Contents

Introduction

Understanding measures

There are two aims that teachers need to bear in mind when teaching about measures. Children need to develop:

— an understanding of the processes involved in using measures

— competence at using measuring to solve problems

Understanding and competence are inseparable: children cannot fully understand measurement unless they have experience of carrying out practical measuring activities; similarly, they cannot become competent without a grasp of the principles. This means that teaching about measures should aim to deal with both aspects: setting practical tasks for children to carry out should be complemented by plenty of discussion about the underlying logic of what they are doing.

In this book most of the activities focus on both aims, although in the first five chapters the first aim — understanding the processes involved in using measures — is uppermost:

Using standard units

A feel for standard units

Developing accuracy

Representing measures

Relationships between units

In the last two chapters the second aim — competence at using measuring to solve problems — is the main focus.

Using and applying measures

Devising measuring systems

Common aspects of measurement

Length, area, volume, angle, weight and so on, all measure different things, and it has been usual to teach them separately. However, there are general ideas that different systems of measurement share, and we have tried to emphasise this in the way the book is structured. If children are offered some insight into the rationale behind what they are doing, and how this rationale holds true for many of the measures they come across, this can greatly accelerate their learning.

Two fundamental ideas used in measuring are 'units' and 'continuity'. Most children will grasp these ideas intuitively. For example, young children experience the difference between continuous and discrete quantities through activities like sharing out biscuits and juice. The juice is a continuous quantity; to measure it out they need to introduce units such as cupfuls. The biscuits are discrete quantities; each biscuit is its own unit, so they can be shared by counting.

Units

Counting and comparing discrete quantities of things such as biscuits is not a matter of measurement, but of number. This book concentrates on length, weight, volume and capacity, time, area and angle, which are all continuous quantities.

Young children will deal with these measures by making direct comparisons — this pencil is longer than that one, this cup is fuller than that one. And adults will do the same when appropriate; we hold a pair of trousers against our body to see if they are long enough, to save the trouble of getting out the tape measure.

Adults will also use an intermediate item, if suitable. For example, to find out if a wardrobe will fit into an alcove, we can use a dressing-gown cord to measure the wardrobe, and then hold this against the alcove to see whether it is big enough.

But when two things are separated by time or distance adults, and children, need a way to record the original measure. For example, if children want to find out how the guinea pig's weight has changed over a term, they need to measure and record the animal's weight at the start of the term, and then later on measure again, and compare the two results. That is where units come in.

In order to communicate or record the size of the thing being measured (whether we are dealing with length, angle or time) we use units of an agreed size. Many measures follow the base ten number system, with sub-units which are a tenth the size of the unit — for example, centimetres and millimetres or kilograms and grams. Other measures follow a system other than metric, though — for example hours, minutes and seconds, or gallons and pints.

Measuring is approximate

Most measuring systems rely on a linear scale to represent the size of what is being measured; the advantage of this is that it allows for increasing accuracy. For example, between 31 cm and 32 cm there are actually an infinite number of lengths. With a good quality ruler we can come to a close approximation of, say, the length of a piece of string. With the help of a magnifying glass we might get

as far as saying the string is about 31·26 cm, but then we have to stop — measuring cannot give us an exact answer. An analogy is the number line, where an infinite number of positions can be imagined between any two points, such as 1 and 2. This is in contrast to counting discrete objects, such as children. Here there is not an infinite number of possibilities between two numbers. There may be five or six children, but there cannot be 5·67 children!

Developing ideas about in-between

When children read a value between units on any linear scale (for example a value between 5·4 and 5·5), they need to know that the measuring instrument represents a continuum and that there are values in the spaces between that are not marked.

5·0   5·1   5·2   5·3   5·4   5·5   5·6   5·7

Children show various levels of understanding of this idea. One six-year-old who was weighing an object between 5·5 kg and 5·6 kg acknowledged the

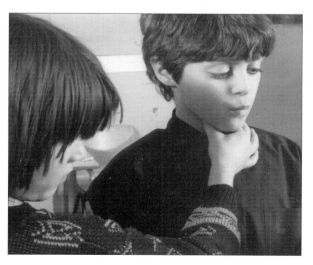

Measuring heart rate as part of a project on the body.

value in between the two points. She talked about it using the language of fractions, despite the fact that the value was not marked: "we have to take a little half away."

Another child was trying to weigh a package with a mass between 250 g and 260 g but the only weights available were in multiples of 10 g. Having got to a certain point she said: "I need a half of that. I need a five."

Children learning about measurement

The Progression in Learning Science and Mathematics Project was set up in 1994 by King's College, London to investigate:

— whether a progression can be identified and described which matches children's learning patterns and so helps the assessment process

— the extent to which progression varies between individual children of the same age and between children of different ages

— the relation between progression in learning and progression in teaching

One of the outcomes of the project, which we draw from in this book, was the development of a framework which identified main ideas which underpin all measurement systems — units, number, continuity and linear scale.

The project developed test items to find out how much children understand as they go through the measuring procedure. For example, children were asked to find the height of a tower and the weight of a package using both standard and non-standard units. The children recognised the need for

sub-units: "Not one of these. It should be a small one like one of these." Some children had difficulty in labelling the sub-units: "It's 10 inches and 4… 4 tiny millimetres." This child confused metric with imperial units, but still recognised the need for sub-units.

There were glimpses of an understanding of the arbitrariness of units: — "I know those aren't the same heaviness" — and the relative size of imperial and metric units of length: "Um, I thought that it would be 15. Then I thought it's in inches. It can't be because inches are quite big so it has to be 15 centimetres and 10 inches."

Using measuring tools

Once children understand what measuring is for, they need to learn how to use measuring tools.

Teach about different tools

Primary classrooms are usually equipped with a wide variety of different tools for measuring, each suited to a particular purpose. Children should be taught how to use these tools properly and with reasonable accuracy; they are unlikely to learn how to do so if left to explore them without guidance, although free exploration has a part to play in becoming familiar with these tools. Practical work with the different tools will help children to evaluate each one's advantages and disadvantages.

Give challenges to make children think

Give children activities which challenge their preconceptions and encourage them to make connections between ideas. For example, measuring length is not always about measuring straight lines. Ask children to measure the circumference of a ball, a route on a map, or the length of a spiral drawn in LOGO. Challenge them to think about how to do it, and what tools to use (possibly a ball of string).

Or ask them find the height of an object, such as a pyramid made from Polydrons.

Encourage discussion

Children should be encouraged to discuss what might be the appropriate measuring tool for a particular activity. They also need to agree the units appropriate to the task, because this will often influence the choice of equipment.

Tools for different measures

Length

Tools for measuring length will probably provide children's earliest measuring experiences. Classrooms will be equipped with a wide variety of tools for linear measurement: rulers, metre sticks, surveyor's tapes, trundle wheels, tape measures, callipers… and each has its own 'rules' for use.

Rulers can cause difficulties because some have a dead end, others do not, and some may look more like a number strip than a tool for measuring length. Children need to learn how to use them and the possible limitations of each kind.

Children need to appreciate when a trundle wheel is and is not a useful tool. For example, it is ideal for measuring long, open distances outside, but it is not suited to measuring the length of the classroom as it is difficult to measure up to a wall accurately with a trundle wheel.

Weight

Balances give a clear visual comparison of weight. They can be used to compare the weights of two objects directly, or an object can be put in one pan and balanced with gram weights in the other. The total of the gram weights tells the child how heavy the object is. There are certain conventions that need to be taught, for example, equalising both sides before starting.

Bathroom and kitchen scales are important pieces of equipment for measuring weight. Most show a conventional dial and children will need practice at reading these, and interpreting the values of the markers between the printed numbers.

Work on number lines numbered in 10s, 25s or 100s can be a useful precursor to reading scales, as can work on rounding numbers up and down.

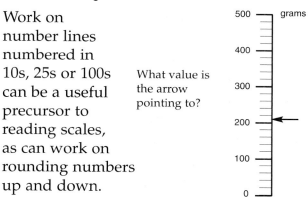

What value is the arrow pointing to?

Scales with digital readouts are comparatively simple to use, although if these display both imperial and metric units they need to be set to the correct units before starting.

Spring balances are a more sophisticated version of the simple tools children may have made lower down the school, when they attached a yoghurt pot to a rubber band and put various different objects in the pot. Again, children need practice at reading the scales on spring balances.

Introduction

Volume and capacity

Sometimes it is appropriate to compare capacities by filling a container with water, sand or some other pourable substance, and pouring it into another container. If this other container is a measuring jug or cylinder, children will need to understand how to read the scale on the side of the jug. The same principles apply to learning to read these scales as to learning to read the weight scales described above.

The capacity of a cuboidal box can be measured by packing it neatly with cubes until it is full, and counting the cubes. If these are centimetre cubes, the volume is in cubic centimetres. Older children will learn from this method that the volume of a cuboid is the length times the breadth times the height, or $l \times b \times h$.

Volumes of solid objects other than cuboids can be found by displacement: the object is lowered into water and the volume of water displaced is measured. This is a sophisticated process, and only suitable for older children.

Time

Much of the equipment in schools for teaching about time concentrates on representing time: clock faces (geared or otherwise), clock stamps, clock face cards, and so on. Children need to become familiar with the two different ways time is represented: analogue (as on a conventional clock face) and digital (as on a video recorder). Work with digital representation of time includes work with the 24-hour clock.

Work on reading the time from a clock face needs to go hand in hand with work on measuring the passing of time. The most important instruments for this consist of sand timers, kitchen timers, ordinary clocks and watches and stopclocks and stopwatches. Clocks and timers are available with varying degrees of sophistication, and it is important to match the complexity of the tool to the level of the children's understanding. A stopwatch that measures time to a hundredth of a second will confuse young children who are still getting a feel for how long a second and a minute last.

Area

The most important equipment for teaching area is squared paper, 1 cm, 2 cm for older children, and 5 cm for younger ones. Transparent plastic 1 cm grids can be very useful; they can be laid over a shape, leaf, book cover or other flat object and the number of squares counted. However, though the equipment might be simple, it is meaningless to children without a conceptual grasp of the meaning of area.

Angle

A circular angle indicator is easier to use than a protractor, and reinforces the idea that angle is a measure of turn.

Protractors, on the other hand, can be confusing. This is largely because children get muddled about which row of numbers to use, especially when failing to consider whether the angle they are measuring is greater or less than 90°.

It is difficult for primary children to be accurate when measuring angles; the difference between degrees is small. When drawing and constructing shapes, it is important to stress the need for a sharp pencil so that the children's work is as accurate as possible.

An important tool, which children need to experience and which is simple to use, is a set square.

The National Numeracy Strategy

The *Framework for Teaching Mathematics* produced by the National Numeracy Strategy outlines the learning requirements for measures and other mathematical areas in each school year. On p111 of this book you will find a reference chart linking each activity in the book to these mathematical objectives. This will help you to plan and assess children's work according to the Strategy's recommendations.

Finding angles the same as a right angle, more than a right angle and less than a right angle.

The different measures

Length

Length is distance between two points.

Metric units

10 millimetres (10 mm)	= 1 centimetre (1 cm)
10 centimetres (10 cm)	= 1 decimetre (1 dm)
10 decimetres (10 dm)	= 1 metre (1 m)
1000 metres (1000 m)	= 1 kilometre (1 km)

Imperial units

12 inches (12 in)	= 1 foot (1 ft)
3 feet (3 ft)	= 1 yard (1 yd)
1760 yards (1760 yds)	= 1 mile (1 m)

Metric/Imperial units

1 metre	= 39·38 inches
1 inch	= 2·54 centimetres
1 kilometre	= 0·61 miles
1 mile	= 1·64 kilometres

Mass and weight

The terms 'mass' and 'weight' often confuse the unwary teacher. There is a difference between mass and weight although in normal circumstances it is not discernible.

Weight depends on how much force is exerted on an object by gravity. If you took a set of bathroom scales to the moon you would find that you weighed less when you got there.

Mass depends on how much substance goes to make up an object, so if you had weighed yourself on a big balance using weights (or masses) and then took all the equipment to the moon your mass would be unchanged because, although you would weigh less, so would the weights (or masses) you had taken with you.

By Year 4, children should be starting to meet the term 'mass', although they are likely to use 'mass' and 'weight' more or less interchangeably at this stage. It is worth discussing the difference between 'mass' and 'weight' at some point, but many will not grasp the difference between the two until they do further science work at secondary school.

Metric units

1000 grams (1000 g)	= 1 kilogram (1 kg)
1000 kilograms (1000 kg)	= 1 tonne or metric ton

Imperial units

16 ounces (16 oz)	= 1 pound (1 lb)
14 pounds (14 lb)	= 1 stone (1 st)
8 stones (8 st)	= 1 hundredweight (1 cwt)
20 cwt	= 1 ton

Metric/Imperial units

1 gram	= 0·04 ounces
1 ounce	= 28·4 grams
1 pound	= 0·45 kilograms
1 kilogram	= 2·2 pounds

Volume and capacity

The volume of an object is the amount of three-dimensional space that it occupies. Liquid volume and solid volume are exactly the same but are generally measured in different units. Liquid volume is measured in litres and millilitres and solid volume is measured in cubic metres and cubic centimetres. A millilitre occupies the same amount of space, and therefore has the same volume, as a cubic centimetre. This is of relevance and interest to children when they discover that a 'big cube' from a set of base ten blocks has the same volume as a litre of water.

Children sometimes get confused over the language of 'cubing'. A length of one centimetre, when cubed, becomes a cube all of whose dimensions are one centimetre — and whose volume is one cubic centimetre. A length of two centimetres, when cubed, becomes a cube whose dimensions are all two centimetres, and whose volume is 8 cubic centimetres.

2 cm

2 cm

2 cm

$2 \text{ cm} \times 2 \text{ cm} \times 2 \text{ cm} = 8 \text{ cm}^3$

Only containers have capacity. The capacity of a container is the maximum volume of liquid which it can hold. For example if a wine glass has 180 millilitres when full to the brim then its capacity is 180 millilitres.

Metric units

1 000 000 cubic centimetres
($1\ 000\ 000\ \text{cm}^3$ or cc) = 1 cubic metre ($1\ \text{m}^3$)
10 millilitres (10 ml)   = 1 centilitre (1 cl)
100 centilitres (100 cl) = 1 litre (1 l)

Imperial units

1 gallon (1 gall) = 8 pints (8 pts)

Metric/Imperial units

1 litre = 1.75 pints
1 pint = 0.57 litres

Time

Everyday units of time were originally based on the rotation of the earth, and so the units are not metric, although they are uniform. (Scientific measures of time are now defined in terms of the resonant frequency of the caesium atom.)

60 seconds (60 secs) = 1 minute (1 min)
60 minutes (60 mins) = 1 hour (1 hr)
24 hours (24 hrs)   = 1 day
7 days   = 1 week
14 days   = 1 fortnight
4 weeks   = 1 lunar month
52 weeks + 1 day   = 1 year

365 days   = 1 year (366 in a leap year)
100 years = 1 century
1000 years = 1 millennium

Area

Area is a measure of two-dimensional space.

Metric units

100 square millimetres ($100\ \text{mm}^2$)
        = 1 square centimetre ($1\ \text{cm}^2$)
10 000 square centimetres ($10\ 000\ \text{cm}^2$)
        = 1 square metre ($1\ \text{m}^2$)

1 hectare = 1 000 square metres

Imperial units

144 square inches (144 sq") = 1 square foot (1 sq')
9 square feet (9 sq') = 1 square yard (1 sq^y)
4 840 square yards = 1 acre

Metric/Imperial units

1 hectare = 2·471 acres
1 acre   = 0·4047 hectares

Angle

Angle is a measure of rotation. Angle was originally based on the rotation of the earth around the sun. As it was then thought that this took 360 days, a full turn was defined as 360 degrees.

$90°$ = a right angle
$360°$ = 1 full turn
$720°$ = 2 full turns

$90°$

Temperature

Celsius has now replaced Fahrenheit as the official temperature scale. Its zero (0 °C) is the freezing point of water and 100 °C is its boiling point.

Using the activity pages

The name of the activity

The name of the activity is at the top of the left-hand page.

Equipment

This section lists what materials you will need to have available.

Children will experience

This section outlines what the children might be learning and hence indicates the main focus of assessment.

Getting started

This section provides an outline of an activity which can be adapted to several different levels of difficulty. It is a good idea to read this section in conjunction with the 'Can the children...' boxes. The suggestions in these boxes offer a guide to what children working at different levels can be expected to achieve in this area, and can help you both to initiate and to continue the activity at appropriate levels.

Important mathematics to discuss

A brief outline of matters to discuss before and during activity work.

Questions to ask the children

These questions can help focus the children's attention on the mathematics and offer you valuable opportunities for assessment.

Take 60

Children will experience

◆ how long a minute lasts
◆ reading and interpreting time recorded on clocks and watches
◆ comparing time events using appropriate language

Equipment

◆ stopclocks and watches
◆ clocks and watches
◆ sand-timers

Getting started

This activity can be done with a group, or with the whole class.

Ask children to think of activities they think will take about a minute to do 60 times — for example, dropping cubes into a box or saying a particular word. One child can try to do it while the others measure the time taken.

Then ask the rest of the children to get into pairs to test out their own ideas for activities to do 60 times in a minute.

Important mathematics to discuss

Following the initial demonstration, discuss whether the activity was the right length, or too quick or too slow.

Remind the children, if necessary, that 60 seconds equals 1 minute. Once they have found an activity that takes 60 seconds to do 60 times they can use it as a means of measuring seconds.

Questions to ask the children

How will you time your partner? How will you ensure you measure accurately?

What do you think will take 60 seconds to do 60 times? How long would it take to do it 30 times?

Would it take you twice as long to do twice as many of that action?

Why did different people take different amounts of time to do the same thing?

How does that timer measure parts of a second? In fifths? Tenths? Hundredths? How can you find out?

How long would it take to drop 600 cubes in that box? Would you get faster or slower the more times you did it?

10

ix

Other ideas

This section offers ways to develop the activity so that the children can continue to work independently, consolidate their ideas, and meet the same mathematics in a different context.

Section and measure

The top of the right-hand page tells you which section the activity belongs in, and which measure it deals with.

Using standard units
Time

Other ideas

- Think of events that would last for approximately a second, a minute, an hour, a day, a year, a century…
- Find out how much time you spend next week watching television.
- Find out how much time you spend next week sleeping.
- How many hours is it until your birthday?

- Have you lived for a million seconds?
- How long does it take you to hop round the hall?
- What is your average walking speed? What is the average speed of a snail? How much faster are you than the snail?

Can the children...

These four boxes indicate ways in which the level of difficulty of the activity can be altered by using different equipment or posing different questions. The ideas in these boxes can be helpful in a variety of ways:

- you can use them in deciding at what level of difficulty to start the activity

- °you can adjust the level of activity once the children have begun working on it, to meet their different levels of attainment

- you can challenge children to begin to work at a higher level of attainment

- you can ask key questions to in assess the level of attainment at which individual children are working

Can the children...

estimate what activity they could do 60 times in a minute?

use a minute sand-timer to time a minute?

compare two different activities, by finding out the number of times they can do each one in a minute?

say which they did most/fewest times?

Level 2

use a watch or clock to time a minute?

estimate a minute by closing their eyes and indicating when the time is up?

give a reasonable estimate of how many hours of TV they watch a week?

record lengths of time using words?

Level 3

measure time using a stopwatch or clock to the nearest second?

work out the duration of a journey using timetables?

using a television magazine, work out a plan for watching 3·5 hours of TV during an evening?

Level 4

measure time using a stopwatch or clock to the nearest $\frac{1}{5}$ or $\frac{1}{10}$ second?

record and analyse the rate of increase of hops per minute they can do after practising for one week and two weeks?

use the 24-hour clock to work out time differences between time zones?

calculate the average (mean) time they take travelling to school?

Level 5

11

X

Using standard units

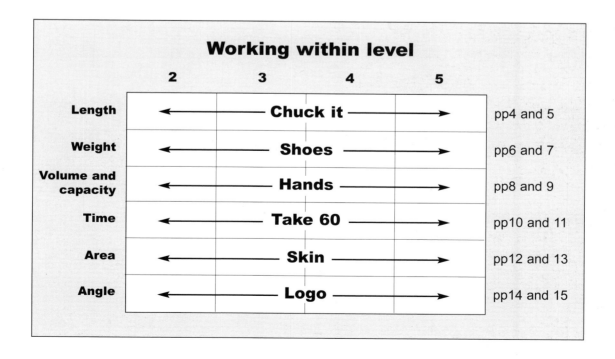

Working within level

	2	3	4	5	
Length	← Chuck it →				pp4 and 5
Weight	← Shoes →				pp6 and 7
Volume and capacity	← Hands →				pp8 and 9
Time	← Take 60 →				pp10 and 11
Area	← Skin →				pp12 and 13
Angle	← Logo →				pp14 and 15

Using standard units

The activities in this section can help children to:

— use the vocabulary of standard metric units of length, weight, volume, and area, and read and write the relevant words

— use the vocabulary of standard units of time and angle, and read and write the relevant words

— use the vocabulary of commonly used imperial units, and read and write the relevant words

— use the abbreviations: km, m, dm, cm, mm; m², cm², mm²; m³, cm³, mm³; kg, g; l, cl, ml; lb, oz

— know the relationships between units

Units

Comparison is at the heart of measurement. Knowing that a desk is 160 cm long is not, in itself, interesting, but when we compare the desk's length to the alcove of 140 cm where we want to put the desk the information becomes useful.

A teacher's instructions for an activity using a protractor, and the resulting piece of work.

Draw a circle with a radius of 9 cm. Using the protractor divide it accurately into 24 sections (24 hour clock)

In order to compare the length of the desk and alcove we use *units*. For comparison purposes once a reference unit is chosen it needs to remain constant but it does not matter what we choose — metres or yards, plastic cubes or gram weights. However, standardising the units we use makes communicating easier. If we all agree to use the same units (grams, metres, degrees Celsius…) it is easier to communicate between classes, towns and countries and in time.

Most of the measures dealt with in this book involve units, whether standard or non-standard, which express the measure as a ratio of that unit; so a weight of 20 conkers means a weight of 20 times one conker; a weight of 55 grams means 55 times one gram. However this only applies in measures with a 'true' zero. Zero centimetres is just that: no length. But zero degrees is an arbitrary point to measure temperature from — 20 °C is not twice as hot as 10 °C.

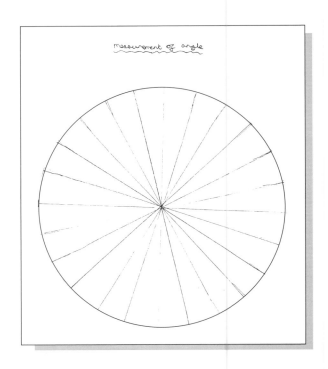

measurement of angle

Important issues to discuss

When children measure using standard units there are important issues to discuss both before and during the work.

For example, if children want to find the distance between two trees they will need to talk about where to measure from and to, what would be the most appropriate units to use, and which tools would work best. They need to talk about how the measuring tools will be used and to consider alternative ways of working should the need arise.

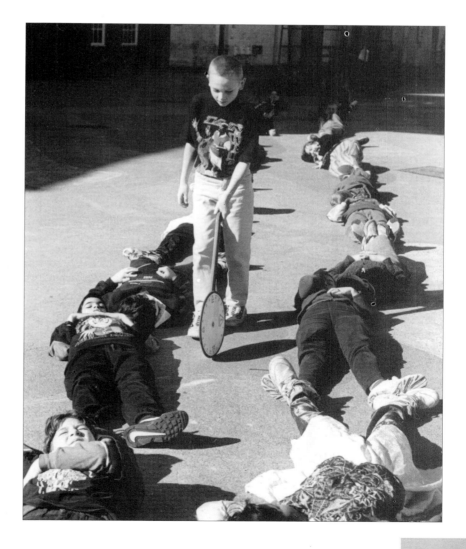

Measuring the total height of the class.

Chuck it

Children will experience

- finding a way of measuring length
- using standard units
- thinking about the need for accuracy
- choosing tools

Equipment

- beanbags/feathers/paper aeroplanes and other objects
- tape measures, rulers, metre rules and other equipment for measuring length
- paper and pencil

Getting started

This activity is best done in groups. Although the purpose is to give children experience in measuring lengths, this activity is best done in the context of a science lesson.

Ask children to guess, then find out, how far they can throw a beanbag/feather/weighted balloon/paper aeroplane and which they can throw the furthest. When children have all had some tries at this ask them to find out if it makes any difference whether they throw the objects inside or outdoors.

Important mathematics to discuss

Talk about the factors that affect the distance. Is how far the object goes affected by its weight? Or its shape? You may also need to discuss the issues of fairness. Is it fair if Kamala threw her beanbag inside but her paper aeroplane outside in the wind?

Ask the children to think about how they will tackle the problem, what equipment they need and how they will record their results. What rules do they need to adopt to ensure a fair test for the flight of each object? Where will they measure from, and to?

Questions to ask the children

What tool will you use to measure the distance?

What units will you use?

Do the same people throw the beanbag furthest each time?

Do the same people also throw the paper aeroplane furthest?

The plane landed back at your feet. Can you measure how far it travelled in the air?

What different units of measurement could you use?

Which do you think are the most appropriate units to use?

Where will you measure from? And where to?

How can you make the measuring fair?

How will you record your measurements?

Other ideas

- How long do you think a toilet roll is? How can you make a good estimate without unrolling it all?
- Draw the longest spiral you can on a piece of paper. How long is it? How will you measure it?
- Make holes 5 cm deep for the bulbs to go in; make a hole about 50 cm deep and 50 cm wide for the tree roots.
- Is your reach with arms outstretched the same as your height?

- Find who has the widest smile.
- Blow up a balloon until it measures 50 cm around the middle. Measure it every day for a week. What happens?
- Find out what length of necklace is comfortable for you, then make one that length.
- Make two circles, one with circumference 1 m, and one with diameter 1 m. Discuss your results.
- Would a dinosaur fit in the school hall?

Can the children...

measure a distance approximately, using non-standard units such as paces or strides?
estimate a distance using non-standard units such as paces or strides, after experience of measuring similar distances?
Level 2

measure a distance using standard units such as metres?
estimate a distance using standard units such as metres?
measure accurately starting from a common base line?
measure a distance using a mixture of units, such as '3 metres and 20 centimetres'?
record their work using whole words and abbreviations?
Level 3

talk about the advantages and disadvantages of various measuring units?
measure a distance in metres and centimetres?
record measurements using decimal notation?
choose their own equipment for measuring?
present their findings in an organised way?
Level 4

estimate a distance in metres and centimetres?
keep coherent records of their work using a range of equivalent decimal measurements?
present their findings in an organised way, bearing in mind what the audience will want or need to know?
calculate the range of their results?
Level 5

Shoes

Children will experience

- comparing the weight of two objects
- estimating weight
- using standard units of weight
- reading a scale accurately

Equipment

- balances (one per pair of children)
- standard weights (10 g, 5 g, 100 g…)
- non-standard weights (conkers, cubes, marbles…)
- shoes

Getting started

This activity is best done in groups of four or eight children, working in pairs.

Ask the children to take off a shoe each, then let the children in turn hold their own and their partner's shoes, one in each hand. Which do they think is heavier? Ask them to record their guesses.

They should now use the balance to find out, and record their results.

When they have done this two pairs should join up and compare all four shoes. First each child in turn estimates what they think the order will be, heaviest to lightest; then they work as a group to find out.

Important mathematics to discuss

Ask the children how easy or hard it is to estimate the difference between the mass of the two objects. Do they think that the larger shoes are also the heavier?

Ask how they could find out the difference more accurately. What units of measurement and/or equipment will they use?

Questions to ask the children

Can you put the four shoes in order of weight?

How much does the heaviest shoe weigh?

What's the difference in weight between the heaviest and the lightest shoe?

How much does each shoe weigh to the nearest 100 g?

What is the average weight of the shoes?

Might there be a relationship between shoe weight and cost?

6

Other ideas

◆ Compare the weight and fabric of the group's shoes.

◆ Make a frequency table of shoe weights.

◆ Make a scatter diagram to see if there is any association between shoe mass and cost, or height and shoe size.

◆ Find the average weights of the shoes in a group and discuss the significance of mode, mean and median in this context.

◆ Compare and make generalisations about different types of shoe — trainers, walking shoes, sandals and so on.

◆ Estimate which packed lunch weighs the most.

Can the children...

---

make a reasonable estimate, by looking, about which of two shoes is heavier?

use a balance to compare two shoes directly, then say which is heavier?

put three or four shoes in order of weight, by comparing two shoes at a time?

weigh a shoe using a balance and non-standard weights such as marbles?

when they have found the weights of three or four shoes, using non-standard units, put these in order?

Level 2

---

make a reasonable estimate of the order of weight of three or four shoes?

weigh a shoe using a balance and standard weights?

when they have found the masses of three or four shoes, in grams, put these in order?

choose appropriate equipment for weighing the shoes?

discuss reasons for using standard units instead of non-standard?

Level 3

---

weigh the shoes to an appropriate level of accuracy?

weigh a shoe using kitchen scales, and read the scale on the dial?

record weights in both grams and kilograms (for example, 567 g and 0.567 kg)

round the weights to the nearest 10 g, or 100 g?

Level 4

---

make a frequency table of shoe weights?

make a scatter diagram showing any correlation between shoe weight and cost, or height and shoe size?

convert weights from metric to imperial?

find the average weights of the shoes in a group, using a calculator if necessary, and discuss the significance of mode, mean and median in this context?

Level 5

Hands

Children will experience

- comparing the capacity of a variety of containers, using direct comparison
- using standard or non-standard units for volume and capacity
- practical exploration of the difference between standard units for volume and capacity

Equipment

- sand and water
- 1 cm cubes
- conkers, beans, lentils, rice, buttons, sorting toys…
- calibrated jugs and cylinders
- yoghurt pots, margarine tubs…

Getting started

This activity can be done with the whole class divided into groups of four or five.

Ask children to find out whose hand in the group holds the most. Encourage them to discuss as a group how to set about the task, and to choose their own equipment from what is provided.

Important mathematics to discuss

Before starting the activity discuss the difference between volume and capacity (one is the amount of space occupied, the other is the amount a container can hold). The children are measuring the capacity of their hands by measuring the volume of matter they can hold.

Children who will be using calibrated containers may need to know that 1 cm^3 (or cc) is the same as 1 ml, but that the former is used for measuring the volume of solids and the latter is generally used for measuring the volume of liquids or the capacity of containers.

Talk with the children about what kind of objects they should hold in order to give the most accurate results and ask about their reasons.

Questions to ask the children

Will you need any rules to make sure the comparisons are fair?

How many centimetre cubes can you hold? How many cc is that?
Can you hold that amount of sand or water?

Which material will give you the most accurate measure of your hand capacity?
Why do you think that?'

How will you measure the rice/sand/lentils?
Do you need to count those lentils, or is there an easier way?

What is the average capacity of your hand?
How many tests would you need to do?

Why can't you hold as many conkers as beans?

Other ideas

◆ Children can hold both hands together to form a scoop and find out who can hold most this way. Is it the same person as before?

◆ Children can investigate the relationship between the area of their hands and the amount they can hold.

◆ Does the person who holds the most conkers also hold the most sand?

◆ Make a box (using 1 cm squared card) which holds exactly a handful of sand. Find the dimensions of the box.

◆ Investigate the significance of 'cc' as it is used in describing car engines.

◆ Which sponge holds the most water (for the school fête)?

◆ Which dishcloth holds most water?

Can the children...

compare the capacity of two hands directly, by pouring, say, beans, from one to the other, then say which holds more?

put three or four hand-capacities in order, by pouring the contents into clear containers?

find the capacities of hands by counting how many non-standard units such as marbles they each hold?

when they have found the capacities of three or four hands, using non-standard units, put these in order?

Level 2

choose appropriate equipment for measuring their hand capacities?

find the capacity of a hand using, for example, sand, and measure this to the nearest 10 ml?

when they have found the capacities of three or four hands, in millilitres, put these in order?

record their work using whole words and abbreviations?

Level 3

read the calibrations on the side of the container?

measure an amount, using calibrated containers, to the nearest 1 ml or 1 cc?

record weights in both litres and millilitres, as well as cc (for example, 123 ml or 123 cc, and 0·123 l)?

compare the number of centimetre cubes they can hold with the amount of water they can hold, and explain the discrepancy?

Level 4

make sensible estimates of the capacity of hands, in cc or ml?

convert volumes from metric to imperial?

find and discuss the significance of the mean average?

use displacement to find volumes and explain their reasoning?

Level 5

9

Take 60

Children will experience

- how long a minute lasts
- reading and interpreting time recorded on clocks and watches
- comparing time events using appropriate language

Equipment

- stopclocks and watches
- clocks and watches
- sand-timers

Getting started

This activity can be done with a group, or with the whole class.

Ask children to invent activities they think will take about a minute to do 60 times — for example, dropping cubes into a box or saying a particular word. One child can try to do it while the others measure the time taken.

Then ask the rest of the children to get into pairs to test out their own ideas for activities to do 60 times in a minute.

Important mathematics to discuss

Following the initial demonstration, discuss whether the activity was the right length, or too quick or too slow.

Remind the children, if necessary, that 60 seconds equals 1 minute. Once they have found an activity that takes 60 seconds to do 60 times they can use it as a means of measuring seconds.

Questions to ask the children

How will you time your partner?
How will you ensure you measure accurately?

What do you think will take 60 seconds to do 60 times?
How long would it take to do it 30 times?

Would it take you twice as long to do twice as many of that action?

Why did different people take different amounts of time to do the same thing?

How does that timer measure parts of a second? In fifths? Tenths? Hundredths?
How can you find out?

How long would it take to drop 600 cubes in that box?
Would you get faster or slower the more times you did it?

Other ideas

- Think of events that would last for approximately a second, a minute, an hour, a day, a year, a century…
- Find out how much time you spend next week watching television.
- Find out how much time you spend next week sleeping.
- How many hours is it until your birthday?

- Have you lived for a million seconds?
- How long does it take you to hop round the hall?
- What is your average walking speed? What is the average speed of a snail? How much faster are you than the snail?

Can the children...

estimate what activity they could do 60 times in a minute?
use a minute sand timer to time a minute?
compare two different activities, by finding out the number of times they can do each one in a minute?
say which they did most/fewest times?
Level 2

use a watch or clock to time a minute?
estimate a minute by closing their eyes and indicating when the time is up?
give a reasonable estimate of how many hours of TV they watch a week?
record lengths of time using words?
Level 3

measure time using a stopwatch or clock to the nearest second?
work out the duration of a journey using timetables?
using a television magazine, work out a plan for watching 3·5 hours of TV during an evening?
Level 4

measure time using a stopwatch or clock to the nearest $\frac{1}{5}$ or $\frac{1}{10}$ second?
record and analyse the rate of increase of hops per minute they can do after practising for one week and two weeks?
use the 24-hour clock to work out time differences between time zones?
calculate the average (mean) time they take travelling to school?
Level 5

Skin

Children will experience

- the idea of area as amount of surface covered
- finding area by counting squares
- using approximation
- developing efficient methods for counting large numbers of squares

Equipment

- 1 cm squared paper
- 2 or 5 cm squared paper (for younger children)
- decimetre squares
- old gloves

Getting started

This activity can be done in groups, or with the whole class. Ask children to find out how much skin there is on one hand. They should use squared paper to measure it.

Important mathematics to discuss

Once the children have been introduced to the activity ask them to plan how they will tackle the task and to decide on the equipment or materials they will need and how far up the wrist to measure. Talk about the skin as being the surface area of the body and how area is measured.

Whatever method children devise for measuring the skin area, they will end up with part squares as well as whole squares to count. Discuss with children what to do about the part squares and help them find a 'fair' way of dealing with them. One method is to count part squares that are more than half and ignore those that are less. Another method, which emphasises the approximate nature of measurement, is 'over and under' estimates'. For the 'over estimate' count both whole and part squares as though they were whole and for the 'under estimate' count only the whole squares. The actual area is somewhere between the two.

Questions to ask the children

Don't forget the sides of your fingers. How can you measure that?

Do you think long thin hands have more skin than short chubby ones?

Do you expect your skin area will be more or less than your partner's? Why is that?

What will you do about the part squares? Will you count them? How accurate do you need to be?

Instead of counting each square could you count a whole lot together? How?

If you did it again would you get a different result? Why is that?

Other ideas

- Who has the biggest footprint?
- How much skin have you got on the whole of your body? (Children could do this by drawing round their bodies and making tubes for their arms and legs. They will need to think about how accurate they want or need to be.)
- Have you got more skin on your hand or on your foot?
- How much area does your body silhouette cover?

- Choose two different shaped junk boxes that you think might have the same surface area. Have they? How will you find out?
- How much paper do you think you will need to wrap a ball? Try, and see if that amount is enough.
- Do boxes with the same volume have the same surface area?
- Draw round the shadow of a shape. Can you cast a shadow of the same shape but with twice the area?

Can the children...

use 2 or 5 cm squared paper to measure the area of their hand- or footprint, and count the whole squares covered?

talk about what to do with the part squares?

compare the area of hand-prints from two different children and say which is the greater/smaller?

Level 2

using 1 cm squared paper, find a way to measure the area of the skin of their hand?

count the whole squares covered and talk about what to do with the part squares?

put the hand areas of the whole group into order?

record their work in terms of number and size of squares?

Level 3

make a reasonable estimate of the area of the skin of their hand in square centimetres?

say that 10 000 cm^2 is the same as 1 m^2?

use, read and write the notation for 'squared' (for example, read '100 cm^2' as 'one hundred square centimetres')?

Level 4

make a reasonable estimate of the surface area of their body in square centimetres?

make a reasonable estimate of the surface area of their body in square metres?

explain that 10 cm^2 is not the same area as 10 cm x 10 cm, and why this is so?

calculate the value of approximately 10% of the surface area of their body

Level 5

Logo

Children will experience

- angle as an amount of turn
- measuring the amount of turn using degrees
- use of angle and distance to solve problems
- the language of angle, position and shape

Equipment

- Pip, Pixie or Roamer
- floor turtle
- any Logo program
- angle indicators
- circular protractor

Getting started

This activity can be introduced to the whole class, then done in groups or pairs.

Ask the children to draw any shape using Logo — for example, a square, a simple face or their initial. Talk with them about the amount of turn the cursor or turtle makes. With floor turtles, you can tape a pointer (pencil or ruler) to the turtle so the children can see the pointer sweeping out the angle of turn.

Then ask them to use Logo to draw the same shape, but turned round by any amount.

Important mathematics to discuss

You may need to help the children focus on the starting and end point of the angle swept.

Talk to the children about turning left and right (this can be reinforced during PE lessons). Which way would the turtle turn if they wanted it to turn anti-clockwise and clockwise? Develop the use of language to include acute and obtuse angles. What happens if the turtle is asked to turn by a negative angle?

Questions to ask the children

(Floor turtle)
Draw where you think the line will go, then see if the turtle goes where you expect it to.

If you ask the turtle to turn 90°, how much will it turn? Show me.
Is the angle you want the turtle to turn greater or less than 90°?

Can you show me with your hand exactly which angle the turtle turns through?

If you want the next line to go here, what angle do you need to turn the cursor through?

On your print-out, draw the angles you turned through.
Can you write the size of the angles?

You've just typed in Right 60°. So where will the turtle go next?

Other ideas

- Use skittles to make a maze or obstacle course on the floor, for the floor turtle to travel around.

- Draw a maze on a sheet of transparent plastic (OHP transparency is perfect). Tape it to the monitor and get the turtle to travel round the maze.

- Plan a maze on spotty paper, then draw it on the screen and get the turtle to travel round the maze.

- Two of you work with a clock face each (you should work back to back so you can't see each other's clocks). Set the clocks to midday. One of you then decides through how many degrees you should both turn your minute hands. Then do it, and compare your results.

- Measure how much a stick's shadow turns in one hour. Will the turn be the same for any hour in the day? At any time of year?

Can the children...

recognise a right angle?

follow instructions with their bodies such as "Go forward 2 paces, turn left, go forward another 3 paces, turn right…"?

Level 2

---

understand that angle is a measure of turn?

recognise a right angle and say whether an angle is larger, or smaller, than a right angle?

say that a right angle is 90°?

say how many degrees there are in a half, three-quarters or full turn?

make simple 2D shapes such as a square or triangle, using LOGO or a turtle?

use a repeat procedure?

Level 3

---

recognise that the exterior angle of a shape can be the degree of turn?

use a circular protractor or angle indicator to measure angles?

use Logo to draw an equilateral triangle?

use inverse operations in Logo to correct errors?

Level 4

---

make any straight capital letter?

measure the exterior angle of a shape in order to construct a copy?

estimate the angle of turn with reasonable accuracy (for example, measure a turn of 40°)?

Level 5

A feel for standard units

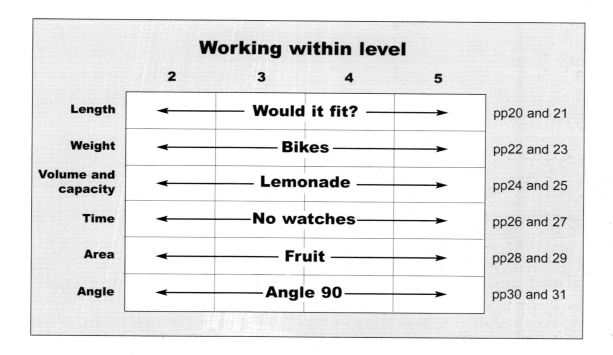

Working within level

	2	3	4	5	
Length	←	Would it fit?	→		pp20 and 21
Weight	←	Bikes	→		pp22 and 23
Volume and capacity	←	Lemonade	→		pp24 and 25
Time	←	No watches	→		pp26 and 27
Area	←	Fruit	→		pp28 and 29
Angle	←	Angle 90	→		pp30 and 31

A feel for standard units

The activities in this section can help children to:

— acquire mental images of the size of standard units and sub-units

— understand the relationships between units in a 'family' such as the metric length family (millimetres, centimetres, decimetres, metres, kilometres)

— acquire and practise skills in estimation

— gain experience in measuring

— choose an appropriate unit to use when measuring

— choose the appropriate measuring instrument to use for a task

The size of various units

In order to estimate successfully using standard units, children need to be able to imagine the size of the unit involved, and to understand the relationship between units of the same family. For example, estimating the lengths of a range of objects requires familiarity with the metric family of units of length. The imperial family of length (inches, feet, yards and miles) should also be learned as it is still in use in many areas of life.

Learning to estimate

In a well-planned curriculum, estimation and exact measuring experiences develop simultaneously and with a purpose. As children gain experience of measurement through a range of activities they acquire a sense of how big are the various units they are using. They also build up a repertoire of everyday objects and quantities they can use as guides or benchmarks for estimation. For example, children who have been measuring the heights of doors, and found they are all approximately 2 metres in height, will be able to use that knowledge to get an idea of the width of the classroom. They might think, "It looks about five doors wide, so it should measure about 10 metres." Checking this estimate adds more information to their store of experience to use another time.

Much of the informal measurement adults do all the time is based on experience: "How long will it take to get to school?"; "Is there enough petrol in the tank?"; "Am I too near the car in front?" These are all very real decisions which children will be inclined to treat as unimportant unless they are given an appreciation of their value.

Angle measurement can be an important part of model making; and the practical nature of the work can help children get a feel for the size of the angles involved.

Getting better at estimation

One of the problems teachers encounter when encouraging children to develop their estimation skills is that too often children lack the confidence to be wrong by even a single centimetre. This means that children may even carry out a rough measurement and then make their 'estimate' afterwards, based on this information. Activities that ask children to estimate and then measure also encourage this view of estimation as a lesser skill. As adults we usually use estimation or measurement, not both.

We must emphasise to children that estimation is a skill, like throwing balls or playing the piano, which develops with practice. In any case, measurement is an area of mathematics where absolute accuracy is not possible, even with highly sophisticated tools, which school equipment certainly is not.

Children who are expected to estimate before they have sufficient experience of measurement may well be inclined to take the view that accurate measurement is unimportant and anything will be good enough.

A way to enhance estimation skills is through games and activities which aid concentration and motivation. A typical game consists of the teacher showing a unit of measure such as a centimetre and asking groups of children to write the number of those units that will be needed to find, say, the width of the table.

Rather than specifying one estimate, which encourages the idea of one 'right' estimate, the children should specify a range within which the answer lies — for example, 'between 80 cm and 120 cm'. The narrowest range containing the actual length scores 5 points, the second narrowest gets 3 points and the third narrowest scores 1. The game continues with the groups estimating other lengths, and the winner is the group with the most points.

RYAN

run in 1 min	Estimate	correct
skips	100 m	140m
	50	22
Steps	65	
		46

How many Steps is it from here to Newcastle

First I got an atlas. I used the Scale to work out that it is 424 km from London to Newcastle. Next I worked out how many steps I take in 1 metre. I took 2 steps. There are 1000 metres in 1 km. It would take me 2 steps x 1000 m to walk 1 km. 2 x 1000 = 2,000 steps for 1 km 424 km x 2000 steps = 848,000 Steps. It would take me 848,000 steps to reach Newcastle

Two pieces of work on length, by Ryan and Dean, which helped the children get a feel for the size of the units involved.

Would it fit?

Children will experience

◆ finding a way of measuring length

◆ familiarity with standard units

◆ thinking about appropriate degrees of accuracy

◆ estimation of length

Equipment

◆ tape measures, rulers, metre rules and other equipment for measuring length

◆ paper and pencil

Getting started

This activity is best done in pairs or small groups.

Ask the children to estimate the dimensions of the hall — try to put the activity in some sort of meaningful context, such as finding out whether it is large enough to fit a netball court. They should estimate by giving upper and lower values that they think the actual value lies between — for example, "I think the length is between 12 and 15 metres" — and then compare their ranges.

They should then measure the hall. After they have measured, discuss with them the estimated ranges which contained the actual length, and which range was the narrowest.

Important mathematics to discuss

Discuss with the children how they might set about estimating the distance — for example, just 'guessing', comparing the distance with a known length such as a child's height, or pacing it out.

"I think it is between ten and twenty metres" is very broad; how could they narrow the range? For example, could they estimate to a range of, say, five metres?

You could repeat the estimation exercise with other distances, both long and short, and discuss whether the children's ability to estimate length improves.

Questions to ask the children

How did you estimate it?
What did you think of in your head?

You say you've measured it and it is 8 and a bit metres.
How could you measure the bit?

Why do you think your range was so near/far out?

What would help you make your estimates more accurate?

Now you've measured 10 metres, do you want to revise your estimate?
Do you still think it's more than 30 metres?

How could you write your estimates/measurements down?

Other ideas

- How far is it from here to the next classroom? Estimate first.
- What total length of shaving comes off your pencil each time you sharpen it? How many sharpenings will your pencil last?
- About how far do you walk in a day? A year?
- If you walked exactly 100 m (or 50 m or 200 m) from the classroom door, where would you get to?
- How long is the perimeter of your hand?

- Is it fair that playtime starts at the same time for everyone? Does everyone have the same distance to go to get to the playground?
- How far is it from school to your home in metres? In kilometres? In paces? Yards? Miles?
- How thick is a sheet of paper?
- If all the words in your book were written out in one long strip, how far would it stretch?

Can the children...

estimate a length, saying whether it is nearer to 1 m, or $\frac{1}{2}$ m?

estimate a length, saying whether it is nearer to $\frac{1}{2}$ m or 1 dm?

measure a distance approximately, using non-standard units such as paces or steps?

say whether the length of the hall is more or less than 3 m?

Level 2

estimate a length, saying whether it is nearer to 1 m, $\frac{1}{2}$ m or 1 cm?

estimate the height of a friend within 10 cm?

estimate the length of a pencil within 2 cm?

measure a distance approximately, using standard units such as metres (for example, say "It's just over 3 metres" or "It's between 4 and 5 metres")?

Level 3

estimate a length, saying whether it is nearer to 1 dm, 1 cm or 1 mm?

estimate lengths in metres, centimetres or millimetres, whichever is appropriate?

measure a distance using standard units such as metres and smaller units (for example, say "It's 3 metres and 25 centimetres")?

use the length of their stride or foot to work out a rough estimate of length?

Level 4

estimate lengths with reasonable accuracy, using metres, centimetres or millimetres, whichever is appropriate?

say that if something measures 6 m it also measures 600 cm or 6000 mm?

estimate length using imperial measures?

Level 5

21

Bikes

Children will experience

◆ getting a feel for weights of 1 kg or 2 kg

◆ using and reading scales

◆ solving problems

Equipment

◆ two identical baskets/bicycle panniers or carrier bags to go in panniers later

◆ things to pack such as: drinks bottle, jumper, swimming kit, map, torch, penknife…

◆ kitchen or bathroom scales, balance and weights

Getting started

This activity can be introduced to the whole class, then tackled by a pair of children at a time, or small groups.

Ask children to decide what to take on a bike ride. (This could fit in with work on journeys, transport, health or a suitable story.) They should then pack this into the two panniers or bags so that the weight is distributed evenly between the two.

In this activity, children should, if possible, use kitchen or bathroom scales, as the aim is to help them develop a feel for standard units of weight — using a balance would encourage direct comparison without using units.

Children for whom the task as a whole is too challenging could tackle a simpler one, trying to fill a pannier with, say, exactly 2 kilograms of items. They will need to use a balance and weights, as these children are unlikely to cope with reading a scale.

Important mathematics to discuss

Ask the children what they need to do first. Would it be helpful to sort the things into two sets of approximately the same weight before they use the scales or balance and weights? How would they decide that the two piles were roughly the same weight?

Use comparative words such as lighter/heavier, too heavy/light, not heavy/light enough.

Questions to ask the children

Before you pack the things, can you arrange them in two sets that you think are roughly equal in weight?

How much does each of the two panniers weigh?
How much weight do you need to transfer to the lighter pannier?

How much does that collection of items weigh?
What could you take off (or add) to make it weigh 2 kilograms?

If you now decided to take a little stove in one pannier, which items would you have to move?

Other ideas

- How many 20 g weights balance 1 kg?
- Find five objects in the classroom, and estimate the weight of each in grams (no cheating!) before weighing them.

  Now do the same thing again with five other objects. Have you got better at estimating?

- Play an estimating game. Each person estimates the individual weight of five objects by giving ranges within which they think each weight lies. The person with the narrowest range containing a correct weight scores 5 points, the next scores 4, and so on.

- Make labels for five objects, saying how much each one weighs. Remove the labels, muddle up the objects, and challenge a friend to match the labels to the objects without using any equipment.

Can the children...

compare the weights of two objects directly, using a balance, and say which is heavier and which is lighter?

use a balance to fill the two panniers with equal weights of items?

say how they know which is the lighter or heavier?

Level 2

estimate whether an item's weight is nearer to 100 g or 1 kg?

weigh an item using a balance, and metal or plastic weights, and say what the weight is?

make a collection of objects that weigh approximately 2 kg?

read and write weights of objects in words and using abbreviations?

Level 3

estimate whether an item's weight is nearer to 500 g or 1 kg?

weigh an object using a balance with a readable scale, and say "It weighs about… grams"?

say what size the intervals are on the scale?

say what value any marker on the scale represents?

Level 4

weigh things to an appropriate degree of accuracy?

read weight on an analogue or digital scale?

read weight on a digital scale and say how this would be shown on an analogue scale?

say the weight of an item using different metric units (for example, "It weighs 250 grams or 0·25 kilograms")?

Level 5

Lemonade

Children will experience

- estimating liquid volumes using standard and non-standard measures
- adding or multiplying fractions
- practical measurement of capacity

Equipment

- one litre bottle of lemonade (or juice)
- cups or mugs
- measuring jugs or cylinders

Getting started

This activity can be introduced to the whole class, then tackled by a pair of children at a time, or small groups.

Give children a litre bottle of lemonade and a cup, and ask them to estimate, then work out, how many such bottles would be needed to provide everyone in the class with one drink. Tell the children they may not pour out the contents of the bottle, so they will need to measure how much a cup holds and then calculate the number of bottles needed.

Important mathematics to discuss

Discuss with the children how they might tackle the problem, and what they need to find out in order to answer the question. How will they ensure everyone has the same amount? How full will the mugs or cups be?

Questions to ask the children

How many bottles do you think will be needed? Don't forget to make a record of your estimate.

How much lemonade does one person need?

How will you measure the amount that cup holds?
What units of measurement will you need to use?

Which cup will you choose to use and why? How full should it be filled?

Can you estimate about how much lemonade there is in that glass before you measure it?

You measured that cupful as 162 millilitres. Would it help to round that figure up or down?

Other ideas

◆ Do this activity every day for a week, using a different size of tumbler/mug each day. What differences do you find in the amount of drink needed? Do you get better at estimating?

◆ Find three very different containers that you think will have much the same capacity. Compare them and see how close their capacities really are.

◆ How many cartons of orange juice should we buy for the open evening?

◆ How many bottles of a concentrated drink would you need for everyone in the class to have a drink? What ratio of concentrate to water would you need to use? How much water would you use altogether?

◆ Estimate the half-way level on a collection of different sized and shaped tumblers; then test and find out how accurate you were.

Can the children...

find out, in a practical way, how many drinks can be got from one bottle?

deal sensibly with a quantity such as cupfuls $5\frac{1}{2}$ cupfuls (for example, say "there is enough for five people but not enough for six")?

find a way to compare several filled glasses and discover whether they have the same amount in them?

Level 2

measure how many millilitres of drink there are in a cup?

say how many millilitres of drink there are in two or four cups (by doubling)?

order a collection of different sized bottles by capacity?

Level 3

make a sensible estimate of how many drinks can be got from one bottle?

make a sensible estimate of how many millilitres of drink there are in a cup?

find a way of solving the problem with minimum adult help?

work to an appropriate degree of accuracy?

Level 4

measure the capacity of one glass and calculate the number of glasses they can fill from a litre bottle?

write the volume of liquid in a glass as a decimal fraction (for example, 0·24 l)?

use ratios when mixing squash for the class?

Level 5

25

No watches

Children will experience

- estimating time
- measuring the passing of time in seconds
- calculation of time differences
- measuring and recording time in seconds and minutes

Equipment

- watch or clock with second hand
- stopwatch
- sand timer

Questions to ask the children

These activities are for the whole class.

a) Cover up any clocks and put any watches — yours and the children's — away in a drawer. Now everyone guesses what the time is. You or one of the children should check this by looking at one of the hidden watches. Do this several times over the space of a week. Do people get better at guessing?

b) Ask everyone to stay silent and guess when a minute is up. You or a child could use one of the watches to time this, or join with the children in the task of guessing — which means you won't be able to find out who was right. Again, do this several times over the space of a week.

As the class becomes familiar with this, progress to working with a two- or three-minute time-span, perhaps using a sand timer.

Important mathematics to discuss

You could point out to the children that:

— time is passing whether or not it is being measured

— the watch and clock faces use arbitrary units that humankind has invented

Questions to ask the children

> How did you estimate the length of a minute?
> Did you use counting? Did you count too quickly or too slowly?
> What will you do next time?

> At what time of day do we have dinner? Playtime?
> At what time do you go home?

> What time did school start today?
> About how long ago was that in minutes? In seconds?

> How long is your playtime?
> Is it really the same every day?
> Why might it be different?

Other ideas

◆ One or more children (perhaps on a rota basis) take responsibility for the class time-keeping. They must make sure you all get to dinner, play and assemblies on time.

◆ Time various class activities. How long does the class usually take to get changed for PE? How long does it take to walk out into the playground?

◆ How long would it take you to count to 100? 1000? 1 000 000?

◆ What things can you do in a minute? How many skips can you do? How many times can you write your name? How far can you run?

◆ About how many times do you breathe in a minute? How many times does your heart beat in a minute?

◆ What units would you use to measure: a running race, the time needed to bake a cake, a holiday, your age, a tree's age…

Can the children...

say that there are sixty seconds in a minute?
say that there are sixty minutes in an hour?
Level 2

use a watch with a second hand to time a minute?
make a reasonable estimate of a minute?
work out the length of time a lesson lasted?
suggest units of time for measuring different time-spans (for example, timing a race, or measuring a person's age)?
time how many minutes they had for playtime?
Level 3

make a reasonable estimate of the time of day (within an hour)?
use a stopwatch competently?
estimate, then time and record, the length of time taken to run a certain distance?
Level 4

discuss times when it might be important to time something accurately and when approximation is acceptable?
record and compare times using both analogue and digital notation?
Level 5

Fruit

Children will experience

◆ finding the surface area of irregular solids

◆ developing a notion of surface area

◆ making choices about use of materials

◆ selecting appropriate units for measuring area

Equipment

◆ various fruits (bananas, satsumas, apples, pears, pineapple…)

◆ 1 cm and 2 cm squared paper

◆ Plasticine

Getting started

This activity can be done with a group, or with the whole class divided into groups.

Introduce the activity by looking at, and handling, the fruits, and discussing their relative sizes. Encourage the children to look in particular at the fruit surfaces and to estimate which they think has the greatest area. Then ask the children to get into threes or fours and give each group a couple of fruits. Ask them to find out which of their fruits has the greatest surface area.

One way of doing this is to open up the fruit and remove the peel (in one piece if possible) then place this on squared paper. Children can then draw round the peel and count the squares.

Another way is to cover the fruit with a thin layer of Plasticine, then open this out and find its area.

Once the groups have worked out the areas of their fruits, encourage a general discussion of the task and the children's findings.

Important mathematics to discuss

The 'squared paper' method of working out area is to count squares that are more than half covered and ignore those that are less; an alternative method, which emphasises the approximate nature of measurement, is 'over and under' estimates. For the 'under estimate' count only the whole squares and for the 'over estimate' count whole squares, and part squares as though they were whole. The actual area is somewhere between the two.

Questions to ask the children

Which fruit do you think has the greatest surface area?

Which would need most paper to wrap it?

Can you estimate the surface area of this piece of fruit? What units will you use?

Now, how might you find out the actual surface area?

Which one of all the fruits did most people think had the greatest area?

And did it?

Can you put the fruits in order of size of surface area?

Other ideas

- Which of these hollow balls has the greatest surface area? Cut them open and find out.

- Have a competition to find the leaf with the greatest area. (How will you compare areas?) Put the leaves in order of size of area.

- Here is a box with a present in it. What is the smallest area of wrapping paper you need to wrap it up?

- What is the area of the clingfilm this coconut is wrapped in? Could the supermarket have used less clingfilm?

- Look at these gloves. Which uses the most fabric?

- Draw the smallest rectangle your foot can fit into. Is it true that the area of your foot is two-thirds the area of this rectangle?

Can the children...

peel their fruit, trace round the peel on 2 cm squared paper, then count the whole squares covered? talk about what to do with the part squares?   **Level 2**

estimate which of two fruits they think has the greatest surface area and explain why they think that? using 1 cm squared paper, draw round the peel and count the squares? count the whole squares covered and decide what to do with the part squares?   **Level 3**

explain that they are looking at the surface area and that this is different from volume? find a way of working out which of their fruits has the greatest surface area? make a reasonable estimate of the surface area of a fruit in square centimetres? work to an appropriate degree of accuracy? **Level 4**

convert a measurement recorded in square centimetres into square millimetres? calculate the difference between their estimate and the actual surface area in square centimetres? work out the differences in surface area of all the fruits?   **Level 5**

Angle 90

Children will experience

◆ opportunities to estimate angle

◆ seeing angle as a measure of turn

◆ giving instructions to other children and to a programmable toy

◆ using inverse operations when estimating angle with a programmable toy

Equipment

◆ Microsmile Pack 2: Angle estimation

◆ Pip, Pixie or Roamer

◆ very large scale-floor map or plan (for example, The Jolly Postman's village with paths connecting the houses)

◆ very large clock face, drawn on floor

Getting started

This activity can be introduced to the whole class by using children as 'robots'. Give them instructions for turning angles of 90°, 45° and so on, and ask them to predict where they will face after turning.

Levels 2 and 3

Put the Roamer in the centre of a large clock face drawn on the floor. Through what angle must it turn to go from the 12 to the 3? What other pairs of numbers give a 90° turn? Get the children to investigate other angles.

Levels 4 and 5

Show children the computer activity Angle 90 from Microsmile Pack 2 — this involves estimating turns between 0° and 90°. Once children are familiar, and confident, with this they may be ready to go on to the other two activities on the disk: Angle 360, which involves estimating turns up to 360°, or Snooker, in which children use their angle estimation skills to hit snooker balls into pockets.

Important mathematics to discuss

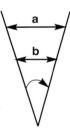

Children need to understand that angle is a measure of turn, not the 'gap' between two arms of a diagram. Children who think in terms of a gap get confused by the fact that the gap is wider further away from the corner.

a is bigger than b, but there is only one measure for the angle, or amount of turn between the two lines.

Questions to ask the children

Is that angle more or less than 90°?
More or less than 180°?
More or less than 270°?

How many degrees are there in a quarter turn?
A half turn? A three-quarters turn?
A full turn?

If you want the Pip to turn 180° will you need to make it go left or right?

How many degrees will the Roamer have to turn to go in a circle?

Where would a turn of 90° take the line to?
And half of 90°?
(What is half of 90°?)

Other ideas

- How much do you need to turn a door handle in order to open it? (How would you measure that?) Are all door handles the same?
- Through how many degrees must you turn the lid on a jar in order to remove it?
- How many degrees is one number on the volume control worth?
- Open that book slowly and stop when the angle between the pages is 30°. Stop again when it is 45°, 90°, 180°.

- Open that book slowly and stop when the angle between the pages is a quarter turn. Stop again when it is a half turn.

  What would happen to the book if you opened its pages more than a half turn?

- Look at the angles made by the gables on houses. Approximately what angle are they?

  Does the angle vary with the age of the house?

Can the children...

tell you where they think they will face if they make a half turn to the right or left? **Level 2**

predict where they will face if they turn a quarter turn to the right or left? find pairs of numbers on the clock face that are separated by a quarter turn? estimate which pairs of numbers on the clock face are separated by less than a quarter turn/more than a quarter turn? **Level 3**

predict where they will face if they turn 45° to the right or left? estimate and test the angle between two consecutive numbers on a clock face, using the Roamer? estimate angles to within about 10°, when playing Angle 90? **Level 4**

place two strips of coloured sticky tape on the floor to create an angle, then estimate its size and test it using the Roamer or Pip? estimate angles to within about 20°, when playing Angle 360? **Level 5**

Developing accuracy

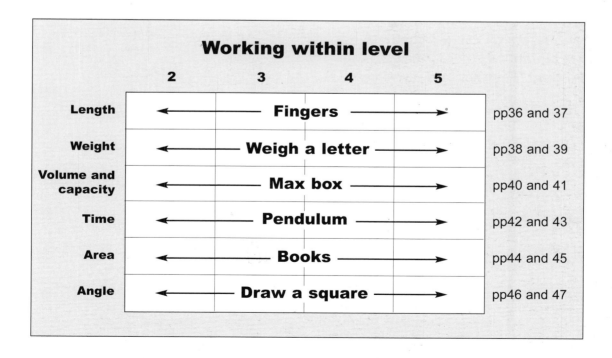

Working within level

	2	3	4	5	
Length	←	Fingers	→		pp36 and 37
Weight	←	Weigh a letter	→		pp38 and 39
Volume and capacity	←	Max box	→		pp40 and 41
Time	←	Pendulum	→		pp42 and 43
Area	←	Books	→		pp44 and 45
Angle	←	Draw a square	→		pp46 and 47

Developing accuracy

The activities in this section are particularly intended to:

— encourage accurate measurement

— help reinforce children's mental images of the size of various standard units

— give experience of handling measuring instruments and paying attention to number representation

When to be accurate

We have said in previous sections that children need to understand that all measurements are only an approximation to the actual size of the thing measured, but they also need to understand the idea of 'degrees of precision'. This latter idea can be understood in the context of cooking or athletics, where attention has to be paid to precision of measurement or the whole activity may fail in its purpose.

When you start focusing with the children on the idea of working with great accuracy, you can ask them to research situations where precision can be important. They can use resources such as the Guinness Book of Records to find the fastest person, the slowest animal, and so on, and think about how those records could be beaten. Another possibility is to make a class book of records which use different degrees of accuracy.

It is also important to discuss with the children the degree of accuracy that might be reasonable when they are measuring certain things. For example, if they are working out how long they spend in school in a year, is it possible — or indeed appropriate — to be accurate to the nearest hour? Does it matter if they are a few hours, or even days, out?

Or if they are measuring angles as part of a project making stars to decorate the school, should they try and be accurate to the nearest degree? Five degrees? Ten degrees? Again, what are the consequences if they are not accurate to the nearest degree?

A child's print-out of squares made in LOGO, drawn as part of the activity *Draw a square*, on p46.

5.1.96	Length

Hand Span

I think my handspan is 18cm

Group 3+4 Handspan

Name	Handspan (cm)
Mr. Wilson	
Rachel	17
Georgina	16
Tom	16
John	16
Oliver	16

Group 3+4 initials

Work on handspans, a follow-up to the activity *Fingers*, on p36.

Accurate use of tools

Although there are occasions when approximate measurements suffice, it is important that children are able to use their measuring tools accurately, and this is something that needs to be taught. It is not always easy to measure something to the nearest millimetre, millilitre, degree or gram, but children's skills need to be developed to cope with this level of precision. Incidentally, the attempt will help them to appreciate just how difficult it is to be absolutely accurate and how measuring something with absolute accuracy is in fact impossible.

Opportunities for accurate measurement come from a variety of tasks; especially valuable is constructing diagrams or models, where accurate measuring is often of prime importance.

Measuring changes in shadow length requires children to be accurate.

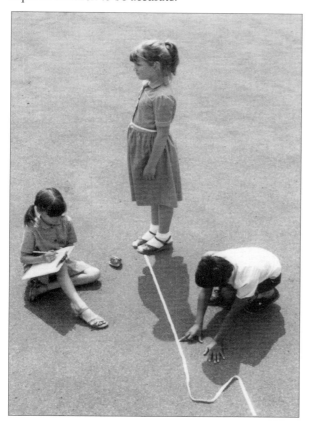

Learning by experiment

'It can be very helpful to children if they do some 'real life' measuring, such as the activity about measuring fingers on p36, and then work together with you to draw up a list of the steps they need to take to ensure that their measurements are accurate.' One class did just that, in trialling these materials, and came up with the list shown below.

> Important things to remember when measuring
>
> 1. Measure from the same start and finish points.
> 2. Don't let the person wiggle about.
> 3. Always measure twice to check for errors.
> 4. Use the same ruler or measure so you don't make mistakes.
> 5. When measuring height, make the person lie down.
> 6. Measure mouths wide open, not top to bottom.
> 7. Measure heads from chin to top of head.

Fingers

Children will experience

- choosing an appropriate measuring instrument
- thinking about the need for accuracy
- making rules for fair testing
- collecting and comparing a set of data

Equipment

- rulers
- tape measures
- home-made tape measures (see *Invention* on p52)
- callipers
- micrometer gauge

Getting started

This activity can be done with one or more groups.

Ask the children to judge by eye, then find out by measuring, who has the longest forefinger in the group. An additional task could be to find out if the longest fingers are also the thinnest.

Important mathematics to discuss

As the lengths of the children's fingers will be fairly similar it is important for children to be as accurate as possible in measuring. 'Fairness' is important too; children will need to measure all fingers in the same way. If children decide to measure the forefingers from the place between the forefinger and middle finger they will have a problem if using rulers with a space before the 0. Make sure children are aware of this, and agree a way to deal with the problem.

Questions to ask the children

What are you using to measure with?
Is it accurate enough?
What units are you using?

Will you include long finger nails?
What about short ones?
Is it fair?

How are you going to measure the fingers?

How can you make it a fair test?

How accurate do you need to be?
These measurements are the same. Would it be possible to measure even more accurately?

Who has the longest forefinger in your group?
And in the class?

Other ideas

- Who in the class has the longest foot?
- Are both your feet the same size? Does everybody have both feet the same size?
- Who has the widest hand-span?
- Make a poster, picture or frieze that will fit on a pillar (or between the two windows) in the hall.

- How would you find the exact length of a wire about 3 metres long?
- Who travels the furthest to school? How can you find out?
- On a map find the shortest route from school to the railway station. (This activity can be adapted to suit any class trip.)

Can the children...

compare two fingers directly and say which is longer?
draw round two hands and compare the fingers by means of a piece of string?
Level 2

draw round two or more hands and find which finger is longest, using a length of string or tape measure?
understand the importance of using a 'fair' method — that is, measuring between the same two points on every hand?
use centimetres and millimetres in measuring fingers, though without great accuracy?
Level 3

choose the appropriate unit for measuring (for example, metres for the hall, millimetres for the circumference of a finger)?
use metres, centimetres and millimetres in measuring, with an appropriate degree of accuracy?
record their work using standard notation for metres, centimetres and millimetres?
use appropriate language (for example, 'circumference', 'unit')?
Level 4

measure distance with reasonable accuracy on a map, using the scale given to translate their measurement into distance on the ground?
find a way of converting distance measured on a map to 'real' distance?
understand that inaccuracy of a centimetre in measuring distance on a map equates with a far bigger inaccuracy in the real world?
use instruments with a fine degree of accuracy, such as a micrometer gauge for measuring the thickness of hair? **Level 5**

Weigh a letter

Children will experience

- weighing with a purpose
- using weights or reading a scale
- using simple problem-solving strategies
- thinking about the need for accuracy

Equipment

- leaflet on postage rates for overseas mail
- card, various weights of paper including airmail paper, various sizes of envelope, stamps
- letter scales or equivalent (with weights)
- weighing scales which display a readable scale
- globe

Getting started

This activity can be done with a group, or with the whole class.

Ask the children to write a letter, or make a card (real or make-believe), to send to someone abroad. They should put the letter or card in an envelope and address it, then weigh it, and use the postage rates chart to work out how much the postage will be.

(The reason for working with letters to go abroad is that finer weight differences apply than when mailing within the UK. However, the activity could also be done with letters to a UK destination.)

Important mathematics to discuss

Discuss how easy or difficult it is to estimate the weight of something like a letter. The children can hold the letter in one hand and think of other things that feel of similar weight.

Questions to ask the children

Hold the letter on the palm of your hand. How much do you think it weighs?

Do you need to put more weights on there, or take some off?

How accurate can you be, weighing the letter that way? Is that good enough?

You can't say exactly what the letter weighs, but can you tell me its approximate weight?

Look at the postage rates chart. Which weight band does it fall in?

How much will it cost? What stamps could you use?

Other ideas

- Children can pack up parcels and work out how much it would cost to send those, within the UK or outside.

- Help children to collect tiny objects (paper clip, brooch, coin, pin…) and put them in order of weight.

- Ask the children to work out how many pound coins are in a sealed envelope, having given them one pound coin to weigh.

- Ask children to find out whether the scales and balances they use in school are accurate.

- At the time of writing you can send a letter first class for 26p as long as it weighs 60 grams or less. What is the biggest letter (and envelope) you can send for 26p?

Can the children...

use a balance to compare the weights of two packets or parcels directly and say which is heavier?
Level 2

weigh a letter using a balance and weights, and say "It weighs more than… grams and less than… grams"?
put several letters into weight order?
explain that grams are used for finding the weight of light objects?
Level 3

weigh a letter using a balance with a readable scale, and say "It weighs between… grams and… grams"?
say what size the intervals are on the scale?
say what value any marker on the scale represents?
Level 4

weigh a parcel and use costing charts from the post office to work out what stamps to put on it?
find the weight of a parcel using both analogue and digital scales and discuss which is the best kind to use?
calculate how much weight could be added or subtracted to make two or more parcels the same weight?
Level 5

Max box

Children will experience

- estimating and measuring capacity
- using standard units of capacity
- recording data for a purpose
- calculations involving capacity
- planning work and working systematically

Equipment

- A4 paper or card
- sticky tape
- cubes, rice, sand, puffed rice, polystyrene 'squiggles'…
- rulers
- calibrated measuring jugs or cylinders
- computer spreadsheet

Getting started

This activity can be done with a group or with the whole class.

Ask the children to make an open box by cutting squares from each corner of a sheet of A4 paper or card and folding up the sides. The box should have the greatest possible capacity.

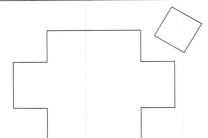

Important mathematics to discuss

Talk about how to measure the capacity. Some children will need to fill their box with a material such as polystyrene 'squiggles', and then pour these into a calibrated measuring jug or cylinder. Some older children will be able to work out the capacity of the box by measuring its dimensions and using the formula 'volume = l × b × h'; they may also be able to use a spreadsheet to explore potential volumes without even making up the boxes.

If children tumble cubes into their box, they will leave gaps which can't be measured; they should organise them neatly in rows to minimise the gaps. Materials such as marbles or polystyrene 'squiggles' will also leave gaps. Discuss with the children whether or not this matters.

Make sure children understand the difference between volume and capacity (one is the amount of space occupied, the other is the amount a container can hold). They are measuring the capacity of their boxes by measuring the volume of matter the boxes can hold.

Questions to ask the children

What is the capacity of your box?
Can you make a box that holds even more?

How do you know that is the biggest box you can make from that piece of card?

You are filling that box with cubes. Does it matter how you arrange them?
Does it matter if you fill your box to overflowing?

Which holds more – your box or Freya's?
How can you find out?

Other ideas

◆ Try using a different size of paper. What is the largest capacity box you can make with A3 paper? (Is it twice the capacity of the A4 box you made?)

◆ Make a box from A4 paper with the smallest possible capacity.

◆ Make a box without cutting off any of the paper.

◆ Make boxes from squared paper; graph their capacities against their surface areas.

Can the children...

measure the approximate capacity of their box, in marbles or cubes, by filling it higgledy-piggledy?

find a way to compare the approximate capacity of two boxes?

Level 2

measure the approximate capacity of their box in cubes by filling it with neat rows and layers of cubes?

fill their box with sand, pour this into a measuring jug, and then read off the two amounts between which the volume of the sand lies?

say how many millilitres there are in a litre?

Level 3

measure the capacity of their box by filling it with rice or sand and then pouring the contents into a measuring jug and reading the scale?

say what is the value of the intervals on the measuring jug scale?

say what value any marker on the scale represents?

work out the volume of their box from measurements of its length, breadth and height?

Level 4

work out what shape the box with maximum capacity would have by trial-and-improvement, reasoning and/or drawing a graph?

use a spreadsheet to explore the maximum possible capacity of their boxes?

give the formula for working out the volume of their box as length × breadth × height?

Level 5

Pendulum

Children will experience

- how long a minute lasts
- telling the time to the nearest minute
- timing events to the nearest second
- decision making relating to the need for measuring time accurately

Equipment

- string
- Plasticine, weights, marbles, stones…
- sticky tape
- junk containers, jar lids, yoghurt pots…
- stopwatch or stopclock
- ordinary watch or clock
- sand timers

Getting started

This activity can be done in groups, or with the whole class.

Ask the children to make a pendulum that can be used to count seconds.

Important mathematics to discuss

The time of a swing of a pendulum is affected only by the length of string. This is why it can be useful for timekeeping. Air resistance will eventually make the swing shorter and shorter in length and so appear slower, but it still takes the same time to do one complete swing.

Talk about how accurate it is possible to be; it is easier to work in chunks of ten seconds, and work towards a pendulum that swings ten times in ten seconds, than it is to work with single swings.

Talk about other ways of measuring a second, such as counting "One elephant, two elephants, three elephants…". Are these methods more or less accurate than the instruments the children have made?

Questions to ask the children

How could you make that move more slowly? How could you make it move faster?

How are you timing your pendulum with the stopwatch?

If your pendulum takes just longer than 5 seconds to do 5 swings, what will happen if you let it do 10 swings?

What might your pendulum be useful for measuring?

Other ideas

- Make a sand or water clock.

- Make a simple marble run about 1 m long. If you increase the angle does the marble move more quickly?

- Use a stopwatch to time your friend running 100 m. Do it several times. What is their best time? What is the average time? (Is that mode, median or mean?)

- Find out about the accuracy that is used for some world records (times in a marathon, athletics races and so on) and compare these with endurance records.

- Measure your pulse: count the number of heart beats in 10 seconds, then multiply by 6 to see how many beats it does a minute.

Can the children...

use a 1-minute sand timer to tell when a minute has passed?

use comparisons between periods of time using words and phrases such as 'longer time', 'shorter time', 'faster', 'slower'?

Level 2

use a watch or minute timer to tell when 10 seconds has passed?

say where the second hand on a watch will travel in three minutes?

Level 3

explain that different degrees of accuracy are needed in different contexts?

convert times from minutes to seconds?

use a stopwatch accurately and for a purpose?

talk about the range of data collected, and calculate differences?

Level 4

find the mode and median of their set of data?

use a stopwatch accurately?

calculate the range and mean average of a set of data?

represent times to the nearest second using digital representations of hours, minutes and seconds?

Level 5

Books

Children will experience

◆ measuring area for a purpose

◆ rounding up

◆ multiplying for a purpose

◆ the use of standard notation for square centimetres and square metres

Equipment

◆ 1 cm squared paper

◆ books

◆ rulers

Getting started

This activity can be done with the whole class divided into groups.

Show children two sheets of 1 cm squared paper, one with an area of 400 square centimetres and one with an area of 800 cm². Allow the children to look closely at, and handle, the sheets, and write up the areas on the board, then hide the sheets.

Now ask children to find a book whose front cover they estimate has an area between 400 cm² and 800 cm². In their groups, they should find the area of each book cover and put the books in order accordingly.

Important mathematics to discuss

Remind the children about the difference between perimeter and area.

Talk about how you can know the areas of the sheets of squared paper — by counting the rows of squares, and the number of squares per row, and multiplying these two numbers. Emphasise that the squares are 1 cm, not 2 or 5 cm (like other squared paper the children may be familiar with).

Questions to ask the children

Approximately what is the area of that book? Can you visualise it covered with 1 centimetre squares? How many would there be?

How will you work out the area of that book cover? What measurements do you need to do?

Which of these two book covers do you think has a larger area?

Other ideas

- Would your school fit on a football pitch?

  Would the playground, if re-arranged, be as large as a football pitch?

  Would the classroom fit on a tennis court?

- Would half a sheet of standard wrapping paper be enough to wrap a shoe box?

- How many of these carpet squares would we need to cover the classroom floor? What would we do about the 'wet area'?

- Which of the classrooms would need the largest number of carpet tiles?

Can the children...

put a book on 2 cm or 5 cm squared paper, draw round it and count the squares accurately?
talk about what to do with the part squares?
Level 2

estimate which of two book covers has the greater area?
find the area of a book using 1 cm squared paper?
deal sensibly with part squares?
put the books in order of area once these are calculated?
Level 3

estimate the area of a book cover in square centimetres?
find the approximate area of a book cover by measuring its length and breadth to the nearest centimetre and multiplying?
use approximation as appropriate?
use the notation cm² for 'square centimetre' and explain what it means?
Level 4

say how many square millimetres there are in a square centimetre?
find the area of a book cover by measuring its length and breadth to the nearest millimetre and multiplying?
explain the formula for finding the area of a rectangle, $l \times b = a$?
Level 5

Draw a square

Children will experience

- working with and measuring angles
- finding ways to construct angles
- accurate drawing of regular polygons
- exploring the relationship beween external and internal angles of polygons

Equipment

- rulers
- set squares
- protractors or angle indicators
- Logo

Getting started

This activity can be done in groups or with the whole class.

Show the children some shapes that are a mixture of real squares and not-quite-squares (cut from paper or drawn) and talk with them about how they know whether a shape is a proper square or not. Then ask them to use instruments to draw a square on plain paper.

More experienced children could make an equilateral triangle, a regular hexagon or the net for a rectangular box or a pyramid (using plain, not squared, paper).

Important mathematics to discuss

Remind children that a square has four right angles and four equal sides, which results in both pairs of oppposite sides being parallel; explain that a square is a special case of a rectangle (that is, like all rectangles it has four right angles, but unlike other ones its sides are the same length).

Talk with the children about the angles and sides of other regular polygons. How could these be measured? If the polygon they have drawn has angles that are very slightly different is it still a regular shape? Regular polygons have all sides equal and all angles equal. A non-square rectangle is symmetrical but not regular.

If the children are using Logo, then every time they get the turtle to turn and move forwards, the amount of turn will relate to the exterior angle, not the interior one. This is very different to the experience of measuring an interior angle with an angle indicator. Make sure that children understand these differences.

The turn made by the turtle, 72°

Interior angle 108°

Questions to ask the children

Do the lines meet where they should do? How can you make sure they meet properly next time?

Are these lines the same length? Do they need to be?

If the angle you are drawing was bigger or smaller by 1°, what difference would it make to your shape?

Other ideas

- Use Logo to draw a square, rectangle, regular octagon, equilateral or isosceles triangle.

- Use Logo to make the net for a box.

- Use Logo to draw a shape such as a square, then make duplicates and turn them. Try to make sure the last one lies exactly on top of the first one.

- Make an envelope for a letter or card.

- You have made your box/square/pyramid. Write out the instructions so another child can make one the same.

- Draw a clock face, putting in the hours at the right places.

- Make a square from geo-strips or plastic Meccano. How can you tell it is a proper square?

- Draw a polygon with one right angle, two right angles, three right angles…

Can the children...

draw a square using a set square?

make a square from geo-strips or plastic Meccano?

say whether or not what they have made/drawn is a proper square?

Level 2

explain that a proper square needs to have four right-angled corners and four equal sides?

tell whether a corner/angle is or isn't a right angle?

explain how to fold and cut a rectangle to make a square and say why this works?

Level 3

use a protractor/angle indicator to measure and draw angles of 90°?

use a protractor/angle indicator to measure and draw angles up to 180°?

calculate the turn needed to draw an angle using Logo?

use a set square to draw a right-angled triangle or a square accurately, and explain what was done?

Level 4

use a protractor/angle indicator to draw angles up to 360°?

measure the angles of drawn shapes accurately?

use appropriate vocabulary to describe the angles they have drawn?

Level 5

Representing measures

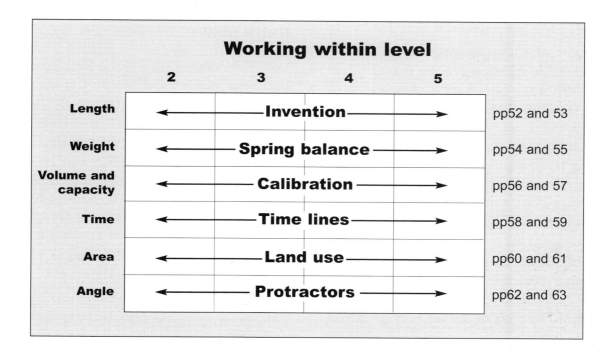

	Working within level				
	2	**3**	**4**	**5**	
Length	←	Invention		→	pp52 and 53
Weight	←	Spring balance		→	pp54 and 55
Volume and capacity	←	Calibration		→	pp56 and 57
Time	←	Time lines		→	pp58 and 59
Area	←	Land use		→	pp60 and 61
Angle	←	Protractors		→	pp62 and 63

Representing measures

The activities in this section are intended to give children experience of the way measurements are represented on scales and recorded on paper. They provide opportunities to:

— read and write measurements such as 2 metres or 5·6 kilograms

— read and write abbreviations for measurements such as 2 m or 5·6 kg

— choose suitable measuring instruments and read their measuring scales

Measurement scales

Measurement scales are of three kinds:

- ordinal
- interval
- ratio

Which they are depends on the properties of the quantity being measured. The first two of these are both linear scales.

Ordinal scales

Ordinal scales are the simplest form of scale, and do not involve the use of units. What they do, as the name suggests, is put things in order — first, second, third, and so on — as happens when 'measuring' IQ, or scoring ice-skating competitions. Such scales do not communicate anything about quantitative differences in performance; knowing that Jo, Sara and Chris came 1st, 2nd and 3rd in the ice-skating competition conveys nothing about the difference between the three competitors. We do not know whether Jo was only just ahead of Sara or a long way in front.

Interval scales

Interval scales not only put things in order, they also tell us about the gap between them; and this gap is a unit of consistent size (often with sophisticated scientific definitions).

The Celsius scale of temperature is one example of an interval scale. In this scale, the zero is defined rather than given: 0 °C is not 'no temperature', but is chosen as the freezing point of water. As each degree represents a meaningful unit, the gap between 3 °C and 5 °C is the same as that between 5 °C and 7 °C, (although 6 °C cannot be said to be twice as hot as 3 °C).

The calendar is another interval scale. Again, zero point is chosen as a particular time on a particular day (midnight on New Year's Eve). The hour is a meaningful unit, and the gap between 3 o'clock and 5 o'clock is the same as that between 5 o'clock and 7 o'clock .

Ratio scales

Length is one example of a ratio scale. Ratio scales combine the properties of ordinal scales and interval scales, but they have special properties of their own as well. When the attribute being measured has a 'true' zero value (no length) the measure can be expressed as a ratio of a known unit. It makes sense, for example, to talk about one object's length being twice that of another's — unlike temperature on the linear Celsius scale, where, as we said above, 6 °C is not twice as hot as 3 °C.

Length, weight, volume and capacity, area and angle are all are measures using a ratio scale.

Accuracy in reading scales

Most scales show units and sub-units. For example, the bold lines on the ruler represent centimetres and the shorter lines represent millimetres. This is similar to the kitchen scales where the kilograms (units) are represented by a bolder line than the grams (sub-units).

Not all scales have room to show single sub-units. A classroom ruler may be able to show centimetres and millimetres, but the kitchen scales may well have a marker only every 25 g — and numbers only every 200 g. This means that reading scales is not straightforward. In order to read the amount accurately children need to understand how the scale is divided: does each small space represent one, two, or more sub-units? If they get this wrong, their measurement will be wrong.

There is another problem children encounter in reading scales: some school equipment is not very sophisticated. For example, balances may not be sensitive to a small number of grams or part grams, and well-worn rulers make close approximations problematic.

Even when children can read a measure off a scale accurately, they can only ever get an approximation, as exact readings are impossible for a continuous measure like volume or length. Children need to be aware of this fact, and it should be raised in discussion as often as you deem necessary.

Children need to be taught how to use rulers accurately. The two most common errors they make are to start measuring from 1:

The stick is 7 centimetres long.

or to include the 'dead-end' (if it exists) on the ruler:

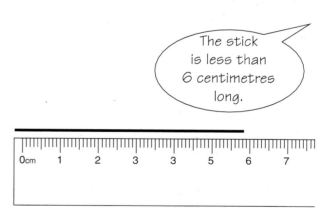

The stick is less than 6 centimetres long.

Invention

Children will experience

- reading measuring scales to the nearest division
- thinking about ways of measuring length
- thinking about the need for accuracy

Equipment

- pedometer
- estate agent's distance measurer, trundle wheel
- tape measures, rulers, metre rules
- paper, glue, sticky tape, tough fabric (non-stretchy)
- cubes, headless matches, paper clips…

Getting started

This activity can be done with the whole class, or a group at a time.

Ask the children to make a tape measure of their own for measuring curved surfaces such as a ball, waist or mug. Younger children might use non-standard units such as thumb-lengths, cubes, headless matches, but older children should use standard units such as decimetres or millimetres.

Older or more experienced children can work in pairs to make one tape measure which uses metric units and another which uses imperial units.

Important mathematics to discuss

Discuss with children what they know about tape measures already. See if they can describe any different types they have used and explain what they have in common. Discuss why there are different types.

Talk about what their measure could be used for and how they will make it as accurate as is necessary for the purpose.

Questions to ask the children

Does your tape measure stretch? Does it matter if it does?

How accurate is your tape measure? Why do you think that?

This piece of paper you are measuring comes to here on your measure. So how long is it?

What is between this mark and this one on your tape measure?

What couldn't you measure with your instrument? Why?

This thing is longer than your tape measure. How can we measure its length?

Other ideas

- Make an instrument for measuring the depth of water.
- Make an instrument suitable for measuring the length of classrooms.
- Make models of classroom furniture.

- Make a tape measure and a mini-trundle wheel and compare the two for accuracy. Can you use the mini-trundle wheel for measuring distances on a map?
- Build a very simple obstacle course (perhaps just one skittle at first) and program the Pip or the Roamer to go around it.

Can the children...

make marks of equal length on a strip of paper (using cubes or paper clips, for example)?
find some objects in the classroom that are longer, shorter or the same length as their measure?
Level 2

make marks of equal length on a strip of paper, using standard measures such as centimetres?
measure something using their own tape measure and say how long it is?
explain the importance of measuring from the zero on a tape measure bought in a shop?
measure some things using both their own and a tape measure bought in a shop and compare the measures for accuracy?
Level 3

make and use a tape measure using centimetres and millimetres?
evaluate the accuracy of their home-made tape measure?
Level 4

make and use a tape measure which shows both metric units and imperial units such as feet and inches?
make scale models?
discuss how measuring instruments such as the trundle wheel work?
suggest what would be the most suitable units and tools to use for a particular measuring task?
Level 5

Spring balance

Children will experience

- devising a scale to measure weight
- working with appropriate accuracy
- solving problems in measuring weight
- reading measuring scales to the nearest division

Equipment

- small polythene bags
- dressmakers' elastic or rubber bands
- safety pins, paper clips
- toothpicks (for pointers)
- a variety of balances and scales
- weights, conkers, cubes…

Getting started

This activity can be done with a group at a time.

Children make a spring balance in this way:

— attach a small polythene bag to one end of a length of elastic (or a rubber band) with a safety pin

— put a pointer at the top of the bag

— attach the elastic to a surface such as a table top, and arrange a sheet of paper behind the bag

— hang various objects in turn in the bag

— note where the pointer reaches for each object

Important mathematics to discuss

The balance can be calibrated by putting in 20 g weights one by one and noting where the pointer reaches each time. However, the balance will never be very accurate, or sensitive to small increments in weight or have a wide range.

Questions to ask the children

What would you expect to happen if you put in one cube, two cubes, three cubes…?

Does a peach weigh more than a pear? Use your spring balance to find out.

Can you calibrate your balance? What units are you going to use?

What are the lightest and the heaviest things you want to weigh with this balance?

What does it mean if you weigh something and it comes just above one of your calibrations?

Other ideas

- Make some 5 g, 10 g and 20 g weights out of plasticine or clay. How can you be sure each one is the weight it should be? What other weights would be useful?

  Use your home-made weights to weigh some things in the classroom.

- Use Plasticine to make a set of weights that can be used to balance any amount (for example, a 1 g, a 2 g and a 4 g weight can be used to balance something weighing 7 g).

- Make a conversion chart showing the relationship between kilograms and imperial measures and use it to find the weight of objects in both units.

- Draw a picture of kitchen scales showing how heavy the guinea pig/book/cake is.

Can the children...

explain that when they hang an object in the bag, the pointer drops because the object is pulling it down?
explain that the further the pointer drops, the heavier the object?
Level 2

explain the need for a pointer to act as a zero point?
explain that two 20 g weights pull the pointer down approximately twice as far as one 20 g weight.
use this to predict that three 20 g weights will pull the pointer down approximately three times as far?
use their spring balance to compare the weight of two objects?
Level 3

calibrate their home-made balance accurately using multiples of a gram?
Level 4

calibrate their balance accurately and evenly?
make a balance that can weigh in metric and imperial units?
Level 5

Calibration

Children will experience

- making a calibrated scale
- multiplying and dividing by 10
- working with ratio
- working with appropriate accuracy
- solving problems in measurement of volume and capacity

Equipment

- clean empty plastic bottles with the tops cut off
- measuring jugs or cylinders
- water, sand or rice
- funnels
- marker pens

Getting started

This activity can be done in groups.

Ask the children to make a calibrated cylinder of their own for measuring capacity. They can do this by using existing calibrated containers to measure an amount of water (or sand or rice) and pouring it into a clean empty plastic bottle that has had the top cut off.

Important mathematics to discuss

Remind the children about the differences between volume and capacity (a cylinder has the capacity to hold a certain volume of material). Ask the children to consider which units of measurement to use and discuss how they will test their measuring cylinder for accuracy.

The volume of solids is generally measured in cubic centimetres (cc) and that of liquids in millilitres (ml). However, as 1 cc is the same volume as 1 ml, the two measures are often used interchangeably.

Questions to ask the children

About how many millilitres would you need to fill a glass?

How could you use your cylinder to measure out a litre of water?

What is the largest volume of rice you could measure with your container?
What is the smallest amount?

What would your scale look like if the container had sloping sides like a pyramid or the neck of a bottle?

Where would 450 millilitres come on your scale? And 425 millilitres?
Where would 450 millilitres come on your friend's scale? And 425 millilitres?

Can you find the volume of 200 grams of sand?

Other ideas

- What do five heaped tablespoonfuls of rice measure in millilitres? And of sugar?

- Make a conversion chart showing the relationship between litres and imperial measures of volume and capacity.

- Make a calibrated cylinder for measuring capacity — in imperial as well as metric units.

- Make a box with a capacity of 500 cc.

- Make a paper cone for measuring and holding 250 cc of popcorn. Show where 50 cc, 100 cc and 200 cc would come to on it.

- Make a chart for converting metric measures to other useful units such as spoonfuls.

- Make some containers using a scale marked in intervals of 10 cc, or 25 cc, and use them to find the capacity of a variety of small containers.

Can the children...

using a half litre and a litre jug, find and mark the half litre and litre points on a large container with reasonable accuracy?
say how many half litres make a litre?
Level 2

using a 100 ml cylinder, mark their container in intervals of 100 ml?
measure quantities using their calibrated cylinder, with reasonable accuracy?
show how they would use their calibrated cylinder to measure 50 ml?
say how many 100 ml make a litre?
explain that the calibration intervals will not all be equal if the container has an irregular cross-section?
Level 3

use a litre container to find the number of litres in a gallon and explain what they have found out?
use their calibrated cylinder to find the capacity of smaller containers to the nearest 10 ml?
express capacities using decimal form (for example, say "That container holds 0·6 litres")?
Level 4

mark their cylinder with appropriate sub-units accurately, and explain their decisions?
find the metric equivalent of a pint of sand to the nearest 10 ml?
mark the cylinder, on the opposite side from the metric scale, with imperial units (pints and fluid ounces)?
make a chart to convert metric units of capacity to imperial units?
Level 5

Time lines

Children will experience

◆ putting events in time order

◆ developing a suitable scale for measuring time

◆ calculations involving the passage of time

Equipment

◆ 1 m or 2 m strips of paper

◆ number lines

◆ rulers

◆ tape measures

◆ calculators

Getting started

This activity can be done in groups, or with the whole class.

Ask each of the children to make a time line showing their life. Encourage them to be as accurate as they can.

Important mathematics to discuss

Talk to the children about number lines and discuss how a time line will have to be different. How many months might it need to show? And would weeks or days be shown too?

Children might want to start by making a list of all the things in their lives that have been important.

Questions to ask the children

You are 9 and a bit. So how many years will there need to be on your line?

Will you divide up the line equally between the years? Or how will you do it?

How will you show events on the time line?

How will you show things that lasted — like your years at school?

Are you going to show each month? Each week?

What is going to be workable?

How long ago in years and months is it since you started school?

Could you work out the number of days as well?

Other ideas

- Make a time line for your ideal day. Be as accurate as possible.

- Make a time line that shows when everyone in your family was born. How many months and years are there between the oldest and the youngest person?

- Make a marble run that takes exactly a minute.

- Make a timer to measure 1 minute, 5 seconds, an hour…

- Make a time line showing how much of a day's TV on your favourite channel is devoted to chat shows, how much to news, how much to soaps…

- Make a chart that you can use to know what time it is in Hong Kong, where your grandmother lives.

- Make a chart that can help you work out the time anywhere in the world.

- Make a calendar for next year to photocopy and distribute round the school.

Can the children...

make a time line showing their lives, where the years occupy different amounts of space?

put events in time order?

use the time line to say how many years ago special times in their lives were?

Level 2

make a time line showing their life, where each year occupies the same amount of space?

explain why each year needs to take up the same amount of space on the line?

find a way of showing events on the time line?

put events into order according to the year they happened?

Level 3

make a time line showing their lives, where each year and month occupies the appropriate amount of space?

calculate the time that has elapsed between one event and another?

Level 4

extend their time line back to show things that happened before they were born?

make a 1-year time line showing annual events?

Level 5

59

Land use

Children will experience

◆ comparison of area

◆ using the scale on a map to solve problems about area

◆ estimation and approximation of area

◆ using an extended vocabulary for discussion of area

Equipment

◆ Ordnance Survey map of area around school

◆ aerial photograph of school and surrounds (possibly enlarged on a photocopier)

◆ old maps of area

◆ local map downloaded from Internet

Getting started

This activity can be done in groups, or with the whole class.

Ask children to look at the map and find an area of 4 km² with your school roughly in the middle.

What is the approximate area taken up by each of the following: buildings, parks, factories, roads, fields…?

Ask the children if they could make a square grid on tracing paper to help them to find the approximate area of important features on the map.

Important mathematics to discuss

Talk about the difference between what they see on the map and the real thing, paying particular attention to the idea of scale. Are the scales on the available maps the same or different?

Older children can be encouraged to talk about the scale factors of the maps.

Questions to ask the children

> Roughly what percentage of the whole area is taken up with fields?
>
> With roads?

> Look at the old and the new maps. What land use has changed most?

> Look at this old map.
>
> How has land use changed?
>
> How much more land is used for buildings nowadays?

> What is the approximate area of the farm land here?
>
> How could you find out?

> How much of the land on the map is taken up by the school?
>
> Is that more or less than the park?

Other ideas

◆ Make an imaginary map of 4 km². Where would you choose to put the school on this map?

How much area would you devote to playing fields, housing, shops…?

◆ Make a large-scale map of 1 km². Imagine you have to build houses or flats for 100 people, and provide gardens or parks for them. Draw on the map how you will use the space.

How much living space will each person have? How much open space?

Can the children...

talk about the map in terms of what a bird might see if it looked down on the school area?
find what looks like the largest building/field?
draw a bird's eye view of the classroom?
Level 2

explain that a square kilometre is a square whose sides are all 1 km long?
explain that the map shows everything much smaller than it really is?
explain that if two things are the same size in real life, they will be the same size on the map too?
compare the main features and say which occupies the largest/smallest area?
Level 3

work out the approximate area taken up by, say, fields (for example, say "It's nearly three square kilometres")?
explain what the scale on the map represents and say how many times larger the features are in reality?
explain that different scales do not alter the actual ground area of a feature?
Level 4

say roughly what percentage of the whole area is taken up by, say, buildings (for example, say "It's about 60% or 70%")?
compare land use over a period of time and calculate differences?
Level 5

Protractors

Children will experience

◆ using angle measuring tools

◆ measuring angles with accuracy

◆ estimating, ordering, measuring and calculating angles

◆ an extended vocabulary of angles

Equipment

◆ protractors or angle measurers

◆ plastic Meccano or geo-strips

◆ flattened straws and paper fasteners

◆ rulers and pencils

Getting started

This activity can be done in groups, or with the whole class.

Children work in pairs. Both children make an 'angle' with plastic Meccano or flattened straws and paper fasteners. They then swap over and use a protractor to measure each other's angles. They will need to keep some kind of record.

Younger children could simply classify the angles as 'more than a right angle', 'less than a right angle' and so on. Older children can draw angles for their partners to measure, rather than make them.

When children have worked in this way for a while you can call the group together and ask them to share what they have done.

Important mathematics to discuss

Talk with older children about acute, obtuse and reflex angles. Explain that :

— **acute** angles are less than a right angle (less than 90°)

— **obtuse** angles are between one right angle and a straight line (between 90° and 180°)

— **reflex** angles are more than a straight line (between 180° and 360°)

Emphasise that an angle is a measure of turn. Introduce the idea that every acute, right and obtuse angle has a corresponding reflex angle and talk about how the size of this can be calculated.

Questions to ask the children

The protractor says both 30° and 150°. Which one is right?

Why does it say two numbers there?

Can you make an acute angle? Can you make an obtuse angle? A reflex angle?

Where do you put the protractor? Where do you start counting the degrees from?

You say your straws make an acute angle. I can see a reflex angle there too. Can you? How big is it?

Other ideas

- Make a large, blackboard protractor.
- Draw two lines that cross. What are all the angles there? Measure them.
- Draw an angle of 90°, making both arms the same length. Join the sides to make a triangle and measure the two new angles. Try some more triangles with a right angle but with different length sides. What can you find out?

- Find out about the angles in a rhombus and a parallelogram and explain their properties.
- Find out where angles have been used in the classroom/school/home. Which can you find most of?
- Draw some quadrilaterals and then draw in the diagonals. What do you notice about the angles made where the diagonals cross?

Can the children...

say whether an angle is exactly a right angle, or more or less than a right angle? find examples of angles in the classroom that are more than, less than or exactly right angles?   Level 2

use the terms 'acute', 'right' and 'obtuse' to describe angles? make an acute, right or obtuse angle to order?   Level 3

classify angles as 'acute', 'right', 'obtuse' or 'reflex', or as straight lines? make an acute, right, obtuse or reflex angle to order? use a protractor or angle measurer properly, knowing how to place it on the lines? explain where to start counting the degrees from on a protractor or angle measurer? Level 4

construct angles of a given size accurately? explain when it might be more appropriate to use a set square instead of a protractor? explain that the internal angles in a triangle add up to 180°? draw acute and obtuse angles of a given size and calculate the size of the associated reflex angle — without measuring? Level 5

Relationships
between units

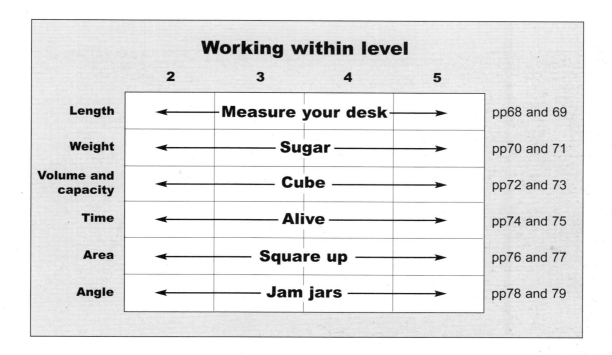

Working within level

	2	3	4	5	
Length	←	Measure your desk		→	pp68 and 69
Weight	←	Sugar		→	pp70 and 71
Volume and capacity	←	Cube		→	pp72 and 73
Time	←	Alive		→	pp74 and 75
Area	←	Square up		→	pp76 and 77
Angle	←	Jam jars		→	pp78 and 79

Relationships between units

The activities in this section can help children to:

— know the relationship within each family of units (a metre is 100 cm, a centimetre is 10 mm, and so on)

— understand the fact that very small units (such as millimetres) are grouped to make the next size of unit (a centimetre) and so on

— understand that within the metric system the ratios are the same as they are in the decimal number system

— learn something of the relationships between different families of units: a metre is just more than a yard; a teaspoon is about 5 ml; and so on

Children who have a wide experience of the relationships between units, and of their relative sizes, are well-equipped to select the appropriate units to work with, whatever the task. So, if asked to decide on the units to use when recording the circumference of the world, the thickness of a piece of paper or the weight of a coin these children will be able to give a

sensible answer. They will also be equipped to deal with problems that require them to 'round to the nearest…'.

Metric families of units

The activities in this section give children experience of working with a variety of units and sub-units, and of using the relationships within the families of units. If children have practical experience like this, they can gain a better understanding of the use of various units and their sub-divisions than if they had only read about them or learned the facts by heart.

> Are you 1000 000 seconds old?
>
> There are 60 seconds in 1 minute
> There are 60×60 seconds in 1 hour
> 60×60 = 3600 second in 1 hour
> There are 24 hour in one day
> 24 × 3600 seconds = 86,400
> seconds in 1 day.
> In one week there are 7×86,400
> seconds.
> 7×86,400 = 604,800 seconds
> This is more than ½ million
> seconds. In two week there are
> more than 1 million seconds.
> 14 day × 86,400 seconds =
> 1209600 seconds.
> I am not 1000000 seconds old I
> am more than 1000 000 old.

Work on the activity *Alive* on p74.

Making a container to hold 500 cc — an extension activity on p73.

Metric and imperial

As well as learning about the relationships within the families of metric units, children also need to experience the relationships between the families of metric and imperial units: for example, that a metre is just a bit more than a yard, that a pint is a bit more than half a litre and a pound is a bit less than half a kilogram. In the everyday world, imperial measures and metric are both used, and some people still prefer the imperial. Many children, when asked how tall they are or what their weight is, answer in feet and inches or stones and pounds, despite the fact that schools have been teaching metric measurement since the 1970s and shops have to use metric measures when selling goods.

<u>Turns & Angles</u>

Description	Turn
Quality Street	360°
Clasic Italyian	46°
White	40°
Square Box	360°

Put the lid on and make a mark   Do the lid up and make a mark   Now measure the angle between the marks

Work done by Year 6 children on the activity *Jam jars* on p78.

<u>Accuracy in Measuring Angles</u>

Type of Jar	Degrees
Sauce Jar	23°
Body Shop Jar	720 r '35 = 855 855°
The Body Shop Cream Jar	295°
Jar With White Lid	35°

<u>Method</u>

On each jar that we chose we made a starting point using a sticker, if the jar was black and a felt pen if it was a clear jar. We turned the lid and when it came off we made another mark. We then measured the length between the two marks with a protractor to see how many degrees it took for the lid to come off. The results are in the chart above.

Measure your desk

Children will experience

- the need for sub-units
- relationships between standard units
- selecting appropriate measurement tools
- estimating length

Equipment

- objects one millimetre, one centimetre, ten centimetres, and one metre wide or long
- tape measures, metre rules, rulers

Getting started

This activity can be done with a group or the whole class.

Show the children a series of objects with at least one dimension of one millimetre, one centimetre and one metre (for example, a drawing pin with 'stalk' 1 mm thick, a centicube, a metre rule). Give the children time to handle the objects, and discuss the relationships between the lengths.

Now ask the children to:

— estimate the length and width of their desk using any of these units

— measure the desk using whatever tools they see fit

— record the measurements, specifying which units they are using

Length	Width
1·56 m	0·79 m
154·6 cm	77·7 cm

Important mathematics to discuss

When the children have completed this, discuss their results with them, and record on the board the various different ways of recording the same dimensions.

Talk about discrepancies between measurements of the same desk: how close are 0·78 m and 77 cm? Talk about degrees of accuracy: does it make better sense to say the desk is exactly 77·7 cm wide, or that it is nearly 78 cm, or that it is between 77·5 and 78 cm wide?

Questions to ask the children

Heather says the desk is 1·56 metres long and you say it is 157 centimetres. What is the difference between your two measurements?

Which of you is most accurate?

You measured it in centimetres, did you? What did you do with the little bits left over?

What is the relationship between metres and centimetres?

Can you write that measurement in centimetres? Can you write it in metres?

Other ideas

- If you wanted to walk a mile up and down your stairs, how many times would you have to make the journey? What if you wanted to walk one kilometre?

- Which travels faster, a train which travels 300 km in 4 hours or one which travels 200 miles in 2 hours?

- Is it possible to measure the height of the school by counting bricks and layers of mortar? How many yards and feet high is it? What is this in metric measurements?

- What are the differences in height between all the children in your group, in metric and imperial units?

Can the children...

explain the limitations of using a non-standard unit, such as their hand-spans, to measure a length such as their desk?   **Level 2**

explain the advantages of using a standard unit, such as a centimetre, to measure a distance such as the width of their desk? say how many centimetres there are in a metre?   **Level 3**

estimate and measure using a unit of their choice, and deal with 'left over bits' by using decimals? give the equivalents in centimetres or millimetres of any length expressed in metres? say which of various metric and imperial units is biggest/smallest? put units of the same family together (for example, yards, feet and inches, or kilometres, metres and centimetres)? say what are the abbreviated forms for writing metric and imperial units?   **Level 4**

say what the relationship is between units of the same family (for example, yards, feet and inches, or kilometres, metres and centimetres)? work out some approximate conversions from metric to imperial and back? use simple time/distance graphs to calculate speeds of travel? explain that a metre is about one yard and three inches?   **Level 5**

Sugar

Children will experience

◆ calculating weight in a meaningful context

◆ making sensible approximations

◆ problem solving using volume and weight

◆ relations between units of weight

Equipment

◆ teaspoons

◆ sugar

◆ computer spreadsheet

◆ balances and weights

◆ scales

Getting started

(The research for this activity should be done by a couple of children or a small group. However, once the data have been collected from the staff, the whole class can work in groups, using the data in their own way.)

Ask the children to find out how much sugar the staff get through in their tea and coffee on a typical day. They should use this information to work out the weight of sugar needed by the staff every week/month/year.

Older children may be able to use a computer spreadsheet to help them with their calculations.

Important mathematics to discuss

Children need to talk about the fact that they are starting with a measure of volume (teaspoonfuls) and translating that into a measure of weight (grams and kilograms).

Children will need to talk through their strategies for tackling this problem, with each other and you. Once they have reached a final figure, how can they check this? (Who buys the sugar for the staffroom? How much and how often?)

Questions to ask the children

What measures are usually used for sugar? Dessertspoons? Teaspoons?

How many teaspoonfuls of sugar are there in 500 grams?
How could you find out?

If you use 2 teaspoonfuls of sugar in each cup of tea, and drink 5 cups a day, how many calories is that?

How do you buy sugar?
What weight package does it usually come in?
How many teaspoonfuls are there in a packet of sugar?

70

Other ideas

- How much sugar do children in the class take in their hot drinks?

- How much does the average adult take in a cup of tea? How much sugar will be needed for tea at the next parents' evening?

- Ask children to discover, through weighing, how many 10 g weights balance 100 g; and how many 20 g weights balance 1 kg.
  What other equivalents can they find?

- What happens to the weight of a litre of water when 100 g of salt is dissolved in it?

- People often weigh themselves in stones. How many pounds is this? How many kilograms? How will you find out?

Can the children...

find out how many teaspoonfuls of sugar fit in an eggcup, by counting?

find out how many eggcupfuls of sugar balance 500 g, by counting?

Level 2

work out how many teaspoonfuls of sugar are used in the staffroom in a day if they know the number of teaspoonfuls each member of staff uses?

work out how many teaspoonfuls of sugar are used in a week, if they know the amount used in a day?

Level 3

discuss whether one day's usage of sugar can be taken as typical?

work out how many teaspoonfuls of sugar there are in a packet?

talk about the fact that they are working with both volume and weight?

explain that though there are x teaspoonfuls of sugar in a 1 kg packet, there would not necessarily be the same number of teaspoonfuls of salt, or sand, in a kilogram?

Level 4

work out the weight of sugar needed by the staff every week/month/year?

find the cost of this?

find a way of checking their calculations?

use a spreadsheet to help them with their calculations?

Level 5

Cube

Children will experience

- a feel for the size of units of capacity and volume
- the relationships between millilitres, cubic centimetres and litres
- the relationship between volume and capacity

Equipment

- squared paper
- plain paper or card
- centimetre and decimetre cubes (plastic or wood)
- measuring jugs or cylinders
- calculators
- sand, rice, polystyrene 'squiggles'…

Getting started

This activity should be done in groups.

Ask the children to make a cube that holds exactly 1000 cubic centimetres or millilitres. As far as possible allow children to work as a group, discussing the problem and devising their own methods for solving it. However, some children will need help from you to get them started.

Younger children may work by trial and improvement, making a box and finding its capacity by filling it with, say, sand and pouring this into a measuring jug. Older children should be encouraged to work out the dimensions such a cube must have before making it.

Important mathematics to discuss

Discuss the fact that 1 l is the same as 1000 ml, and that millilitres and cubic centimetres have the same volume, so that 1 l is also equivalent to 1000 cc. (Conventionally, millilitres are used to measure the volume of a liquid and cubic centimetres the volume of a solid.)

Questions to ask the children

How might you set about this?
What information do you need to find out?

Is your box a cube?
What is special about a cube?

About how big is a cubic centimetre?
Can you show me with your hands?
About how big is a litre? Can you show me with your hands?

If you know the length, breadth and height of a box, how do you find its volume?
So if you know the box's volume, how can you find the length, breadth and height?

Other ideas

- Make a measuring cylinder that shows both pints and litres. Or mark pints, gallons and litres inside a bucket.
- Find a way of making a 100 ml measure. How many cubic centimetres is that?
- What would you need to move 1 000 000 mm³ of sand? A jug? A wheelbarrow? A truck?

- Cowboys were supposed to wear ten-gallon hats. Can you find out how many litres this is? What is it in cubic centimetres?

  How big would a ten-gallon hat be? Could you show me?

- Make or find three containers which hold 500 ml, 250 ml and 100 ml. What amounts could you measure with them?

Can the children...

make a box and tell you how many centimetre cubes they have used to fill it?
fill their box with sand, pour this into a measuring jug, and then say whether their box holds more or less than a litre?
Level 2

make a cube-shaped box?
fill their box with sand, pour this into a measuring jug, and then read off the two amounts between which the volume of the sand lies?
say how many millilitres there are in a litre?
Level 3

say that one cubic centimetre is 'as big as' one millilitre?
work out the dimensions their cube needs to be, with support?
make a cube 10 cm x 10 cm x 10 cm and measure its capacity?
find a container of given capacity such as a shampoo bottle, and calculate how many times it could be filled from a litre jug?
Level 4

work out the dimensions their cube needs to be, independently?
explain the difference between volume and capacity?
calibrate a litre jug using displacement?
Level 5

Alive

Children will experience

- learning and using the relationships between the various units of time
- using and applying number operations
- solving problems involving time
- calculations using days, months and years
- working with large numbers

Equipment

- calculators
- spreadsheets

Getting started

This activity can be done in groups, or with the whole class.

Ask the children to find a way to solve one of the following problems:

Level 3
How many weeks (or months) have you been alive?

Levels 3 and 4
Have you been alive for a thousand days?

Levels 4 and 5
Have you been alive for a million seconds?

Important mathematics to discuss

Children will need to use the relationships between the various units of time when working on these problems. You or the children could make a chart showing these, to display on the wall. (It is worth pointing out to the children that this is one of the few measures which is not based on the number ten.)

Questions to ask the children

> How many months are there in a year (or weeks in a month or a year)?
>
> How does this knowledge help to solve the problems?

> You've found your age in months.
>
> How will you find out how many weeks old you are?

> A million minutes sounds a very long time. Do you think anyone in this room has been alive that long?
>
> How can you check?

> How will you get the spreadsheet to change your age into months (or weeks or days)?

> How will you find out if you have lived for 1000 weeks?

Other ideas

- How much of your life have you spent cleaning your teeth? Sleeping? Watching TV? Eating?

- Is it possible for someone to have lived for 1 million hours?

- Find out the age of the oldest person in the world and work out the number of hours that person has lived.

- Make a table to work out the number of days (or hours) that people of any age have been alive.

- How long do you spend at school in a year?

- How many hours of their life has your teacher/parent spent washing their hair/shaving/cooking?

- Has anyone in your family been alive for 3000 weeks?

Can the children...

say how many months there are in a year?
explain that for every year they have been alive there are 12 months?
appreciate that there will be more months than years in a person's age?
Level 2

talk confidently about the relationships between hours, days, months and years?
use a calculator to work out the number of months or weeks they have lived?
record their results?
organise their work, sustaining the calculations until they have the 'answer'?
Level 3

say how many days there are in a year?
say the number of seconds in a minute and the number of minutes in an hour?
calculate their age in days without a calculator?
use a calculator to calculate their age in minutes or seconds?
find the approximate length of time taken to perform everyday tasks, and from this calculate the amount of time spent on each during a year?
Level 4

calculate their age in seconds without a calculator?
deal appropriately with leap years?
round answers up or down appropriately?
write appropriate formulae into a spreadsheet to convert ages from one unit to another?
Level 5

Square up

Children will experience

- the relationship between linear and square measures
- the relationship between units of area
- using and applying multiplication
- solving problems involving area and perimeter

Equipment

- newspaper or scrap paper
- 1 cm squared paper
- calculators
- square decimetres (plastic or wood)
- rulers

Getting started

This activity can be done in groups, or with the whole class.

Ask the children to make a rectangle or square of area 1000 cm^2, using paper. (Younger children can be offered square decimetres and asked to make a rectangle ten times as large.)

Important mathematics to discuss

You may want to remind children about the difference between perimeter and area. Give a concrete example such as a field, where the fence goes round the perimeter and the animals feed on the area enclosed.

When children have completed their task, discuss the wide range of rectangles that can be made with an area of 1000 cm^2 (long, thin ones; fatter, squarer ones…). Making a square of that area would involve finding the square root of 1000 with the calculator — using the square root button, or by a trial-and-improvement method.

Talk about the fact that their rectangles, at 1000 cm^2, are one tenth the area of a square metre (1 m^2).

Questions to ask the children

How long will your rectangle be?
And how wide?
So what will the area be?

If you wanted to make a square of area 1000 square centimetres, how long would the sides be? How could you find out?

Is that the only rectangle you could make with that area?

How big is your rectangle?
Do you need to count every square?

How could you work out the number of square millimetres there are in your rectangle?

Other ideas

- How much space (area) is there in your class? How much does each person have at their desk?

  Is there any wasted space? How much? Could it be used better?

- What could you keep in a pen with a floor area of 1 000 000 cm²? A mouse, a guinea pig, a horse, an elephant?

  What could you keep in a pen with a floor area of 1 000 000 mm²?

- Get house or flat particulars from an estate agent. In the playground, draw out the dimensions of two of the rooms. Which has the greatest area?

- Make different shapes, all with an area of 1 m².

Can the children...

find things in the classroom with an area greater or lesser than a square decimetre (using a sample square decimetre as a check)?

Level 2

draw or make a rectangle from squared paper and find its area by counting the square centimetres?

draw or make a rectangle with an area ten times that of a square decimetre?

explain the difference between perimeter and area?

Level 3

work out the dimensions of a rectangle of area 1000 cm²?

make such a rectangle?

explain that they would need ten of their rectangles to make 1m²?

Level 4

tackle the problem independently?

work out what would happen to the area of their rectangle if all the dimensions were doubled?

use a calculator to work out the dimensions of a square of area 1000 cm²?

Level 5

Jam jars

Children will experience

- the notion of angle as an amount of turn
- the need for a reference point to start measuring from
- using angles in a 'real life' situation
- the relationship between amount of turn and angle

Equipment

- jars and screw-top lids
- vacuum flasks
- drink containers

Getting started

This activity can be done in groups.

Give the children several jars or other containers with screw-top lids (two each, or more). Ask them to screw the lids on, then find out how much each lid must be turned in order to remove it. It is a good idea to help children make marks on the jar and lid when the lid is on, to show the 'closed' position.

Younger children can investigate whether a lid needs more or less than a whole turn, and perhaps how many turns to the nearest quarter.

Older and more experienced children can investigate approximately how many degrees each lid takes. (One possibility is to actually measure the amount of turn by glueing a circular protractor on the lid of the jar.)

Important mathematics to discuss

Younger children may need to stick to working with whole, half and quarter turns. You can introduce the terms 'right angle' and 90° turn, but these may not have much significance for the children.

Older children who are dealing with degrees may need reminding, or telling, that a quarter turn is worth 90° and a full turn is the same as 360°.

Questions to ask the children

How will you know when you have done one full turn?
Or a half turn?

Is a quarter turn on a little bottle smaller than a quarter turn on a big jar?

Do you need more or less than a full turn to get that lid off?

How can you measure the amount of turn you use to get that lid off?

Do little lids need to be turned a smaller angle than big lids before they open?

Other ideas

- Do containers of runny liquids (honey, drinks…) need more turns to open or close them than containers of less runny things (set jam or pickle)?
- Are deep and shallow lids any different in the amount of turn needed?

- When the minute hand of a clock has turned through 90°, how much time has passed? Suppose it turns through 30°: how much time has passed?

  How much time has passed when it turns through a full rotation?

  When the hour hand of a clock turns through 60°, how much time has passed? What about if it turns through 390°?

Can the children...

say whether a lid needs more or less than a whole turn to open it?

Level 2

say how many quarter turns make a whole turn?

find out how many turns are needed to open a lid to the nearest half turn?

use the term 'right angle' correctly in relation to turns?

Level 3

find out how many turns are needed to open a lid to the nearest quarter turn?

discover approximately how many degrees are needed to open a lid?

say that a quarter turn is worth 90° and a full turn is the same as 360°?

Level 4

estimate with appropriate accuracy how many degrees a lid has been turned through?

measure with appropriate accuracy how many degrees a lid has been turned through?

make reasoned statements about the connection between the amount of turn and the amount of thread on the container?

Level 5

Using and applying measures

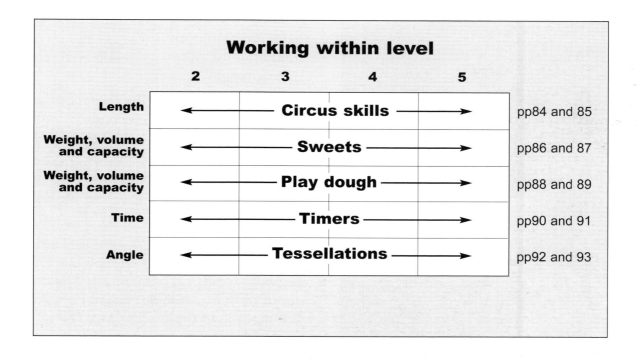

Working within level

	2	3	4	5	
Length	◄───────	Circus skills	───────►		pp84 and 85
Weight, volume and capacity	◄───────	Sweets	───────►		pp86 and 87
Weight, volume and capacity	◄───────	Play dough	───────►		pp88 and 89
Time	◄───────	Timers	───────►		pp90 and 91
Angle	◄───────	Tessellations	───────►		pp92 and 93

Using and applying measures

The tasks in this section give children the opportunity to:

— develop their higher order thinking skills

— apply their existing knowledge to a realistic challenge

— extend their learning through activity and enquiry

Why 'using and applying'?

Many of the problem-solving situations we have to deal with as adults involve measurement in some way or another. For example, working out how much paint to buy to decorate the kitchen, or which size of pruners will reach the top of the apple tree. Similar situations can be used in school to help children to see the relevance of their school mathematics to everyday life, and to develop their skills at problem solving.

Making a model boat involves children in tackling various measurement problems.

When children engage in applying the knowledge and skills they have developed, they gain greater responsibility for developing their learning and learn to work with increasing independence. Mathematical problems give them the opportunity to develop skills of cooperation by requiring them to work as part of a group and to communicate through discussion about the work.

Making decisions

In order to solve the problems presented in this section it will be necessary for the children to clarify how to set about their task, and what to do first. This will involve making some important decisions about what sort of measurements are needed, which units will be most appropriate, which tools would be best, what recording needs to be done and what calculations might be needed — all to be decided through discussion and negotiation. This decision making provides a valuable context for extending children's grasp of the mathematical language associated with measurement.

The decisions that need to be made in a measuring context can be very demanding because of the range of possible tools and units. Many children find this harder than deciding, for instance, which of the four rules to use in a number situation.

When children first look at a problem, and declare they don't know what to do, it can be tempting to make suggestions about how the problem might be solved. But the role of the teacher must be to enable the children to think their way through the problem.

This is best achieved through skilful open-ended questioning, asking, for example, "What information do you need?", "What do you know already?", and "What could you try first?"

Once children have managed to 'get into' the problem they should be encouraged to keep notes of their workings. This will help later when they prepare to present their work to their peers, perhaps in a plenary session at the end of the activity. These plenary sessions should be a regular part of the classroom life, and provide an opportunity for children to reflect on their learning, and appreciate just what they have achieved, as well as learning from other children's efforts.

Ria, Reyland, Louise and Daniel worked on one of the *Other Ideas* on p85, about making a doll one tenth of Ria's measurements.

What We did: We got ourselves in a group and we chose one person and measured that person. We wrote down the size of the things on the person that we measured and we split up the numbers into one tenth. Then we used the answers to make a paper doll.

Measurement	Actual	$\frac{1}{10}$
Height	139 cm	13.9
Shoulder	33 cm	3.3
Arm Length	60 cm	6.0
Arm Width	8 cm	0.8
Rib to Rib	30 cm	3.0
Down Leg	61 cm	6.1
Across Leg	14 cm	1.4
Down head	18 cm	1.8
Across head	15 cm	1.5
Shoulder to hip	30 cm	3.0
Down Neck	6 cm	0.6
Across Neck	13 cm	1.3

Circus skills

Children will experience

- finding a way of measuring length
- calculations involving measurement of length
- thinking about the need for accuracy
- selecting the appropriate tools and recording methods

Equipment

- wall-mounted height chart
- measuring tape
- metre stick

Getting started

This activity can be done with the whole class, organised in groups.

Ask the children to discuss one or more of these problems and find a way of solving them:

Imagine you are all doing a workshop in circus skills.

Levels 2 and 3

You are learning to walk on stilts 30 cm high, with long trousers to cover your legs. How tall will you appear to be when on stilts?

Levels 3 to 5

Everyone in your group is doing work on stilts. You all want to be the same height. How tall will everybody's stilts need to be?
You are doing a tumbling trick that involves standing on another person's shoulders. How high will you be able to reach standing on your partner's shoulders?
Will she/he be able to reach to exactly the same height?

Important mathematics to discuss

Talk about what units of measurement children will use and how accurate they need to be. Remind the group which is aiming to be the same height that everyone needs to be on stilts, not only the shorter people.

Questions to ask the children

How can you measure someone who is taller than the metre stick?

What rules will you make about the height you will reach — will it be with arms stretched as high as possible?

Will it make a difference to the height you and your friend reach if you include upstretched arms?

Now you've worked out the height you have to be off the ground, how tall will the stilts have to be for you to hold them comfortably?

All of your group have to be the same height. What length will the tallest person's stilts be?

Other ideas

- You've worked out how tall you will be with stilts. How long would your trousers have to be?

- The ringmaster wants you to do cartwheels across the circus ring. How far would you travel if you did ten cartwheels? How many cartwheels would you have to do to cover a distance of 30 m? What if she asked you to do somersaults?

- Sometimes in the circus people have to jump on a horse. What is the highest horse you could jump on? What about your friends?

- Who travels the furthest to school? How can you find out?

- Who in the class has the longest foot?

- Find the shortest route out of the school in case of fire.

- Make a doll whose measurements are $\frac{1}{10}$ of yours.

Can the children...

measure their height in centimetres using a wall-mounted height chart?
demonstrate approximately how much taller they would be with 30 cm added?
Level 2

find a way to measure their height without the use of a wall-mounted height chart?
calculate their 'height' when on 30 cm stilts?
calculate the extra length of trousers they would need with 30 cm stilts?
Level 3

work accurately to the nearest centimetre?
find ways of solving the problems to an appropriate degree of accuracy?
discuss what degree of accuracy is appropriate?
explain and record their methods of working clearly?
Level 4

record and calculate measurements using decimal notation (for example, 3·45 m)?
make deductions (for example, say that a person with long neck and head will give extra height in the tumbling trick only if they are the top person)?
Level 5

Sweets

Children will experience

- developing a feel for how much 100 gm is
- estimation of weight
- comparisons of weight and volume
- calculations with weight
- selecting the mathematics for a practical task

Equipment

- heavy sweets such as butterscotch
- lighter sweets such as flying saucers
- weighing scales
- balances and weights
- small paper bags

Getting started

This activity can be introduced to the whole class, then done by a group at a time, working in pairs.

Ask the children whether they would rather have 100 g of butterscotch or a bagful and whether they would rather have 100 g of flying saucers or a bagful. Show them a bagful of sweets in each case.

Important mathematics to discuss

Discuss with the children what their definition of a bagful will be; for example, must it be possible to twist the top to keep the sweets safe and clean? Ask what equipment they might need to use and how will they record their work.

Questions to ask the children

How much does that bagful of sweets weigh? How do you know?

How will you work out the difference in weight between the bag of flying saucers and 100 grams of them?

If you wanted 1 kilogram of sweets for a party, and the shop only sold butterscotch and flying saucers, which would you choose to get? Which would you get most of in a kilogram?

Which would you prefer, a bagful or 100 grams? Why? Which weighs more, a bagful or 100 grams?

You've found the weight of a bag of flying saucers. How would you find the weight of one of them?

Other ideas

- Can children find the weights of the juice, fruit and container in a tin of peaches? What proportion of the total weight is actual fruit?

- Give children three eggs and ask them to find which one weighs most. Is it also the largest?

- Get children to follow a simple recipe without your help. If it is successful, can they now make double the quantities?

- Three very hungry sand-eating monsters have just landed in the school. Can the children share out a bag (or 1 kg) of sand fairly between the three of them?

- Suppose big and little oranges are sold by weight, and they cost the same per kilo. Are big ones or little ones better value, given that you cannot eat the peel?

Can the children...

compare the weights of a flying saucer and butterscotch directly, using a balance, and say which weighs more?
weight out 100 g of sweets using a balance and weights?
compare the weight of 100 g of sweets with the weight of a bagful of the same sweets, using a balance?
Level 2

find out whether a bagful of sweets weighs more or less than 100 g?
find a way to solve the problem?
give a reasonable justification for their decision to choose either 100 g of sweets or a bagful?
Level 3

say whether they would get more butterscotch or flying saucers in a kilogram, and give reasons?
weigh sweets using a balance with a readable scale, and say "They weigh about... grams"?
say what size the intervals are on the scale?
say what value any marker on the scale represents?
Level 4

calculate the number of butterscotch or flying saucers they would get for 1 kg and explain their reasoning?
generalise that things of similar size do not necessarily weigh the same?
explain that you will get fewer heavy items than light ones for the same weight?
Level 5

Play dough

Children will experience

◆ converting from one unit to another

◆ using and applying number operations

◆ decision making using measures

◆ estimation

◆ using simple ratios

◆ using all four operations to solve problems involving mass and capacity

Equipment

◆ recipe for play dough

◆ ingredients and utensils as in recipe below

◆ kitchen scales

◆ measuring jug or cylinder

◆ cups, plastic bottles, yoghurt pots

◆ funnel

Getting started

This activity can be done in groups.

Pose the children this problem:

"In the USA, to save people weighing ingredients, recipes such as this one for play dough use cupfuls rather than grams. Can you translate this recipe into an American one, replacing grams and millilitres with whole or part cupfuls?"

Important mathematics to discuss

Tell the children that one US cup is approximately the same as 240 ml of liquid, or 224 g of flour (tightly packed).

Children could start by making a US cup from a plastic bottle or yoghurt pot.

(Discuss how accurate the children need to be.)

Recipe for play dough

Utensils	Ingredients
mixing bowl	500 g plain white flour
wooden spoon	250 g salt
2 or 3 flat baking tins	5 teaspoonfuls cream of tartar
pastry board	about 750 ml water
rolling pin	

Method

1 Set the oven to 160 °C.

2 Grease the baking tins.

3 Mix the dry ingredients together with a wooden spoon, and add the water slowly (you may not need it all).

4 Mix the dough with your hands.

5 Make your models and put them on the baking tins.

6 Bake them (15 to 30 minutes for thin, flat models, up to an hour for larger pieces).

Questions to ask the children

Approximately how many US cups of flour is 500 grams?
How can you find out?

Do you think all those cups will measure out the same amount of flour?

How can you measure half a cup?

Other ideas

- Divide into two groups; one group make the recipe using cupfuls and one using grams.

- How many models did you manage to make from your recipe? Can you find the volume of each one?

- Do all flours weigh the same per cupful (gram flour, wholemeal flour, maize flour, rice flour…)?

- Two and a quarter pounds of jam weigh about a kilogram. Is this true?

- An old recipe book says that a pint of water weighs a pound and a quarter. Does it? What does a litre of water weigh?

- A lot of recipes call for the ingredients to be measured in tablespoons. Could you rewrite the play dough recipe using tablespoonfuls?

  If you only wanted a small amount of dough, how could you work out a tenth of the recipe?

Can the children...

given a container holding one US cup, how many cupfuls of flour balance the 500 g weight?

find out whether an ordinary teacup holds more or less than one US cup?

Level 2

compare the capacity of a set of containers and say which holds the most/least?

given a container holding one US cup, find out how many cups can be filled from 750 ml water?

Level 3

measure to an appropriate degree of accuracy?

calculate the ingredients for quarter, half or double the quantities?

divide the play dough into equal-sized pieces and say what each one weighs?

make a set of containers that hold one US cup, $\frac{1}{2}$ US cup and $\frac{1}{4}$ US cup?

Level 4

translate the play dough recipe into an American one using US cups, by calculation alone?

discuss the ratio of flour to salt?

look at other recipes and discuss how the amounts could be increased or decreased by keeping the ratios constant?

Level 5

Timers

Children will experience

- practice in timing
- using and applying number operations
- decision making using measures
- estimation

Equipment

- empty plastic pots and bottles
- large needle
- dry sand
- water
- stopclocks and stopwatches
- ordinary clocks and watches
- funnel

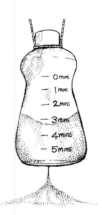

Getting started

This activity should be done in pairs.

Ask each pair to make a clock or timer by putting sand (or water) in a leaky plastic bottle and calibrating the container.

Important mathematics to discuss

Talk about what effect the size of the hole in the container will make. What is the longest stretch of time they could measure with a really small hole?

When the timers are made, talk about how to check their accuracy. Ask children to swap timers and check each other's with a clock or watch.

Questions to ask the children

> What are you going to do first?
> What do you need to find out?

> Is the sand coming out at a constant rate?
> Does it matter whether it does?

> How long does it take for all the sand to come out?

> Do you expect the distance between '0 minutes' and '1 minute' on the side of the bottle to be the same as the distance between '3 minutes' and '4 minutes'?
> Why?

Other ideas

◆ Find out how sundials work.

◆ Find some sand timers and check how accurate they are. If they are not accurate, how much out are they?

◆ Make a machine, of any sort, that measures one hour exactly.

◆ In your group, compare watches. Do they all keep the same time? If they don't, how could you check which — if any — is the most accurate?

◆ Make an egg-timer that will tell you when 3 and 4 minutes are up (for a soft or hard-boiled egg).

Can the children...

use a 1-minute sand timer to tell whether their bottle takes more or less than a minute to leak all its sand?

use comparisons between periods of time using words and phrases such as, 'longer time', 'shorter time', 'faster', 'slower'?

Level 2

use a watch to tell when five minutes has passed?

with help, mark '0 minutes' and '5 minutes' on their bottle to indicate the level of sand before it starts emptying, and after 5 minutes?

understand what this simple calibration means?

Level 3

make and calibrate a timer as directed?

convert times from minutes to seconds?

use a stopwatch or stopclock accurately and for a purpose?

Level 4

discuss the limits of the accuracy of their timer?

represent times to the nearest second using digital representations of hours, minutes and seconds?

Level 5

Tessellations

Children will experience

◆ practical exploration of angle using regular shapes

◆ calculations based on work with angles

◆ reasoning about the angles of regular shapes

◆ the language and properties of shapes

◆ investigating general statements about shapes and angles

Equipment

◆ tessellating tiles (hexagons, rectangles, rhombuses, squares, triangles...)

◆ pattern blocks

◆ Mathematical Activity Tiles

◆ squared paper

◆ hexagon (honeycomb) paper

◆ isometric (triangle) paper

Getting started

This activity can be done in groups.

Give the children materials which tessellate. Ask them to find out whatever they can about the angles of the shapes. (They will not need to use protractors for this.)

Important mathematics to discuss

There is a lot of mathematics waiting to be discovered in this activity. For example, when equi-angled shapes tessellate (for example, a square or regular hexagon) equal corners fit together to make 360° and children can use this fact to work out the size of the internal angles — although they may need quite some time exploring before they realise this.

When a rhombus tessellates, children may see that two of its angles add up to 180° (a straight line), and that the opposite angles are equal. They may be able to work out that the internal angles add up to 360°.

Questions to ask the children

Here is one corner of your shape. How many more of the same shape can you arrange around that corner without overlaps?

You have found some shapes with equal corners that fit together. Can you find some mixtures of regular shapes that do the same thing?

Can you see any angles that add up to 180°? What do those two angles make?

Are there any right angles in your shapes? Are there any angles less than a right angle? Or more?

Do you know how big that angle is? Are there any other angles the same size as that one?

Can you work out the size of that angle in any way?

Other ideas

◆ Draw a scalene triangle, cut it out and use it to make some more identical triangles. Can you make them tessellate?

Try the same thing with a quadrilateral.

◆ Here are two OHP transparencies of a hexagonal grid. Overlap the transparencies to make a pattern and describe it to a friend. Photocopy the new pattern and find out about the angles at any point.

◆ Find out from a book how to find the height of a tree or tall building. Use this method to find the height of the school. Find a tree that looks nearly the same height and find out whether it is taller or shorter than the school.

Can the children...

name some of the shapes they are working with?
discover some shapes which fit together without gaps?
say where similar shapes that fit together can be seen around the school (for example, a square tile pattern on the dining hall floor)?
Level 2

say how many right angles there are in a complete turn and in half a turn?
explain that a square has four right angles
say that squares tessellate?
discover how many of the same shape can be arranged around a point without overlaps?
Level 3

explain that a right angle is equal to 90°?
calculate that four right angles (or 4 x 90°) equal 360°?
explain that a half right angle is equal to 45°?
make and describe turns of 30°, 60° and 90°?
recognise which of two angles is greater?
Level 4

make various deductions about angle size? (for example, work out that if angle **A** is 150° then angle **B** is 30°)
explain why some regular shapes will tessellate and others will not?
discuss the angles in a rhombus and a parallelogram and discover the size of the internal angles of regular triangles and hexagons?
use a clinometer to measure the angle to the top of a building or tree? **Level 5**

Devising measuring systems

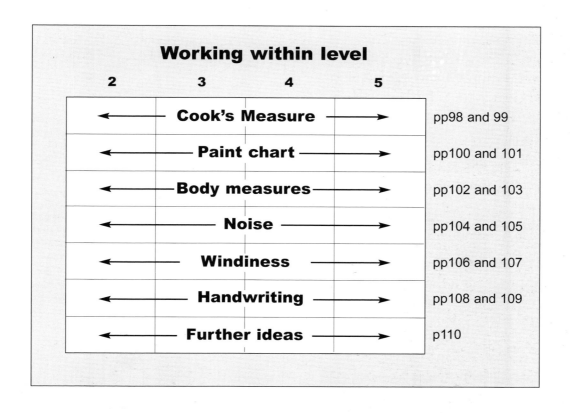

Working within level

	2	3	4	5	
← Cook's Measure →					pp98 and 99
← Paint chart →					pp100 and 101
← Body measures →					pp102 and 103
← Noise →					pp104 and 105
← Windiness →					pp106 and 107
← Handwriting →					pp108 and 109
← Further ideas →					p110

Devising measuring systems

The tasks in this chapter give children opportunities to:

— think about why measuring systems are necessary

— explore how measuring systems do and don't work

— develop their own workable systems for measuring

In this chapter there are several different kinds of activity:

Cook's Measure asks children to calibrate a container for a particular substance, with marks showing how far to fill it for particular weights of that substance.

Paint chart asks them to devise a way of matching any pink colour mixed from red and white paints. Ways of measuring these already exist, but children need not concern themselves with that. They need to devise a system they can use themselves.

Body measures requires them to devise a system of measuring length based on their own bodies.

Noise and *Handwriting* ask them to devise a way of measuring two things that are not commonly measured. Again, the main concern is that children devise a system they can use themselves.

Windiness asks them to devise a way of measuring wind speed.

Some of the above activities will enable children to use elements of the knowledge they have gained through working on other tasks in the book. Others will encourage them to develop a divergent approach and to be inventive in finding a workable solution to a measuring problem.

Researching other systems

As part of the work on devising measuring systems, children can be encouraged to research how people measured in the past. The use of body measurements in history is a particularly interesting study and, in addition to being of significance mathematically, is part of historical inquiry. Children may find out the names of some of the old measures of length; they will discover that the word 'inch' derives from the Latin 'uncia', which means a twelfth part, and that in Roman times the width across a person's thumb was equal to one twelfth of the length of their foot (and they could investigate whether this is still true). They may discover that the word fathom (six feet) meant 'two outstretched arms' and was measured across the full span of a person's arm from finger tip to finger tip; similarly, 'cubit' meant forearm.

As a class you can discuss how these compare with present day methods. Questions to research include: how do

Some Year 6 children's attempt to measure windiness.

people in other countries measure? is it the same throughout the world?

Children can also explore measures not normally covered in the mathematics curriculum. They might include the Beaufort scale for measuring wind, Richter scale for earthquakes or decibels for sound. All of these can lead to an exploration of both the scales and the ratios that will be involved in the measurements. Thinking about some of the ways in which we measure the world around us can help children when they try to develop their own measuring systems.

Sources of information

Encyclopaedias, mathematical or ordinary dictionaries and the Internet can be useful sources of information. Many museums or town halls have collections of the old standard measures which could possibly be borrowed for the children to investigate. Alternatively, a friendly museum might be able to get some replicas made, especially of the bushels and pecks once used for capacity.

Handwriting System   Maria Zoe Helen

Each piece of writing has 30 marks to begin with. Points are deducted for each fault. If the final mark is:
between 20 - 30 points, an 'A' grade is given.
between 10 - 20 points, a 'B' grade is given
between 0 - 10 points, a 'C' grade is given.

Faults are given — a rating - each point fault is worth so many deducted points - as below.

5 points are deducted for
i) not joining handwriting
ii) not keeping handwriting vertical.
iii)

4 points are deducted for
i) not keeping small letters half the size of the line

3 points are deducted for
i) not keeping letters next to the margin.
ii) not crossing out mistakes with a ruler and a pencil.
iii) not keeping all letters sitting on the line.

2 points are deducted for
i) tall letters not touching the top of the line.

1 point is deducted for
i) not keeping all small letters the same size.

Maria, Zoë and Helen devised a detailed system for judging handwriting. Further work (not shown) consisted of several samples of handwriting together with their detailed assessments of these.

Cook's Measure

Children will experience

- calibrating a linear scale to represent weight
- measuring small distances
- using problem-solving skills
- comparing weight and volume of the same substance

Equipment

- clean empty tins or plastic bottles with the tops cut off
- kitchen scales (analogue and digital)
- measuring jugs or cylinders
- cups
- funnel
- rice, flour, salt, raisins, water, sugar lumps, dried peas...

Getting started

This activity can be done with a group at a time.

Tell the children you want to simplify things for cooks who don't want to have to use kitchen scales. They are to make a 'Cook's Measure' for a particular ingredient such as rice or flour — that is, a container with marks showing how far to fill it for particular weights of that ingredient.

Important mathematics to discuss

Children will need to think about the fact that the same weight of different substances may well have different volumes — hence the need to specify what substance their 'Cook's Measure' is for.

The children need to appreciate that when measuring in this way it is important for the ingredient to be level in the container and to consider how they might ensure it is level.

Discuss how the 'Cook's Measure' will be used, what measures are usually quoted in recipes, and so how the Measure should be calibrated. For example, will it be useful for the Measure to show intervals of 10 g, 100 g, 200 g? Discuss how, if the intervals are, say, 250 g or 100 g, they would measure 50 g?

Questions to ask the children

One of you is making a measure for rice and one of you is doing flour. Would just one measure do for both substances? Why is that?

You have marked your measure to show multiples of 250 grams. How could you use it for 100 grams?

Are the distances between the intervals on your Measure all the same? Why is that?

Can you find the volume of 1000 grams of sugar?

Would it matter if your Measure was not a cylinder? Suppose it had sloping sides?

Other ideas

- Can you make one Cook's Measure for measuring different ingredients — say, flour, rice and sugar?
- Lots of people still use pounds and ounces when weighing ingredients for their recipes. Could you make a Cook's Measure to help those people? Could you have one Cook's Measure for metric and imperial measurement?

- Make a recipe using your Cook's Measure. How well does it work?
- Rewrite a recipe using 'different' measures such as '2 yoghurt-potfuls of flour' or 'five conkers in weight of sugar'. Can you be as exact as you are when using grams or ounces?
- Make a paper cone for measuring and holding 200 g of chips or 100 g of popcorn.

Can the children...

use a balance to find 100 g of flour?

mark where the 100 g of flour comes on the container and explain why the flour needs to be level?

say how they could use the measure to find 200 g?

Level 2

choose materials appropriate to the task?

show how they will use the measure for different amounts of flour?

explain why 100 g of different ingredients do not all reach the same height on the Cook's Measure?

Level 3

predict that 100 g of different ingredients will not all have the same volume?

mark more than one scale on the same container?

explain their calibrations and how they can be used to measure any amount of the relevant substance?

say that 1000 g is the same as 1 kg and that 500 g is $\frac{1}{2}$ kg?

write their calibrations in grams and as decimal fractions of a kilogram?

Level 4

devise a measure for both metric and imperial units?

say that there are more than two pounds in every kilogram?

make a measure for 100 g of a substance with subdivisions of 10 g for greater accuracy?

Level 5

Paint chart

Children will experience

◆ working systematically

◆ recording for a purpose

◆ practical use of simple ratios

Equipment

◆ pre-mixed red and white paint

◆ teaspoons, ice cream spoons, dolls' teaspoons

◆ colour charts from a paint manufacturer

Getting started

This activity can be done with a group at a time.

Each child needs some red and some white paint. Children work in pairs: one mixes a pink and paints with this on a sheet of paper; the other child tries to make a matching pink.

Introduce the idea of paint charts with specific instructions for mixing a paint so it can be reproduced at any time, then ask the children to devise such a system for mixing a range of pinks.

Important mathematics to discuss

Get the children to think about how a paint manufacturer can be sure of getting the same colour each time when mixing their colour charts.

Discuss the idea of using small amounts for a test sample and how can they be sure the shade will be just the same next time. Ask them to think about what they will need to do to make larger amounts.

Questions to ask the children

Here is a pink that Sammi made. Can you use your chart to find out how she made it?

What amounts of each colour have you used to make the light pink and the dark pink?

If you made a sample that was half red and half white would it be darker or lighter than that one? Why?

You have two shades of pink there. How might you make a shade in between?

What amounts of each colour might you need if you wanted a very pale pink?

You have used a teaspoon to measure amounts of red and white paint for that pink. How much of each would you need if you wanted to make a litre?

Other ideas

◆ Children can work with three colours.

◆ What different effects can they make with just one colour and water? Can they devise a system for this?

◆ Children can make a series of hand prints using the different tones of pink, going from palest to darkest.

◆ If children have access to computer programs that use different percentages of grey (or of a colour) children can experiment with making a chart of these greys.

◆ Children can try making jelly with different amounts of water, and use this to devise a system for describing the consistency of school dinner jellies.

Can the children...

talk about the notion of degrees of pinkness (that is, say that some shades are denser, darker, or pinker, than others)?
say whether they have used more white, more red or the same amount of each?
count and record how many spoonfuls of each colour they use for one shade?
Level 2

observe that more white than red gives a paler shade and vice versa?
begin to count and record systematically?
Level 3

say what fraction of the whole is red and what fraction white?
work and record systematically?
calculate the quantities needed to make 10 or 100 times the amount used for the sample?
Level 4

talk about the ratios of each colour and use them to calculate larger quantities?
say what percentage of the whole is red and what percentage white?
Level 5

101

Body measures

Children will experience

- the need for a standard system
- ratios between body measures
- developing strategies for estimation

Equipment

- paper strips
- string or tape
- spreadsheet

Getting started

This activity can be done with a whole class.

Talk with the children about how measures of length in many cultures have been based on the human body or human activities. In this country measures and length include:

— the foot

— the inch (an adult's thumb width)

— the yard (the distance from an adult's nose to the tip of their outstretched arm)

— the cubit (the length of an adult forearm) was about 18 to 22 inches, named from the Latin for forearm, 'cubitum'

Tell them that the inch (in Latin, 'uncia') means a twelfth part of a linear foot, and ask if anyone in the class has got twelve 'thumb-width inches' to their foot.

Now ask them to devise a system of measuring length based on their own bodies.

Important mathematics to discuss

Each child will be able to devise their own system, and can discover useful relationships between the units (for example, 'eleven thumb's widths equals one hand-span'). However, two children's systems will have different values unless their bodies are much the same size, and a child's system will of course have different values from an adult's.

This means that a child can use their own system successfully (for example, to measure whether a table will fit a certain space without moving it). But sharing information with others may be more problematic — "The table's length is six hand-spans and three thumbs" is useful information only if we have an idea how big the hand-span is.

Questions to ask the children

Can you use your measuring system to see if the fish tank would fit on that table?

In your system, how many thumbs equal a hand?
Write down your system and how it works.

Three of you measure the length of the carpet. Do you all agree on its width?

In your group everyone's measure is slightly different. How could you be more accurate?

Other ideas

◆ Find who in your group (or the class) has used 'thumbs' and hand-spans. Explore how many 'thumbs' there are to a hand-span in each system and comment on the results.

◆ Collect information about the foot (or other body measure) in your class. What are the mean, mode and median measurements? What does each of these averages mean?

Can the children...

make a hand-span measure and use it with reasonable accuracy?

estimate short distances in hand-spans?

say approximately how many of their thumb-widths are equal to a hand-span?

find things in the classroom that are more or less than, or equal to, a hand-span or a thumb-width?

Level 2

make a hand-span measure with thumb width intervals?

measure distances in hand-spans, and use thumb-widths as sub-units where necessary?

work with other body measures, such as their reach or stride, to estimate and measure distances?

Level 3

draw up a system of measurement using body measures, with fixed ratios, and use this consistently?

explain when and how this form of measurement is inaccurate?

talk about when body measures are useful for estimating distances in real life?

make generalised statements about the ratios they have found (for example, "about three times around my head is the same as my height")?

Level 4

take several measurements of the same distance, and find the median and mode of their data?

take several measurements of the same distance, then calculate the mean average of their data?

explain that the mean average can be seen as giving a more accurate value than a single measurement?

Level 5

Noise

Children will experience

◆ thinking about how non-tangible quantities can be compared and measured

◆ deciding on a scale for measuring sound and applying it consistently

◆ exploring which shapes and materials might amplify sound

◆ using and developing problem-solving skills

Equipment

◆ children

◆ sensor connected to a computer for measuring sound

◆ bell, megaphone, drum, radio

Getting started

This activity can be done with one or more groups.

Say to the children that you want them to devise a system for measuring noise in the classroom.

Important mathematics to discuss:

Talk with the children about two different methods: one would be to stay put, and find a way to measure the rise and fall of the noise level; another method would be to keep the noise constant and measure the distance they have to go before it becomes inaudible.

Ask the children if they could make up a scale for measuring noise in the classroom. What units would they use?

Discuss recording. Could they show on a graph how the sound might increase or decrease over a short period of time?

Questions to ask the children

Can you make a picture of the sound getting louder and softer?

How could you make the sound of the little bell louder?

You have drawn a line graph to show noise going up and down. What is happening at that point there?
What is the smallest noise you heard?

You stopped hearing the little bell 20 m away. How far might you go before you stop hearing the bigger one?

Other ideas

◆ Think of a system which sets off a signal to indicate that the classroom noise is getting too loud.

◆ Find ways of making sounds louder. Do some shapes amplify sounds more than others?

◆ The saying goes that "It was so quiet you could hear a pin drop". How far away can you hear a pin drop? Is it the same distance for everybody?

◆ There is another saying that, "Empty vessels make the most sound". Is this true and how will you test it?

◆ Test the length of time it takes for a tuning fork to stop making a noise. Is the time the same for all sizes of fork?

◆ Investigate volume scales on computers, radios, CD players and so on.

Can the children...

---

say when a noise is loud, soft or just about right?

compare two or three noises and put them in order of loudness?

Level 2

---

find a way to record the increases/ decreases of sound over a short period (by, for example, drawing a simple line graph)?

measure the distance at which a sound becomes inaudible?

Level 3

---

assign different volumes of classroom noise a scale value (for example, 5 for very loud to 1 for very quiet)?

find ways of muffling sounds with barriers or distance and measure the difference in volume on their scale?

appreciate that their scales of noisiness may be subjective?

Level 4

---

interpret a computer-generated read-out of sound levels over a period of time?

Level 5

Windiness

Children will experience

- thinking about how non-tangible quantities can be compared and measured
- developing a scale to measure wind
- opportunities to apply fair testing
- researching wind measures used by forecasters
- using and developing problem-solving skills

Equipment

- card, corroflute, wire, paper cups, fabric
- doweling, lolly sticks
- tools for making holes
- glue
- anemometer

Getting started

Children work in groups to devise a system for measuring how windy it is on a particular day. The aim is to be able to:

— decide whether it is more or less windy than the day before

— ring somebody up and discuss whether it is more or less windy where they are

— listen to a weather forecast to find out how windy it will be the next day in their area, then compare their findings with the level of wind predicted

Important mathematics to discuss

Talk with the children about how they know when it is windy. Is the wind always the same strength or are there times when there is no wind at all? Does the wind always blow from the same direction and how do they know? Are there some places around the school where it seems to be windier than others?

Can they find a way of measuring the windiness of each day? What sort of scale will they use to measure the wind and how accurate does it have to be?

You could show the children an anemometer, and talk about how to use it; or children could make their own.

Questions to ask the children

Do you think you can find a windier place around the school?

How will your wind measure tell you if there is more or less wind?

Do you think there will be more or less wind tomorrow?
Why do you think that?

You have shown me how your wind measure works on a very windy day.
Will you know when it is half as windy?

Other ideas

- Devise a system for measuring the direction of the wind.
- Decide on a way of measuring rainfall.

- Find a way of measuring the warmest place out in the school grounds.
- Research the Beaufort scale for measuring wind. Use the scale to find the approximate wind strength each day.

Can the children...

say whether it feels more or less windy in different places around the school grounds?   **Level 2**

invent and record a simple system for measuring windiness (not using equal intervals)? explain how their system works?   **Level 3**

invent and record a system for measuring windiness (not using equal intervals)? explain how their system works? count the revolutions of an anemometer in a minute and calculate the number of revolutions in 10 minutes? **Level 4**

use an anemometer over a period of a minute and convert the revolutions into the number of times it will turn in an hour? measure accurately the distance covered by one revolution of an anemometer and calculate the approximate distance travelled in a minute/an hour? **Level 5**

Handwriting

Children will experience

- thinking about how non-tangible quantities can be compared and measured
- data collection and analysis
- developing problem-solving skills

Equipment

- samples of adults' handwriting
- samples of 'old-fashioned' handwriting (manuscripts, old letters, and so on)
- samples of handwriting from different countries
- samples of different computer fonts

Getting started

Children work in groups to devise a system for measuring handwriting or another form of lettering such as computer fonts. They could measure:

— how legible it is

— how beautiful it is

— how convenient it is for the writer

or some other quality of their choice. (Different groups may well choose different aspects to work on.)

The aim is to be able to compare and assess any sample of writing.

It is best if they use examples of adults' writing, or print, in order to avoid judgements of the children's own writing ability. However, when one or more systems have been worked out, children could use these to judge their own handwriting.

Important mathematics to discuss

You could discuss: the need for a standard against which to measure; that this standard must be consistent; that the measure must be applicable to all handwriting (or if not it must state which it is applicable to). You may also want to discuss how subjective are the judgements made.

Questions to ask the children

Can you use your work to put these samples in order of...?

Was there an example of handwriting that most people chose as being easy to read? Why did they choose that one?

Can you explain how your scale works? Could you use it for any writing?

What rules could you have for making sure writing is easy to read?

Other ideas

- Explore various computer fonts, and analyse them for legibility.
- Use an optician's wall chart for evaluating writing.
- Find a size of print that everyone in the class can read from a distance of three metres.

- Make a collection of commercial advertising posters. What strategies do the poster designers use to make them easy to read?
- Look at old letters and postcards and photographs of handwriting going back through the ages. Can you apply your scale to these handwriting styles? What changes and what stays the

Can the children...

give sensible criteria for judging handwriting (for example, "The letters are large and all the same height")?
Level 2

select a number of criteria for making judgements about handwriting?
collect data using their criteria to measure handwriting?
Level 3

design and use a scale for judging handwriting based on a range of criteria?
Level 4

design and use a scale for judging handwriting?
give different weightings to different criteria, depending on how important they are deemed to be?
collect data and analyse the results?
Level 5

Devising measuring systems: further ideas

You and the children are likely to find your own things that need measuring.

In trials of these materials, children devised systems for measuring:

- how healthy plants are
- the speed of children's reactions
- how furry animals are

Other ideas you might consider are listed below.

Metric Time

How would you metricate time (that is, invent a system based on tens)? Get rid of 7-day weeks, 24-hour days, 60-minute hours and so on and start again.

Metric Clock

Design a clock face that shows time in a metric system (that is, invent a system based on tens).

Football

Devise a system for measuring the transfer value of footballers.

Bounce

Explore how bouncy different balls are — football, golf ball, table tennis ball, super ball... Then devise a system for measuring the bounciness.

Speed

How might you measure the speed of: a car, a child running, a jelly setting, a plant growing, water filling a bath...? (Think of some more things to add to the list.) Choose one of those things and measure its speed.

Heat

How might you measure temperature without a thermometer?

Trainers

Investigate all the various qualities of trainers, then devise a system for measuring their monetary value.

Music

Devise a system for measuring the musical worth of pop songs. How could you put them in order?

What about the value of pop groups?

Light

How could you devise a system for measuring the light in the classroom?

Ripples

Drop pebbles into various containers of water. How can you measure and compare the ripples in different containers?

Chart linking the activities in this book with the mathematical objectives from the Framework for Teaching Mathematics

Objectives from the Framework for Teaching Mathematics

Group	Activity	Using vocabulary related to length	Using vocabulary related to mass	Using vocabulary related to capacity	Using vocabulary related to angle	Understanding and using angle measures in degrees	Measuring and comparing using standard units	Using a ruler to measure and draw lines	Knowing and using relationships between standard units	Suggesting suitable units to estimate and measure	Suggesting suitable equipment to estimate and measure	Recording estimates and measurements	Reading measuring scales	Using vocabulary related to area and perimeter	Understanding, measuring and calculating area	Reading and writing vocabulary related to time	Using units of time and knowing relationships between them	Reading clocks, calendars and timetables
Using standard units	Chuck it	★					★		★	★	★	★	★					
	Shoes		★				★			★	★	★						
	Hands			★			★			★	★	★	★					
	Take 60								★			★					★	★
	Skin													★	★			
	Logo				★	★												
A feel for standard units	Would it fit?	★					★		★	★	★	★	★					
	Bikes		★						★	★	★	★	★					
	Lemonade			★			★		★	★	★	★	★					
	No watches																★	★
	Fruit													★	★			
	Angle 90				★	★												★
Developing accuracy	Fingers	★					★		★		★	★	★					
	Weigh a letter		★				★		★	★	★	★	★					
	Max box			★			★		★	★	★	★	★					
	Pendulum						★										★	★
	Books						★					★		★	★			
	Draw a square				★	★	★	★										
Representing measures	Invention	★					★		★			★						
	Spring balance		★				★		★			★	★					
	Calibration			★			★		★				★					
	Time lines								★								★	★
	Land use													★	★			
	Protractors				★	★												
Relationships between units	Measure your desk	★					★		★	★	★	★	★					
	Sugar		★	★			★		★	★	★	★	★					
	Cube			★			★	★	★		★	★						
	Alive								★								★	★
	Square up						★		★					★	★			
	Jam jars				★	★						★						
Using and applying measures	Circus skills	★					★		★	★	★	★	★					
	Sweets		★	★			★		★	★	★	★						
	Play dough		★	★			★		★	★	★	★						
	Timers								★	★		★	★				★	
	Tessellations				★	★												
Devising measuring systems	Cook's Measure		★	★			★		★	★	★	★	★					
	Paint chart			★					★			★						
	Body measures	★							★			★						
	Noise								★			★	★					
	Windiness								★			★	★					
	Handwriting								★			★						

111

Resources

Resources

Books

Exploring Volume and Capacity

Practical ideas for teaching about volume and capacity. Each activity has extensions and reinforcement suggestions.
BEAM Education   ISBN 1 874099 61 8

Exploring Weight

Practical and interesting ideas for teaching about weight. Each activity has extensions and reinforcement suggestions.
BEAM Education   ISBN 1 874099 58 8

Starting from Scratch: Measures

Practical ideas for teaching about measures, primarily aimed at Levels 1–3. Also provides valuable experiences for Key Stage 2 children working at the lower levels of the National Curriculum.
BEAM Education   ISBN 1 874099 47 2

Making LOGO Work

Janet Ainley and Ronnie Goldstein
Explains the rationale for including LOGO in the curriculum. Provides a number of valuable and practical case studies of children using LOGO in the classroom.
Basil Blackwell Limited   ISBN 0 631157 03 8

Teaching Measures

Janine Blinko and Ann Slater
A book of useful and practical ideas for teaching various aspects of measurement, particularly at the lower levels.
Hodder   ISBN 0 340630 95 7

Lines of Development in Primary Mathematics

Mary Deboys and Eunice Pitts
Offers useful guidance on the development of mathematical topics throughout the primary school. The sections on the teaching and learning which relate to measures are especially useful.
The Blackstaffe Press   ISBN 0 856401 94 3

Primary Mathematics Today

Elizabeth Williams and Hilary Shuard
An essential reference book for any primary school teacher, particularly the non-specialist. Provides valuable information on all aspects of primary mathematics, including measures. Contains explanations of a wide range of mathematical topics within the primary curriculum and makes practical suggestions for their teaching.
Longman   ISBN 0 582360 04 8

Websites

ATM (Association of Teachers of Mathematics)
http://acorn.educ.nottingham.ac.uk//SchEd/pages/atm

A helpful professional organisation. Details of conferences and resources can be found, together with good links to other sites.

BEAM (Be A Mathematician)
http://www.beam.co.uk

The site includes details of INSET courses and downloadable extracts from publications, as well as links to other interesting mathematics sites.

Dictionary of Measures, Units and Conversions
http://www.ex.ac.uk/cimt/dictunit/dictunit.htm

A good site for older Key Stage 2 pupils researching measures.

Cookery unit conversions
http://www.cuisinedumonde.com.convert.pl

A good site for finding equivalent units.

Maths Net
http://www.paston.co.uk/users/mathsnet/contents/html

A good range of resources and ideas for using IT to enhance mathematics activities. Details of other useful sites are also provided.

MathSphere
http://www.mathsphere.com

This site has example worksheets (some linked to measurement) for the daily numeracy lesson and a maths dictionary. Solutions to regular problems can be emailed.

NRich
http://www.maths.org.uk

Online maths club, with activities for all key stages, which is devoted to mathematical problem-solving. Pupils can send their solutions to monthly problems.

Mass and Weight
www.exploratorium.edu/ronh/weight/index.htm

Although this site is more concerned with physics, it enables users to find out their weight on places ranging from our moon to Callisto, one of Jupiter's moons.

Equipment list

Length
tape measures — dressmaking, woodworking and surveyor's
rulers
metre rules
home-made 'tape' measures
callipers
micrometer gauge
pedometer
estate agent's distance measurer
trundle wheel
PE mats
height chart

Mass/weight
standard weights (5 g, 10 g, 100 g, 1 kg)
balances
spring balances
scales — analogue, digital, bathroom
letter scales
centicubes

Volume and capacity
sticky tape, rulers
1 cm cubes
calibrated measuring jugs and cylinders
litre jugs
funnels
centimetre and decimetre cubes (plastic or wood)

Time
stopwatches
stopclocks
watch or clock with a second hand
sand timers
1 and 2 metre strips of paper
number lines
rulers
tape measures
calculators
spreadsheets

Area
1 cm, 2 cm, 5cm squared paper, decimetre squares, rulers
Ordnance Survey maps
aerial photographs of school and surrounding area
calculators

Angle
Roamer, Pixie, Pip (programmable toys*)
Logo
turtle graphics program
angle indicator
protractors, including circular ones
angle indicators
Microsmile* pack 2: Angle estimation
rulers
set squares
plastic Meccano
geo-strips
tessellating tiles (hexagons, rectangles, rhombuses, squares, triangles)
hexagonal grid paper
isometric paper

*See page 117 for addresses and suppliers.

Additional materials that may be needed

Length

Chuck it	beanbags, feathers
Invention	tough fabric, cubes, headless matches, paper clips
Measure your desk	objects with dimensions of 1 mm, 1 cm, and 1 m
Circus skills	wall-mounted height chart

Mass/weight

Shoes	shoes, conkers, cubes, marbles
Bikes	bags, baskets, cycle panniers with items such as clothes, drinks bottle to pack in them
Weigh a letter	leaflet showing postage rates for sending mail abroad, letter and airmail paper and envelopes, stamps
Spring balance	small polythene bags, dressmakers' elastic or rubber bands, toothpicks, safety pins, paper clips
Sugar	teaspoons, sugar
Sweets	heavy sweets such as butterscotch, lighter sweets such as flying saucers, paper bags

Volume and capacity

Hands	sand, water, conkers, beans, lentils, rice, yoghurt pots, margarine tubs
Lemonade	1-litre plastic bottles, lemonade or fruit juice, cups or mugs
Max box	rice, sand, puffed rice, polystyrene 'squiggles'
Calibration	plastic bottles, sand, water, rice
Cube	sand, rice, polystyrene 'squiggles'
Play dough	various ingredients and utensils — see recipe, p88

Time

Pendulum	string, Plasticine, marbles, stones, junk containers
Timers	empty plastic pots and bottles, large needle, sand, funnel

Area

Skin	old gloves
Fruit	fruits such as bananas, satsumas, apples, Plasticine
Books	books
Land use	Ordnance Survey map of area around school, aerial photograph of school, maps of area
Square up	newspaper or scrap paper

Angle

Angle 90	very large scale floor map or plan, very large clock face drawn on floor
Protractors	plastic Meccano or geo-strips, straws and paper fasteners
Jam jars	jars and screw-top lids, drink containers
Tessellations	tessellating tiles, pattern blocks, Mathematical Activity Tiles, hexagon and isometric paper

Devising measuring systems

Cook's Measures	tins or plastic bottles, cups, funnel, rice, flour, salt, raisins, dried peas
Paint chart	red and white paint, different sizes of spoon, paint charts
Noise	sensor connected to a computer for measuring sound, bell, megaphone, drum, radio
Windiness	corroflute, wire, paper cups, fabric, dowelling or lolly sticks, glue, anemometer
Handwriting	samples of writing, samples of computer fonts

Suppliers' addresses

Roamer:
Valiant Technology, Valiant House,
3 Grange Mills, Weir Road,
London SW12 0NE
0181 673 2233

Pixie and Pip robots:
Swallow Systems, 134 Cock Lane,
High Wickham,
Buckinghamshire HP13 7EA
01494 813471

MicroSMILE:
Smile Mathematics,
108a Lancaster Road,
London W11 1QS
0171 221 8966

Sherston Software Ltd,
Angel House, Sherston,
near Malmesbury,
Wiltshire
SN16 0LH
01666 843200

Acknowledgements

We wish to thank the following for taking part in trialling the book before its publication:

Frances Bestley and the South London Science and Technology Centre, London

Lin Bullard and Milwards Primary School, Essex

Barbara Carr and Cranford House School, Oxon

J E Harris and Henham and Ugley CP School, Essex

Sonya Hockley and Bishop Winnington Ingram CE School, Middlesex

Lynda Jackson and Warton Nethersole Primary School, Staffordshire

Adèle Markey and Bury and Whitefield Jewish Primary School, Lancashire

Brenda McCourtney and Holly Hill Primary School, Nottinghamshire

Clare Neuberger and Menorah Primary JMI School, London

Janet Parfitt and Balfour Junior School, East Sussex

Karen Pearse and Winsor Primary School, London

L Proctor and Marsden CP School, Lancashire

Claire Swanney, A Wright and Selwyn Primary School, London

Ann Todd and Beech Street CP School, Manchester

Andrew Warren and Amherst Junior School, Guernsey

Contents

Specification lists

AQA A AS

Module (Unit)	Specification topic	Chapter reference
ENGA1	**Seeing Through Language**	
	Language and Mode	1, 2
	Language Development	3
ENGA2	**Representation and Language**	
	Language Investigation	4
	Language Production	5

AQA A A2

Module (Unit)	Specification topic	Chapter reference
ENGA3	**Language Explorations**	
	Language Variation and Change	6
	Language Discourses Task	7
ENGA4	**Language Investigations and Interventions**	
	Language Investigation	8
	Language Intervention	8

Examination analysis

Unit 1 – ENGA1 **Seeing Through Language** 60% of AS, 30% of A-Level
You will sit a 2 hour written examination worth 90 marks.
1 Language Analysis task – one question only
1 Language Development essay – choice of two tasks.

Unit 2 – ENGA2 **Representation and Language** 40% of AS, 20% of A-Level
Coursework 60 marks
1 Investigation
1 Production Task Plus Commentary (2000–2500 words).

Examination analysis

Unit 3 – ENGA3 **Language Explorations** 30% of A-Level
You will sit a 2 hour 30 minutes written examination worth 90 marks.
1 Language Variation and Change task
1 Language Discourses task.

Unit 4 – ENGA4 **Language Investigations and Interventions** 20% of A-Level
Coursework 60 marks
1 Investigation
1 Intervention task (3000–3750 words).

AQA B AS

Module (Unit)	Specification topic	Chapter reference
ENGB1	**Categorising Texts (focusing on three specific social contexts)**	
	Language and Power	4, 7
	Language and Gender	4, 7
	Language and Technology	4, 7
ENGB2	**Creating Texts** Writing in different genres for different audiences and purposes	5

Examination analysis

Unit 1 – ENGB1 **Categorising Texts** 60% of AS, 30% of A-Level
You will sit a 2 hour written examination worth 96 marks.
1 text categorising exercise
1 essay from a choice of two in these options:
- *Language and Power*
- *Language and Gender*
- *Language and Technology.*

Unit 2 – ENGB2 **Creating Texts** 40% of AS, 20% of A-Level
Coursework 80 marks
You will produce **two** *pieces of writing in different genres and for different audiences and purposes, and* **two** *commentaries (2500–3500 words).*

AQA B A2

Module (Unit)	Specification topic	Chapter reference
ENGB3	**Developing Language**	
	Child Language Acquisition	3
	Language Change	6
ENGB4	**Investigating Language**	
	Language investigation	8
	Informative media text and commentary	7, 8

Examination analysis

Unit 3 – ENGB3 **Developing Language** 30% of A-Level
You will sit a 2 hour 30 minutes written examination worth 96 marks.
1 Child Language Acquisition essay from a choice of two.
1 Language Change essay from a choice of two.

Unit 4 – ENGB4 **Investigating Language** 20% of A-Level
coursework – 80 marks
1 language investigation
1 informative media text and commentary (2500–3000 words).

Edexcel AS

Module (Unit)	Specification topic	Chapter reference
6EN01	**Language Today**	
	Language and Context	4, 7
	Presenting Self	4
6EN02	**Exploring the Writing Process**	
	Reading Audience	5
	Listening Audience	5

Edexcel A2

Module (Unit)	Specification topic	Chapter reference
6EN03	**Language Diversity and Children's Language Development**	
	Language Diversity	6
	Children's Language Development	3
6EN04	**English Language Investigation and Presentation**	
	Independently researched a language investigation	8

Examination analysis

Unit 1 – 6EN01 Language Today 60% of AS marks
30% of total A-Level marks
You will sit a 2 hours 15 minutes examination worth
100 marks.
Section A: Language and Context – short data response
questions.
Section B: Presenting Self – essay-based response to texts.

Unit 2 – 6EN02 Exploring the Writing Process 40% of AS
marks, 20% of total A-Level marks
Coursework 80 marks
You will submit a folder with two pieces of your own writing
accompanied by commentaries:
● one for a reading audience
● one for a listening audience
(2000–2500 words maximum).

Examination analysis

**Unit 3 – 6EN03 Language Diversity and Children's
Language Development** 60% of A2 marks, 30% of total
A-Level marks.
You will sit a 2 hours 45 minutes examination worth
100 marks.
Section A: Language Diversity over Time and in Global
Contexts – short data response questions, followed by a
longer essay.
Section B: The Development of Children's Spoken and
Written Language – short data response questions, followed
by a longer essay.

**Unit 4 – 6EN04 English Language Investigation and
Presentation** 40% of total A2 marks
20% of total A-Level marks.
Coursework 80 marks
1 presentation of the language investigation to a non-
specialist audience (24 marks)
1 independently researched language investigation
(56 marks)
(2500–3000 words maximum).

OCR AS

Module (Unit)	Specification topic	Chapter reference
F651	**The Dynamics of Speech**	
	Speech and Children	3
	Speech Varieties and Social Groups	4, 7
F652	**Texts and Audiences**	
	Comparative essay	5, 6
	Adaptive writing with commentary task	5

OCR A2

Module (Unit)	Specification topic	Chapter reference
F653	**Culture, Language and Identity**	
	Language and Speech (compulsory)	1, 2
	The Language of Popular Written Texts	4, 7
	Language and Cultural Production	4, 7
	Language, Power and Identity	4, 7
F654	**Media Language**	
	Analytical essay	8, 6
	Media production task and commentary	8, 6

Examination analysis

Unit 1 – F651 **The Dynamics of Speech** 60% of the marks for AS (30% of A-Level)
You will sit a 2 hour written paper worth 60 marks.
Speech and Children – 1 long data response question from a choice of 2.
Speech Varieties and Social Groups – 1 long data response question from a choice of 2.

Unit 2 – F652 **Texts and Audiences** 40% of the marks for AS (20% of A-Level)
Coursework 40 marks
1 essay analysing written and multi-modal texts
1 adaptive writing task with commentary.

Examination analysis

Unit 3 – F653 **Culture, Language and Identity** 30% of the total A-Level marks
You will sit a 2 hour written paper worth 60 marks.
Two essays are required.
1 from **Section A:** Language and Speech (compulsory)
And 1 other from:
Section B: The Language of Popular Written Texts (optional)
Or Section C: Language and Cultural Production (optional)
Or Section D: Language, Power and Identity (optional).

Unit 4 – F654 **Media Language** 20% of the marks for A-Level.
Coursework 40 marks
1 essay analysing written, spoken and multi-modal texts
1 piece of original media writing with commentary.

WJEC AS

Module (Unit)	Specification topic	Chapter reference
LG1	**Introduction to the Language of Texts**	
	The language of texts	1, 2
	Language focus	1, 2, 4
LG2	**Original Writing and Exploring Spoken Language**	
	Original writing	5
	Exploring spoken language	5

WJEC A2

Module (Unit)	Specification topic	Chapter reference
LG3	**Language Investigation and Writing for Specific Purposes**	
	Language investigation	6, 7, 8
	Writing for specific purposes	6, 7, 8
LG4	**Analysing and Evaluating Language Modes and Contexts**	
	Analysis of spoken language	1, 2
	Analysis of written language over time	6

Examination analysis

Unit 1 – LG1 **Introduction to the Language of Texts** 60% of AS, 30% of A-Level
You will sit a 2 hour 30 minutes written paper worth 60 marks.
Section A: The language of texts – two or more texts. 40% of AS, 20% of A-Level
Section B: Language focus – usually a single text, 20% of AS, 10% of A-Level.

Unit 2 – LG2 **Original Writing and Exploring Spoken Language** 40% of AS, 20% of A-Level.
Coursework 3000 words folder
Section A: Original writing and commentary
Section B: Exploring spoken language analytical study.

Examination analysis

Unit 3 – LG3 **Language Investigation and Writing for Specific Purposes** 40% of A2, 20% of A-Level
Coursework 3000 words
Section A: Language investigation
Section B: Writing for specific purposes – genre piece and commentary.

Unit 4 – LG4 **Analysing and Evaluating Language Modes and Contexts** 60% of A2, 30% of A-Level
You will sit a 2 hour 30 minutes examination.
Section A: Analysis of spoken language – analysis of at least two spoken texts
Section B: Analysis of written language over time – analysis of at least two texts, one from the past.

Revision tips

Examiners use instructions to help you to decide the length and depth of your answer:

State, define, list, outline: These key words require short, concise answers, often recall of material that you have memorised.

Explain, describe, discuss: Some reasoning or some reference to theory is needed, depending on the context. Explaining and discussing require you to give a more detailed answer than when you are asked to 'describe' something.

Apply: With an 'apply' question, you must make sure that you relate your answer to the given situation (this is always good practice in English Language exams).

Evaluate: You are required to provide full and detailed arguments, often 'for' and 'against', to show your depth of understanding.

Some dos and don'ts

- **Do** answer the question. No credit can be given for good linguistic knowledge that is not relevant to the question.
- **Do** use the mark allocation to guide how much you write. Writing more than necessary will not result in extra marks.
- **Do** use real-life examples in your answers. These often help illustrate your level of knowledge.
- **Do** write legibly. An examiner cannot give marks if the answer cannot be read.
- **Do** use the correct terminology. Marks will be lost if you fail to use terms appropriately.
- **Don't** feel that you have to fill all the space allocated to a short form question. If you write too much on one question, you may run out of time to answer some of the others.
- **Don't** contradict yourself. Present reasoned and consistent arguments.
- **Don't** get bogged down on difficult points. Exam time is limited, and you can always return to the difficult part if you have enough time at the end of the exam.

What grade do you want?

Everyone would like to achieve the highest grades, but you will only manage this with a great deal of hard work and determination. Your final A-Level grade depends on the extent to which you meet the assessment objectives. The hints below offer advice on how to improve your grade.

A* or A grade

To achieve a grade A* or a grade A, you have to:
- show in-depth knowledge and critical understanding of a wide range of linguistic theories and concepts
- apply these to familiar and unfamiliar situations, problems and issues, using appropriate linguistic techniques
- evaluate effectively evidence and arguments
- make reasoned judgements in presenting appropriate conclusions.

You have to be a very good all-rounder to achieve a grade A* or A. The exams test all areas of the specifications, and any weaknesses in your understanding will be exposed.

C grade

To achieve a grade C, you have to have a good understanding of the aspects shown in the criteria to gain an A grade (shown above), but you will have weaknesses in some of these areas. To improve, you will need to work hard to overcome these weaknesses, and also make sure that you have an efficient and effective exam technique.

AS/A2 English Language courses

AS and A2

As with all A-Levels, English Language courses are divided into two sections. You study the AS (Advanced Subsidiary) course first, and then go on to the second part called A2.

There are two modules (units) at AS level and two at A2 level. The AS and A2 courses are designed so that the level of difficulty increases from AS to A2:

- AS English Language builds on GCSE English Language
- A2 English Language builds on AS English Language.

How will you be tested?

Assessment units

For AS English Language, you will be tested on two assessment units. For the full A-Level in English Language you will take a further two units. AS English Language forms 50% of the assessment weighting for the full A-Level.

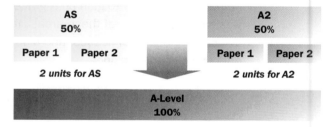

All exam specifications include coursework at both AS and A2. You can usually only submit coursework once a year, but the written papers are available in January and June. If you are disappointed with a module result, re-sits are possible, and the higher mark will count towards your final grade.

A2 and synoptic assessment

After having studied AS English Language, you may wish to continue studying English Language to A-Level. For this you will need to take two further English Language units at A2.

The A2 units assess the course using a 'synoptic' approach. Synoptic assessment tests your ability to apply knowledge, understanding and skills you have learnt throughout the course, and to make linguistic judgements and/or apply linguistic understanding. It takes place across the two A2 units and encourages you to...

- treat language matters holistically
- develop the ability to apply linguistic approaches in a wide variety of contexts.

What skills will I need?

The Advanced Subsidiary GCE and Advanced GCE in English Language draw on the subject criteria for English Language, which are prescribed and are compulsory. AS and A-Level English Language should encourage you to...

- develop enthusiasm about the English language
- gain a broad overview of linguistic approaches
- develop a critical understanding of how language and society interact
- understand some of the debates that surround issues in linguistics
- explore your own creative writing ideas
- understand some of the ethical issues related to the use of language in everyday life
- build up a toolkit of linguistic perspectives that can be used in the analysis of language and of rhetoric.

It is important that you develop your key skills throughout your AS and A2 courses. These are important skills that you need whatever you do beyond AS and A2 levels. The main key skill areas relevant to English Language are...

- communication
- information and communication technology
- working with others
- improving own learning and performance
- problem solving.

Each examination board will 'signpost' where key skill developments can best take place whilst studying A-Level English Language. You will have opportunities during your study of A-Level English Language to develop your key skills.

You will have to meet the following assessment objectives:

- **AO1:** Select and apply a range of linguistic methods to communicate relevant knowledge using appropriate terminology and coherent, accurate written expression.
- **AO2:** Demonstrate critical understanding of a range of concepts and issues related to the construction and analysis of meanings in spoken and written language, using knowledge of linguistic approaches.
- **AO3:** Analyse and evaluate the influence of contextual factors on the production and reception of spoken and written language, showing knowledge of the key constituents of language.
- **AO4:** Demonstrate expertise and creativity in the use of English in a range of different contexts, informed by linguistic study.

Types of exam questions

In English Language examinations, different types of question are used to assess your abilities and skills. Unit tests mainly require more extended answers. These questions are often linked directly to a given context, requiring you to read and study stimulus material. Some specifications use structured short-answer questions.

Short-answer questions

Short-answer questions can be set at AS and A2 level. A short-answer question may test recall, or it may test understanding. Short-answer questions may have space for the answers printed on the question paper.

Here is an example (a brief answer is shown below):

1 Extract: Nice! Cheers! <3

(i) Describe two features of this text message.

1. <3 is an emoticon.

2. Use of graphology to represent sentiment.

Structured questions

Structured questions are in several parts. The parts usually have a common context, and they often become progressively more difficult and more demanding as you work your way through the question. A structured question may start with simple recall, then test understanding of a familiar or an unfamiliar situation.

An example of a structured task based on text messaging might involve:
- identifying the features of a set of messages (2 marks per feature)
- explaining the reasons behind certain stylistic features (10 marks)
- identifying a particular message by its stylistic features (15 marks).

You will need to respond to as many parts of the question on the exam paper as possible, but you will not score well if you allow yourself to get bogged down on the early questions. Attempt all parts for maximum marks.

Extended answers

The majority of English Language exam questions require extended answers, either based on a passage or passages for commentary, or as stand-alone essay questions. These questions are designed to test your ability to structure ideas cogently, and communicate effectively.

The 'correct' answers to extended questions are often less well-defined than those requiring shorter answers. Examiners will often be marking you on more than one assessment objective, and giving separate scores for each one.

Marks for your answer may be allocated using a 'levels of response' mark scheme. Such a scheme for a 12-mark section might be written as follows:

- **10–12 marks:** You have discussed a linguistic issue in a thorough and evaluative manner.
- **7–9 marks:** You have discussed the issue, but not considered its practical aspects fully.
- **4–6 marks:** You have shown some knowledge of the issue, but only at a basic level.
- **1–3 marks:** You show only a limited knowledge of the issue.

AS and A-Level specifications will assess your quality of written communication (QWC). Marks are likely to be allocated for legible text with accurate spelling, punctuation and grammar, and for a clear, well-organised answer in which you use specialist terms effectively.

1 Language modes

The following topics are covered in this chapter:

- Spoken, written, blended and multimodal texts
- Phonology, graphology and text structures
- Rhetorical strategies and reader and writer positioning

1.1 The spoken mode

LEARNING SUMMARY

After studying this section, you should be able to:

- identify the key features of the spoken mode
- describe how the conventions of the spoken mode convey meaning
- analyse the strengths and weaknesses of spoken communication

An overview of the different language modes

AQA	A P1, B P1
Edexcel	P1
OCR	P1
WJEC	P1

The two main methods of communication through language are the **written** and the **spoken modes**. Your main focus to date is likely to have been on achieving competence in the written mode. A-Level English Language courses seek to redress this balance to some extent.

The spoken mode:
- takes place in real time and space
- involves face-to-face communication, telephone and Skype
- involves speakers and listeners who use different ways of communicating ideas in context.

The written mode:
- is usually permanent and checkable
- is impersonal – writers do not know who will read their texts
- has a limited repertoire of ways to show how a text is meant to be conveyed (such as spelling, punctuation and graphology).

Recent developments in information technology have added a third **electronic mode**, which combines elements of both written and spoken communication and is therefore **multimodal**.

In this part of the examination, your knowledge of grammar will enable you to meet Assessment Objectives (AOs) 1 and 3.

AO1: Select and apply a range of linguistic methods to communicate relevant knowledge using appropriate terminology and coherent, accurate written expression.

AO3: Analyse and evaluate the influence of contextual factors on the production and reception of spoken and written language, showing knowledge of the key constituents of language.

In both of these areas you will need to focus **not** on spotting the characteristics of the mode, but on **applying** your knowledge intelligently.

Features of the spoken mode

AQA **A P1, B P1**
Edexcel **P1**
OCR **P1**
WJEC **P1**

The spoken mode is largely **unplanned** and happens in **real time and space**. Without a great deal of planning or editing, most speech is temporary, ephemeral and **impermanent**. Speakers can change topics with ease and freely move backwards and forwards in a conversation. Comments and asides are frequent, whilst misunderstandings can be cleared up with simple questions.

In contrast, writing is often **deliberately constructed** and usually more **permanent**.

> Because they are easier to study, the rules for writing are more widely known.

Writers cannot fully anticipate their readers' responses, but they do know that their words can be re-read. Things like topic changes have to be managed carefully to make sure that readers can follow the thread of the writing – writers have to edit and re-arrange parts of their text. However, speakers can use phrases such as 'as I was just saying', or 'but to return to your point'.

In the spoken mode, speakers can switch between different **accents, dialects** and **registers** according to context. Speakers use **different levels of formality** to suit their audiences, whereas writers tend to plan and control their writing, and maintain a single level of formality.

The comedians Armstrong and Miller make amusing use of accents and levels of formality in their sketches. One example is where World War II airmen speak in modern street slang, but using the 'posh' accents that we are used to from World War II films.

Speaking is usually **face to face**, and as we communicate we are alert to feedback. This allows speakers to adjust what is said, and to collaborate in the creation of mutual meanings.

Longer forms of speaking exist, for example stage monologues, political speeches and jokes, but most talking involves interaction with listeners.

People:
- finish each other's comments and statements
- interrupt
- compete for turns
- argue
- disagree with – or extend – what is said.

> This is also known as **backchannelling**.

As they talk and listen, participants in a conversation give feedback to each other.

This feedback process might involve:
- **specific words** – 'exactly', 'definitely', 'right', 'absolutely', 'good', 'oh I see', 'that's interesting'
- **vocalisations** – 'yeah', 'mmm', 'uh huh', 'oh'
- **non-verbal signals** – 'smiling', 'nodding the head', 'wincing'.

Non-verbal communication – such as eye contact, hand gestures, body movements, intonation, volume, pauses and silences – conveys meaning, usually by supplementing what is said. Speakers can also undermine meaning, for example by remaining silent in a discussion or not replying to someone.

Consideration for others is an essential part of spoken language. **Modal expressions** such as 'possibly', 'probably', 'maybe', 'I guess', 'I suppose' and 'perhaps' help speakers to negotiate meaning in a non-assertive, non-aggressive way. In addition, there are hundreds of expressions that help to soften and adapt a speaker's requests or demands. These include 'so to speak', 'would you mind?', 'if I may', and so on.

Writing cannot compete with a living voice in conveying subtle shades of meaning, although there are ways to express nuances in speech in the written word:
- Capital letters, italics and underlining can be used for emphasis.
- Dots can show silence.
- Exclamation and question marks can indicate voice pitch and volume.

Writers also find it difficult to show that there is more to a message than what the words alone say, or that the words are not intended to be taken at face value.

In spoken communication, speakers and listeners constantly signal how they want things to be taken and interpreted. This spoken punctuation reflects the need for speakers to give structure and shape to how they talk.

Speakers frequently **signpost** things for their listeners.

'Now', for instance, shows a change of topic or the end of an utterance, for example, 'Now, that's it for the money. What about packing?'

In more formal speech, numerals such as first, second and third are used to indicate the order of events.

> **KEY POINT**
>
> Writing is almost entirely **visual** – words on a page or screen. Speaking and listening are mainly **aural**, but there are many visual elements.

Single word units of meaning are rare, and are even discouraged in writing. In speech, single words or phrases are frequent and **meaningful in context**. Examples are 'anyway', 'right', 'OK' and 'really'.

The fact that speakers can usually see each other and their surroundings means that things do not have to be described or even named explicitly – **pointing** or **deictic words** such as 'this', 'that', 'these', 'here', 'now' and 'over there' can be used instead.

Writing relies much less on immediate context. Isolated words or phrases can be used for effect, but if overused they are confusing.

> **PROGRESS CHECK**
>
> ① Give three reasons why talking face to face is probably the best way of communicating with another person.
>
> **1** Instant feedback possible; speaker can adjust to listener; speech has more resources than writing, e.g. tone, gestures, backchannelling, pointing, etc.

Non-verbal communication

AQA	**A P1, B P1**
Edexcel	**P1**
OCR	**P1**
WJEC	**P1**

When face-to-face speech takes place, a great deal of meaning can be communicated **non verbally**. Backchannelling, for instance, might consist of encouraging nods and smiles rather than words. Anger might show in the colour of someone's cheeks, or in the distance between speakers. Almost all speakers respond to non-verbal signals, but they are very difficult to record and study.

The psychologist Michael Argyle concluded that there are five main functions of non-verbal communication:
1. Expressing emotions.
2. Expressing interpersonal attitudes.
3. Managing interaction cues between speakers and listeners.
4. Self-presentation of one's personality.
5. Rituals (e.g. greetings).

A very important aspect of non-verbal communication is the speaker's and listener's **gaze** or making eye contact. Looking someone in the eye is very important in some social groups, whereas it is inappropriate in others.

Non-verbal messages interact with speech in a number of ways, including accenting, complementing, conflicting, regulating, repeating and substituting:
- **Accenting** allows speakers to control how they will be understood through factors such as touch, voice pitch and gestures. For instance, a negative statement can be emphasised by shaking the head, and a seemingly angry statement can be softened by maintaining eye contact.
- Speakers can **complement** their verbal messages with non-verbal cues. This kind of behaviour can be seen when singers make gestures that are appropriate to the meaning of their song, or when someone puts a hand on their heart to show sincerity.
- **Conflicting** verbal and non-verbal messages can often be a valuable source of information; for example, someone who is telling a lie may fidget or avoid eye contact. As people are usually less conscious of their non-verbal communication, it is often a good idea to trust body language over spoken words when there is a conflict.
- Non-verbal behaviour is often used to **regulate** conversations. A person might touch someone's arm to show that they want to speak next.
- **Repeating** gestures, such as pointing at the object of discussion, can convey the same information as a verbal message.
- Finally, non-verbal behaviour can be a **substitute** for verbal communication. People who do not share a common language can make themselves understood in this way, but even in everyday life people can be greeted with a smile and a wave instead of words.

PROGRESS CHECK

1 What messages is the following non-verbal behaviour conveying?
  a) hunched up, head down
  b) saying 'trust me', but looking down, avoiding eye contact
  c) looking over the shoulder of the person being spoken to.

1 a) does not wish to talk
b) might be lying
c) not interested in speaking to that person – wishing to speak to someone else.

Transcripts

AQA   **A P1, B P1**
Edexcel **P1**
OCR   **P1**
WJEC   **P1**

People tend to remember the content of a conversation rather than the exact words that were spoken. This tends to make us think that speech is much more coherent than it actually is. **Transcripts** of actual conversations show us that real speech is often disjointed and discontinuous.

Here, for example, is a transcript of a conversation between a manager and an employee in a shop.

> The conversation is about a sales order.
>
> They have a jokey aside about another employee.
>
> They return to business.

Manager:	Has the new batch of sweaters come in yet?
Employee:	Er... which ones do you mean?
Manager:	Oh, you know…, the ones coming over from, um, the Cheshire shop. The ones I asked you to contact Bob about last week.
Employee:	Cute Bob?
Manager:	Yeah, cute Bob! (laughter) So, you order 'em?
Employee:	Yeah, yeah I did. They're gonna be in later today.

Some characteristic features of the spoken mode are listed in the table below.

Features of the spoken mode	How they are shown in writing
Pause	. , ; : –
Hesitation	– … 'er'
Fillers	'er', 'like', 'you know'
Non-fluency features	– … 'er', 'em'
Expression of emotion	'aagh!', '!', *italics* and **bold**
Incomplete syntax	…
Overlaps	… or with comment: 'x interrupted'
Pronunciation, accent	Through spelling
Redundancy	Often omitted
Sentences not marked off	Capital letters and full stops
Deictic behaviour	Explicit comment: 'x pointed'
Gesture and body language	Explicit comment: 'x smiled'
Seamless topic change	New sentence or paragraph

> Notice how writing has far fewer resources than speech.

For information about the common conventions that you need to follow when writing a transcript, see chapter 8 (page 250).

PROGRESS CHECK

1. What is a transcript?
2. How are sentences marked in speech?
3. How are accents marked in writing?

1 A record of all the words, noises and gestures in a conversation.
2 Usually they are not marked off.
3 Usually through spelling, to match them phonologically.

1.2 The written mode

LEARNING SUMMARY

After studying this section, you should be able to:

● identify the key features of the written mode
● describe how written mode conventions convey meaning
● analyse some of the ways in which writing extends itself beyond words on a page

Features of the written mode

AQA **A P1, B P1**
Edexcel **P1**
OCR **P1**
WJEC **P1**

As we have already noted, the written mode is usually planned and deliberate so that writers can control and manipulate many aspects of texts as they appear to the reader. Features under a writer's control might include graphology, phonology, lexis, semantics, textual structures, and discourse.

Graphology

Graphology is a term used to describe the visual features of a text – it might include layout, choice of font, and even the colour and size of a piece of text. Just as non-verbal communication supplements meaning in speech, graphology supplements meaning in writing.

Helpful graphological features include:

● underlined words
● boxes
● bullet points
● italicised text
● bold text
● headings and sub-headings
● illustrations (graphics, images, maps, diagrams)
● headlines, sub-headings and pull quotations in newspapers
● chapters, an index and a table of contents in information books.

> How many of these techniques can you spot in this book?

Figure 1.1 A London street scene by John Parry, 1835

A good example of how **font choice** and colour affect our reception of a text can be seen in this illustration of a street scene in Victorian London. Cheap printing and a more literate general public led to the development of text-based advertising in this period. In this image, different coloured posters battle for attention using a bewildering variety of fonts and cases. Few pictures are used because they were more expensive to generate. Notice the predominance of upper case writing as each poster 'shouts' its message to the general public before being replaced by a newer one.

A basic **layout** feature is the paragraph. Writing without paragraphs makes it difficult for readers to find their way around a text and is therefore off-putting. The rule 'New speaker, new line' is often taught at primary school, as a way of making dialogue layout clear and easy to follow.

In *Alice in Wonderland*, meaning and layout go hand in hand in 'The Mouse's Tale', as shown in Figure 1.2.

The Mouse's Tale

> "Fury said to
> a mouse, That
> he met in the
> house, "Let
> us both go
> to law: I
> will prose-
> cute *you*. –
> Come, I'll
> take no den-
> ial; We
> must have
> the trial:
> For really
> this morn-
> ning I've
> nothing
> to do."
> Said the
> mouse to
> the cur,
> 'Such a
> trial, dear
> sir, With
> no jury
> or judge,
> would
> be wast-
> ing our
> breath.'
> 'I'll be
> judge,
> I'll be
> jury,'
> said
> cun-
> ning
> old
> Fury:
> 'I'll
> try
> the
> whole
> cause,
> and
> con-
> demn
> you to
> death."

'The Mouse's Tale' is shaped like a mouse's tail, and is therefore a visual pun.

Figure 1.2 'The Mouse's Tale' from *Alice's Adventures in Wonderland* by Lewis Carroll

Some graphological features are extremely conventional and well known, such as a newspaper's layout in columns, or a play script with the character names down the side. Other forms of communication deliberately break graphological conventions in order to stand out. They might use **deviant spellings** like Kwik-Fit or Phones 4U, or combinations of writing and graphics, such as the use of an arrow connecting the 'a' and 'z' of 'Amazon' in the Amazon logo.

Modern means of writing – such as word processors and html editors – allow users to control all aspects of how a text appears to a reader. This freedom means that writers can be much more creative than before, but it can also lead to some poor choices, such as over-busy MySpace pages, or the distracting use of flashing texts.

The combination of the right kinds of text with the right kind of visual elements results in **graphical cohesion**.

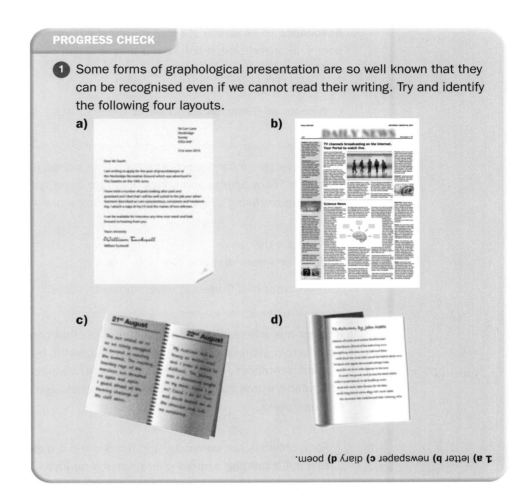

1. Some forms of graphological presentation are so well known that they can be recognised even if we cannot read their writing. Try and identify the following four layouts.

a)

b)

c)

d)

1. a) letter b) newspaper c) diary d) poem.

Phonology

It might seem odd to discuss the sound-related, or **phonological**, features of written texts, but generally it is only when a text is written down or deliberately committed to memory that alliteration, assonance, rhythm and rhyme can be manipulated. It is easy to assume that these features are only aspects of poetry or song, but they can also be found in prose texts.

KEY POINT

The **deliberate** nature of phonology is emphasised when rhymes are **accidentally** made, e.g. 'I'm a poet and I didn't know it'.

Alliteration is when the sounds at the beginning of a set of words are the same, or similar. It is a very emphatic way of writing and is therefore not used extensively in prose, but it can be striking and effective when used subtly, as the following example shows.

> It is (Death) that puts into a man all the wisdom of the world without speaking a word.
>
> *Extract from* A History of the World, *Sir Walter Raleigh*

Alliteration is also common in advertising slogans, for instance 'Allied Irish Bank: Britain's best business bank'.

Assonance uses similar internal vowel sounds and is relatively common in poetry. In advertising, it can hold a phrase together more subtly than rhyme or alliteration.

> It beats as it sweeps as it cleans.
>
> *Hoover vacuum cleaner*

Rhyme places similar sounds at the ends of words, and is the distinguishing feature of many poems and songs. It is rare in everyday prose, but can be used to make advertising slogans memorable. Below are a couple of examples.

> A Mars a day
> Helps you work rest and play
>
> The flavour of a Quaver is never known to waver.

Rhythm has a less localised effect than the other phonological features. It can occur within a single sentence or it can be created by using, say, a whole series of short sentences. In the following example, a series of short phrases using polysyllabic words builds up to a sobering conclusion which uses only monosyllables.

> For a crowd is not **company**, and faces are but a **gallery** of **pictures**, and talk but a **tinkling cymbal** where there is no love.
>
> *Extract from* Of Friendship, *Francis Bacon (emphasis added)*

The **onomatopoeic** word 'tinkling' also adds to the soundscape of this sentence, and makes lack of friendship seem bleak and empty.

PROGRESS CHECK

1 Identify the phonological features in the following quotations from Samuel Taylor Coleridge:
   a) 'The fair breeze blew, the white foam flew, the furrow followed free.'
   b) 'That solitude which suits abstruser musings.'
   c) 'In Xanadu did Kubla Khan a stately pleasure dome decree.'
   d) 'To meet, to know, to love – and then to part,
      Is the sad tale of many a human heart.'

1 a) alliteration b) assonance c) rhythm; alliteration d) rhyme.

Text structures

The way that a text is organised helps readers to find their way around it and, to some extent, determines how it will be interpreted.

A number of **text structures** have been identified, including:
- description
- problem–solution
- chronological sequence
- compare and contrast
- cause and effect
- directions–process
- generalisation.

Each of these structures are explained below and followed by an example.

Description can often consist of statements about something in no particular order. Typical words and phrases include **is, for example, involves, can be defined, an example, for instance**.

> The cat lay in the sunlight basking in the warmth of the day.

In a **problem–solution** text structure, a problem is set up, discussed and solved. Typical words and phrases include **because, cause, since, therefore, as a result, so, if...then**.

> The cat had only one problem. He was feeling hungry. He began to mewl loudly, in the confident expectation that food would be brought.

Chronological sequence is a very common organisational strategy. Typical words and phrases include **first, second, third, now, before, after, then, next, finally, while, meanwhile, since**.

> The cat had behaved in this way since it was a kitten. It had never ever bothered to look for food itself.

The **compare and contrast** text structure is used to discuss similarities and differences between two or more ideas, objects, or processes. Typical words and phrases include **same as, alike, similar to, unlike, but, as well as, yet, either...or, compared to, in contrast, while, although, unless, however**.

> The cat's sister, however, was the best mouser we had ever owned. She saw all mice as a personal affront to her peace of mind and would not let even one escape.

The **cause and effect** text structure shows how one event is a consequence of another. Typical words and phrases include **so that**, **because of**, **thus**, **unless**, **since**, **as a result**, **then**, **consequently**, **thus**, **accordingly**.

> We tried to encourage the male cat to hunt mice; as a result he sulked for over a week.

The **directions–process** text structure gives instructions or directions; most verbs are in the imperative.

> If you want to find the male cat, go to the warmest place in the house. The female cat will find you.

Generalisation draws conclusions from observations, or outlines rules based on previous experience. Typical words and phrases include **most**, **all**, **some**.

> On nature programmes, you see male lions lounging about doing nothing much. Perhaps all male felines are lazy.

Different text structures are appropriate for different types of writing. For instance, you would expect chronological sequences in newspaper stories and generalisations in newspaper editorials.

> The fact that readers can move on to the next story forces newspaper articles to 'front load' information.

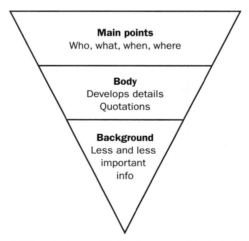

Main points
Who, what, when, where

Body
Develops details
Quotations

Background
Less and less
important
info

Figure 1.3 Inverted pyramid showing a possible text structure

Knowledge of text structures helps readers, particularly of non-fiction, to find their way around texts and to pinpoint information easily. At paragraph level, for instance, readers know that the first sentence of any given paragraph is often a **topic sentence**, which effectively summarises the information that is about to be given. Dictionaries and encyclopaedias are principally structured using alphabetical order.

KEY POINT

Text structures govern **readers' expectations**. It would be extremely disorientating, for instance, to arrange a novel alphabetically, or a 'how to' guide in the style of a newspaper.

An informational text may include a range of graphological features (see page 21). It is also possible to find examples of different text structures within a single paragraph.

However, different types of text require particular overall structures.

Here are some examples:
- A **biography** is usually **chronological**.
- A **geographical account of a country** uses a **description** structure.
- A **newspaper article about a local issue** uses a **problem–solution** text structure.
- A **recipe** uses **directions–process**.
- A **consumer report on new mobile phones** uses the **compare and contrast** text structure.
- An **article about why we should recycle** uses **cause and effect**.

PROGRESS CHECK

1. Which text structure would you choose for the following?
   a) persuading someone to give up smoking
   b) explaining how bonfire night celebrations came about
   c) explaining why you bought a particular type of phone.

1. a) cause and effect b) chronological c) compare and contrast.

1.3 Blended forms

LEARNING SUMMARY

After studying this section, you should be able to:
- identify the key features of blended forms
- understand how text conventions position both writer and reader
- analyse how speech is represented in writing

Key features of blended forms

AQA **A P1, B P1**
Edexcel **P1**
OCR **P1**
WJEC **P1**

Blended forms make use of the features of both speech and writing. Some forms attempt to present the spoken word on the page, whilst others are delivered orally, but are prepared in advance in writing. In both cases written conventions tend to predominate, so that speeches tend towards the formal and rhetorical – even the most 'spontaneous' seeming speech, when presented in writing, ignores features such as the repetition, overlap and redundancy of real speech.

In our daily lives we are on the receiving end of **planned speeches** from a range of people, including advertisers and politicians. Planned speeches are written first and then delivered orally. This means that they combine many of the advantages of writing with the immediacy of speaking. In many societies, from Ancient Greece onwards, the ability to deliver a speech effectively – either in a political debate or in a court of law – has been highly valued, and the art of public speaking or **rhetoric** has been extensively studied.

Well-constructed speeches, by people like Abraham Lincoln, Winston Churchill and Martin Luther King, are famous and frequently quoted. Equally, the elaborate set piece speeches of characters in plays – ranging from the patriotic fervour of Shakespeare's Henry V at Agincourt, to the wit and word play of characters in plays by Oscar Wilde – are admired and often referenced.

Rhetorical strategies

AQA	**A P1, B P1**
Edexcel	**P1**
OCR	**P1**
WJEC	**P1**

Henry V's Agincourt speech is delivered to a group of men about to engage in a battle, and deliberately appeals to their emotions.

Henry makes them think of the future and of surviving the battle.

> This day is call'd the feast of Crispian.
> He that outlives this day, and comes safe home,
> Will stand a tip-toe when this day is nam'd,
> And rouse him at the name of Crispian.

He reminds them that their deeds will always be remembered.

> And Crispin Crispian shall ne'er go by,
> From this day to the ending of the world,
> But we in it shall be remembered-

All those who take part – from King to commoner – will have a special bond.

> We few, we happy few, we band of brothers;
> For he to-day that sheds his blood with me
> Shall be my brother; be he ne'er so vile,
> This day shall gentle his condition;

Those who were not at the battle will be jealous.

> And gentlemen in England now-a-bed
> Shall think themselves accurs'd they were not here,

Extract from Henry V *(Act 4, Scene 3) by William Shakespeare*

In making this speech, Henry has chosen a particular **rhetorical strategy**. He has made himself the equal of his listeners. He has shared their concerns and their pride, and contrasts their situation with 'gentlemen in England now-a-bed', so that their desperate situation is made to look preferable. He is speaking to ordinary soldiers and so keeps his language and his ideas simple and close to their lives.

Effectively, all speakers and writers adopt rhetorical strategies to make their points more effectively. Some strategies are highly formal, for example a summing-up speech in a court of law, whilst others are highly informal, for instance a friendly tone adopted by a blogger. You may have noticed that this sentence begins with 'you may have noticed…'! How would it have been different if it had begun 'We can see…'?

To identify a rhetorical strategy, you need to ask yourself the following questions:

- **How does the writer present him or herself?** Does he/she present him/herself as an expert with years of experience, or as someone coming fresh to the subject? Is the tone friendly or severe? Does the writer seem to be trying to shock or offend you, or to show consideration for your feelings?
- **How does the writer connect with the reader?** Does he/she show shared feelings of concern; is he/she willing to share experience through anecdotes; does he/she show a sense of humour?
- **What language choices has the author made, and are they appropriate?** Are emotive terms being used when logic is required? Are difficult ideas being cloaked in euphemism?

- **What text structures and organisation has the writer used?** As we noted earlier, examples may include chronological, descriptive, cause and effect, directions–process, problem–solution or generalisation. Is the organisation appropriate for the ideas?
- **Does the writer acknowledge other points of view?** Are ideas developed in isolation or are other points of view taken into account? What attitudes to others are displayed?
- **How are the ideas expressed?** What lexical and syntactic choices has the writer made? Are they appropriate for the topic and the presumed audience?

> **KEY POINT**
>
> A rhetorical strategy or framework can be complex or simple, but all speech and writing has to adopt one. For instance, what is the difference between saying 'Alright mate?' and 'Hello!'?

Positioning

AQA **A P1, B P1**
Edexcel **P1**
OCR **P1**
WJEC **P1**

In **positioning** themselves, writers and speakers also position their audience. In this poster, the viewer is made to feel that he is not doing his bit for the war effort. The John Bull figure in the foreground represents the nation, but the men in the background could be family or friends.

Note the graphological features of this text. 'Is it *you*?' is in a handwritten font to give it a familiar feel.

In his speech to encourage the people of Great Britain in one of the most desperate moments of World War II, Winston Churchill makes repeated use of the word 'we' to emphasise the fact that everyone is in the same boat, and that success can only come from collective action.

> We shall go on to the end,
> we shall fight in France,
> we shall fight on the seas and oceans,
> we shall fight with growing confidence and growing strength in the air,
> we shall defend our Island, whatever the cost may be,
> we shall fight on the beaches,
> we shall fight on the landing grounds,
> we shall fight in the fields and in the streets,
> we shall fight in the hills;
> we shall never surrender...

> After so many repetitions of 'we shall fight', the final 'we shall never surrender' comes as an emphatic ending.

The rhetorical framework that a speaker or writer chooses will depend on its **context**, and will take into account:

- the **audience** – who is being addressed
- the **purpose** – why the text is being created
- the **mode** – how the text is to be delivered and received
- **format** or **genre** – what rules of presentation it will follow.

Public speaking

The rhetoric of **public speaking** is highly artificial and has a number of readily identifiable features. Because the spoken word cannot be returned to, as in a written text, **repetition** is frequently used, as are carefully planned and **balanced structures** that make contrasts clear. Many speakers make use of **triplets** – lists of three that give a sense of climax to what has been said. Audiences can be engaged through rhetorical questions that imply their own answers, and **figurative language** is often employed to provide striking imagery.

PROGRESS CHECK

1 How do the following extracts from well-known speeches position the speaker and listener?

a) **William Wilberforce** – '... when I turn myself to these thoughts, I take courage, I determine to forget all my other fears, and I march forward with a firmer step'.

b) **John F Kennedy** – 'And so, my fellow Americans: ask not what your country can do for you – ask what you can do for your country'.

a) sharing something personal
b) friendly, but authoritative.

Speech in literature

AQA **A P1, B P1**
Edexcel **P1**
OCR **P1**
WJEC **P1**

In complete contrast to public speaking are the ways in which **inner monologues** are represented in writing. In real life, we only have access to the words of other people, but literature can give access to the innermost thoughts and feelings of individuals.

Shakespeare's texts use soliloquies – speeches in which characters talk to the audience and reveal their inner thoughts. Hamlet's 'To be or not to be' speech, for instance, represents his meditation on the difficulties of human existence, whilst Macbeth's 'Tomorrow and tomorrow and tomorrow' speech is a reflection on the meaninglessness of life.

Later poets – such as Tennyson, Browning and Carol Ann Duffy – have used **dramatic monologues** to explore a character's mental state.

These efforts may work as poetry and provide insights into other minds, but real thoughts on a topic are rarely so 'organised'.

Many dramatic monologues construct an **implied audience** other than the reader of the poem. For instance, in *My Last Duchess* by Robert Browning, a duke confesses to having his last wife murdered as a way of showing how powerful he is and above the law. He confesses to an ambassador who has come to arrange a new marriage.

'The Count your master's' tells us that the listener is on a mission for someone else, and a 'dowry' implies a marriage.

> Will't please you rise? We'll meet
> The company below, then. I repeat,
> The Count your master's known munificence
> Is ample warrant that no just pretence
> Of mine for dowry will be disallowed;
> Though his fair daughter's self, as I avowed
> At starting, is my object.
>
> *Extract from* My Last Duchess *by Robert Browning*

In novels, an all-knowing author can simply tell us what a character is thinking.

> "The woman's an idiot," thought Morris; but he was obliged to say something different. It was not, however, materially more civil.
>
> *Extract from* Washington Square *by Henry James*

Or a first person narrator can report his or her thoughts and feelings.

'I said to myself' implies an internal dialogue.

> I used to dream of the poor old woman at nights. I really am not superstitious, but two days after, I went to her funeral, and as time went on I thought more and more about her. I said to myself, "This woman, this human being, lived to a great age. She had children, a husband and family, friends and relations; her household was busy and cheerful; she was surrounded by smiling faces; and then suddenly they are gone, and she is left alone like a solitary fly ... like a fly, cursed with the burden of her age".
>
> *Extract from* The Idiot *by Fyodor Dostoyevsky*

Some authors have attempted to reproduce the flow of thoughts inside someone's head, otherwise known as stream of consciousness.

In *Mrs Dalloway*, a character is taking a bicycle ride. Her thoughts seem to flow freely from one topic to another.

The subject of the thoughts moves in a free-flowing way, as it might in a conversation.

> What a lark! What a plunge! For so it had always seemed to her when, with a little squeak of the hinges, which she could hear now, she had burst open the French windows and plunged at Bourton into the open air. How fresh, how calm, stiller than this of course, the air was in the early morning; like the flap of a wave; the kiss of a wave; chill and sharp and yet (for a girl of eighteen as she then was) solemn, feeling as she did, standing there at the open window, that something awful was about to happen; looking at the flowers, at the trees with the smoke winding off them and the rooks rising, falling; standing and looking until Peter Walsh said, 'Musing among the vegetables?' – was that it? – 'I prefer men to cauliflowers' – was that it? He must have said it at breakfast one morning when she had gone out onto the terrace – Peter Walsh. He would be back from India one of these days, June or July, she forgot which,...
>
> *Extract from* Mrs Dalloway *by Virginia Woolf*

Dialogue

Dialogue is the name given to conversations between characters in novels, plays and films. In most cases, dialogue allows an audience to get to know characters at first hand. We hear what they say without the intervention of a narrator, for instance. In some film and theatre pieces, the dialogue is improvised or made up on the spot, but even such apparently unstructured talk is a long way from real speech.

You will have encountered various rules about setting out dialogue, and probably know that there are different conventions for different genres of writing. Some examples are illustrated below.

Comic books use speech bubbles that 'point' to the speaker.

Novels use rules like 'new speaker, new line' and phrases such as 'said Alice'.

Plays place the name of the speaker at the side. Some actions are indicated in stage directions.

Macberry the Play (based on *Macbeth*)

ACT II SCENE I: Outside Macberry's castle. It is a cold and dark night, the wind is howling through the trees.

Enter Banktop, and Fleapit bearing a candle before him.

BANKTOP	Are you alright, boy?
FLEAPIT (angrily)	Erm, the moon is down; I have not heard the clock.
BANKTOP (confidently)	And she goes down at twelve.
FLEAPIT	It is later, you silly man! (walking around agitatedly) There's something funny going on. Mark my words, you scoundrel!
BANKTOP	What do you mean, you, you... demon!
FLEAPIT	I mean that YOU were never to be trusted.
BANKTOP (pausing)	ME! ME never to be trusted?

Film scripts place names above the dialogue, and usually contain descriptions of visuals. You can see this in the example below, and in the extract from the *An Education* script, written by Nick Hornby, which is on pages 146–148.

```
The inside of a hotel ballroom.

[The band have just finished playing and a member of
the audience approaches the lead singer]

              AUDIENCE MEMBER
    Hi. Would you mind having a word with that
    girl over there? She doesn't know the
    difference between Cajun and Zydeco music.

              LEAD SINGER
    She doesn't?

              AUDIENCE MEMBER
    I'm sure she'd appreciate it if you could go
    over and explain. She's a bit shy, you see, and
    doesn't want to ask in person. Her name's Emma.

[Cut to: Long shot of other band members gazing
jealously at the lead singer, who is approaching the
girl. They turn to look at each other and nod in
agreement]

              BAND MEMBER
    Right. That's the final straw. He's got to leave
    the band now.

[Cut to close-up of the lead singer and the girl
talking]
```

The function of dialogue within a story might be to:
- show character
- make characters seem natural and lively
- reveal the emotional states of characters
- establish character relationships
- reveal conflicts in the story and between characters
- move the story on
- give information to the reader
- comment on the action
- foreshadow future plot developments.

This list shows how important dialogue is in conveying character; just as it is in real life. In addition, aspects of dialogue like lexis, regional or social accents, and attitude can reveal a great deal about particular speakers.

The way dialogue is written varies considerably across genres and historical periods.

In *Hamlet*, for instance, the main character is talking to two of his friends, who are meant to find out why he is sad.

Guildenstern

My lord, we were sent for.

Hamlet

I will tell you why; so shall my anticipation prevent your discovery, and your secrecy to the king and queen moult no feather. I have of late (but wherefore I know not) lost all my mirth, forgone all custom of exercises: and, indeed, it goes so heavily with my disposition, that this goodly frame, the *earth*, seems to me a steril promontory, this most excellent canopy, the *air*, look you, this brave o'er-hanging firmament, this majestical roof, fretted with golden *fire*, why, it appears no other thing to me, than a foul and pestilent congregation of *vapours*. What a piece of work is a man! how noble in reason! how infinite in faculties! in form, and moving, how express and admirable! in action, how like an angel! in apprehension, how like a god! the beauty of the world! the paragon of animals! and yet, to me, what is this quintessence of dust? man delights not me, nor woman neither; though, by your smiling, you seem to say so.

Rosencrantz

My lord, there is no such stuff in my thoughts.

Extract from Hamlet *by William Shakespeare (emphasis added)*

Side annotations:

Here Hamlet interrupts himself.

Hamlet makes a series of comparisons using the elements of earth, air, fire and water.

Rhetorical trope repeating the word 'how'.

He makes a slightly risqué comment about sexual attraction.

This is recognisably a conversation that might go on between three young men, particularly the risqué comment at the end, but Shakespeare has structured Hamlet's depressed thoughts into a carefully thought through piece of rhetoric.

In the film *Pulp Fiction*, two friends are talking about Vincent's recent trip to Europe.

> **Vincent:** ... you know what they call a Quarter Pounder with Cheese in Paris?
>
> **Jules:** They don't call it a Quarter Pounder with Cheese?
>
> **Vincent:** Nah, man, they got the metric system, they wouldn't know what ... a Quarter Pounder is.
>
> **Jules:** What do they call it?
>
> **Vincent:** They call it a 'Royale with Cheese'.
>
> **Jules:** 'Royale with Cheese'.
>
> **Vincent:** That's right.
>
> **Jules:** What do they call a Big Mac?
>
> **Vincent:** A Big Mac's a Big Mac, but they call it 'Le Big Mac'.
>
> **Jules:** *[in mock French accent]* 'Le Big Mac.' *[laughs]* What do they call a Whopper?
>
> **Vincent:** I don't know, I didn't go in a Burger King.
>
> *Extract from* Pulp Fiction *by Quentin Tarantino*

Jules echoes Vincent's lexis here and at other points.

Jules asks questions to allow Vincent to make his points.

They attempt to move on to a related topic.

Again, the conversation is one that most people would recognise, but it is much closer to real speech. There are repetitions and redundancies, one swear word has been edited out, and the lexis is informal and colloquial, but the conversation is slightly too well organised.

> **KEY POINT**
>
> Dialogue is an artificial construct and can never hope to be like real speech, even when writers have a 'good ear'. In fact, readers and viewers quickly become bored with too many speech-like features.

> **PROGRESS CHECK**
>
> 1. What is the one major purpose of using dialogue in writing?
> 2. What does Hamlet's speech show about his character?
> 3. What do you think having a 'good ear' for dialogue means?
>
> 3 Being able to convince readers that dialogue is realistic.
> 2 He says he is depressed, but he clearly enjoys developing ideas elaborately.
> 1 To present characters.

Colloquial language

A colloquy is an old-fashioned name for a chat or conversation. Colloquial language, therefore, is the sort of language you might find in conversations, and is thus present in everyday speech by definition. Its presence in writing will depend on the degree of formality or informality a writer wishes to achieve.

Colloquial language is avoided in official documents or in information texts, but it is a frequent feature of dialogue in stories, novels, plays and films. The friendly informal tone of colloquial speech also makes it a natural choice for many advertisements.

Starbucks uses many colloquial features in its advertisements to convey the idea that the company is both friendly and informal, but is also concerned about its economic and social impact. The headline 'It's not just what you're buying, it's what you're buying into' uses an informal understated construction – 'It's not just what you're buying' – and then plays on this with the expression 'buying into' as an informal way of saying 'showing approval of'. The relaxed tone is also underlined by the headline's use of contractions and its direct address to the reader, using 'you'. Starbucks's customers, it seems to be implying, are discerning and thoughtful about world affairs, as well as about their coffee.

Colloquial speech is different from slang or jargon – it is generally understood by all speakers of English, so that it tends to be inclusive rather than exclusive. Some colloquial expressions, such as 'bloke' for a man, are at least a hundred years old, and some, like 'booze' (meaning to consume alcohol), go all the way back to the Middle Ages.

Colloquial language can be found in places like magazines and blogs, and even on the side of buses. The atheist message shown in the image below employs contractions, speech-like discourse markers ('now'), and the unthreatening word 'probably'. Theist bus advertisements claim that there is 'definitely' a God, and can come across as hectoring their audience.

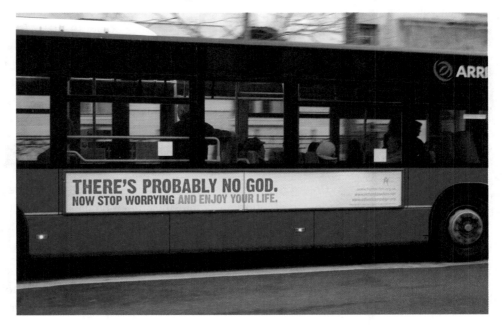

PROGRESS CHECK

1. Do you think that swearing is colloquial language?
2. What is the main phonological feature of colloquial language?
3. Why might a politician use colloquial language in a speech?

3 To seem friendly and approachable.
2 The use of contractions.
1 Yes, some English swear words are very old and well understood.

1.4 Multimodal forms

LEARNING SUMMARY	**After studying this section, you should be able to:** • identify the key features of multimodal forms • understand how multimodal forms have grown and developed • analyse the impact of new text forms on our society

Key features of multimodal forms

AQA **A P1, B P1**
Edexcel **P1**
OCR **P1**
WJEC **P1**

A person carrying a banner and shouting slogans is using a multimodal form of communication, but generally this term is used to describe the many new ways of interacting that have developed with modern technologies. These range from telegrams and ham radio, to SMS texting, e-mail and instant messaging. These ways of interacting are particularly interesting to linguists because they combine aspects of both speaking and writing.

Multimodal texts are mixed, so they sometimes follow the rules of speech and sometimes follow the rules of writing. This can be confusing for people who are unfamiliar with the rules of multimodal texts. For instance, people who are not used to the written aspect may not be aware that WRITING WITH CAPS LOCK ON is the equivalent of shouting, whereas people used to writing using traditional modes may find the abbreviations and short cuts of texting confusing and sometimes upsetting. Linguists are very interested in the way people compensate for the features of speech in writing with such things as emoticons, and abbreviations like LOL.

The development of multimodal forms

AQA **A P1, B P1**
Edexcel **P1**
OCR **P1**
WJEC **P1**

One of the most significant features of electronic modes of communication is the degree of interactivity that they make possible. A hundred years ago it was possible to send a letter and receive a reply the next day. Today, SMS texting and instant messaging allow written communication with almost instant replies.

Communication involving two or more people at the same time is called **synchronous**, whilst forms of communication that do not require the presence of all participants, like letters and e-mails, are called **asynchronous**. The more closely communication is associated in time the more speech-like it becomes, so that with instant messaging, for instance, phenomena like **adjacency pairs**, where two speakers create a single unit of meaning, are common.

The table on the next page shows different ways of communicating, ranging from carvings in stone to direct face-to-face communication. Each communication strategy has advantages, and rules for them differ in various places and times.

How might you extend this table? For example, what about radio, telegrams, planned speeches?

Type of communication	Advantages	Disadvantages	Comment
Stone carving	Extremely long lasting	Slow and difficult to produce; expensive	Only for very important messages; public
Poster	Easy to produce in large numbers; inexpensive	Not long lasting	Public messages – no feedback
Novel/play	Large audience	Expensive	One-way process; feedback is delayed (reviews/ book clubs/ author website)
Letter	Easy and cheap	Takes time to deliver	Private; feedback in kind
E-mail	Very cheap; instant delivery	Often written in haste	Private; feedback in kind; stored electronically
Text message	Often free	Phone keyboards can be difficult to use	Very quick feedback; short-form message
Tweet	Very cheap – wide audience; word limit	Same as for texts; word limit	Public; almost instant feedback; ephemeral
Blog	Available to all at any time	Can be time-consuming	Feedback in comments – people get annoyed
Instant message	Two-way conversation	Typing, not speaking	Written form can lead to misunderstanding
Telephone call	Quick	Person may not be available	Sound only; no non-verbal communication
Video conference	Almost face to face	Picture and sound may not match up	Subtle gestures can be missed
Face-to-face talk	Verbal and non-verbal communication possible	Have to be in the same place at the same time	Unplanned and ephemeral; instant and accurate feedback

Who are you communicating with when you write a personal private diary?

You might want to consider your own communication strategies and the context in which you use them:

- When do you write a letter?
- When do you send an e-mail rather than a text?
- What conversations have to be face to face?
- Which form of communication do you use most frequently?

> **KEY POINT**
>
> No method of communication is perfect. Fortunately, most of the time we have a variety of methods at our disposal and just need to pick the most appropriate.

As well as the many everyday methods of multimodal communication, there are some formats that allow us to exercise a number of communication strategies at once. Making a film, for instance, involves sound, vision, and sometimes text beyond the script. One of the most common multimodal means of communicating in school and in business is presentation software, for instance **PowerPoint presentations**, which usually involve text and speech, but which can include music and video.

The impact of new text forms on society

AQA	**A P1, B P1**
Edexcel	**P1**
OCR	**P1**
WJEC	**P1**

One of the advantages of electronic forms of communication is their speed, but this can also be a disadvantage. People do not have time to construct their messages carefully but, because they are more permanent than talking, written messages can be re-read by their recipients and possibly misinterpreted. In response to this, people using instant messaging, texting and even e-mail have developed a number of strategies to avoid confusion and possible offence.

Emoticons

Emoticons are symbolic representations of faces meant to be read sideways. Modern chat and e-mail programs can often detect their use and turn them into actual smiley or frowny faces.

Here are some common emoticons.

:-) :)	Happy; smile; funny
;-)	Wink; ironic
:-() 8-|	Surprised
8-o :-O	Very surprised; amazed
:-(:(	Sad; frowning
:-|	Disgusted; bored
'-(	Crying
:-D :D	Laughing; big grin
:-O	'Wow!'
:-s	Sarcastic
:-e	Disappointed
: P	Tongue sticking out
;-@	Swearing; angry

Emoticons have been in use since at least 1982. Their growth in popularity shows that there is a real need for them.

Texting abbreviations

Computer users have keyboards, but most texting is done using mobile phones equipped with number keypads – texting some letters therefore involves three or four key presses. So it is not surprising that texting, which also began in the 1980s, quickly developed a set of standard abbreviations. The table below shows some of them.

b/c	Because
B4	Before
BRB	Be right back
FYI	For your information
Gr8	Great
GTG	Got to go
IMO	In my opinion
L8R	Later
LOL	Laughing out loud
NE1	Anyone
OMG	Oh my god
thx	Thanks
U2	You too

As texting has become more popular, some people have started to worry that 'text speak' will somehow invade ordinary language. In reality, people tend to know when certain types of language are appropriate.

However, the fact remains that both instant messaging and texting need something more to cope with communication than traditional punctuation and orthography. The reason for this can be found in politeness theory, which is discussed below and on the next page.

PROGRESS CHECK

1. What does BRB mean?
2. What is the normal reason for putting a 'smiley' emoticon after a comment?
3. What is meant by 'dumbing down'?

3 Making things easier so people can understand/cope.
2 To show that a joke is intended.
1 Be right back.

Politeness theory

Politeness theory was formulated by Brown and Levinson.[1] It refers to the way speakers or writers attempt to soften threats to the '**face**' or social prestige of others. Brown and Levinson defined **positive face** as the desire of everyone to be

1 Brown, Penelope and Stephen C. Levinson. 1987. *Politeness: Some universals in language usage.* Cambridge: Cambridge University Press.

liked and admired, and **negative face** as the desire not to be imposed upon. They claimed that these concerns about face are universal in human culture.

Face-threatening acts are interactions that might damage the face of the speaker or the person being spoken to. They can be:

- verbal, e.g. 'You don't know what you are talking about'
- tonal, e.g. 'That's **really** clever' (said sarcastically)
- non verbal, e.g. looking away from a speaker.

Orders, requests, suggestions, advice, reminders, threats and warnings are all face-threatening acts – they either damage positive face by suggesting that there is something the listener should do, or they damage negative face by imposing on the listener's freedom of action. Compliments and expressions of envy or admiration both build up the hearer's face, as do expressions of thanks and obligation. Finally, offers and promises show that the speaker is willing to restrict his or her freedom of action for the sake of the listener.

In ordinary conversation, we try to avoid threats to our own face and forestall damaging that of others. If we have made a mistake, we can quickly correct our error through apologies and other strategies.

Face can be repaired through:

- polite requests, e.g. 'Would you mind if I borrowed that?'
- apologies, e.g. 'Oh, I'm terribly sorry'
- tone, e.g. using a rising intonation so that statements sound like questions
- non-verbal cues, such as not staring
- a change of accent, up or down the social scale, but usually closer to Standard English; this also shows consideration for one's listener.

In electronic messaging we can write quickly and without forethought, but unfortunately we do not have quick enough feedback to avoid all offence. Emoticons – and other extra textual features – allow writers to avoid giving offence by providing a range of considerate alternatives. A harsh sounding comment can be softened by a smiley icon, and sarcasm and irony can be labelled to avoid confusion.

> **KEY POINT**
>
> Through history, writing conventions have adapted to fit the available technologies.

One problem in politeness is that different groups have different standards. Young people might be offended if a text from a friend did not end with an 'x' for a kiss, and older people might not recognise deviant spellings such as 'thankyooooo' as attempts at politeness. Without these vital clues, tempers get lost and 'flame wars' – violent exchanges of messages – break out.

> **PROGRESS CHECK**
>
> 1 What is positive face?
> 2 What is negative face?
> 3 What is the phrase 'I don't mean to be rude but...' usually followed by?
>
> 3 Someone being rude.
> 2 The desire for freedom of action.
> 1 The desire to be liked.

Sample question and model answer

Text A is a passage from the novel *Emma* by Jane Austen.

Text B is from a blog about strawberry picking on the Best of Wirral website.

- Identify and describe the main mode characteristics of the texts.
- Examine how the writers of the two texts achieve their purposes and create meanings.

In your answer you should consider:
- vocabulary and meanings
- grammatical features and their effects
- topics and how they are structured
- interactive features of language in Text A
- how the language of Text B addresses the reader and shapes their response.

(45 marks)

Text A

The whole party were assembled, excepting Frank Churchill, who was expected every moment from Richmond; and Mrs. Elton, in all her apparatus of happiness, her large bonnet and her basket, was very ready to lead the way in gathering, accepting, or talking—strawberries, and only strawberries, could now be thought or spoken of.—"The best fruit in England—every body's favourite—always wholesome.—These the finest beds and finest sorts.—Delightful to gather for one's self—the only way of really enjoying them.—Morning decidedly the best time—never tired—every sort good— hautboy infinitely superior—no comparison—the others hardly eatable— hautboys very scarce—Chili preferred—white wood finest flavour of all— price of strawberries in London—abundance about Bristol—Maple Grove— cultivation—beds when to be renewed—gardeners thinking exactly different — no general rule—gardeners never to be put out of their way—delicious fruit—only too rich to be eaten much of—inferior to cherries—currants more refreshing—only objection to gathering strawberries the stooping—glaring sun—tired to death—could bear it no longer—must go and sit in the shade."

Such, for half an hour, was the conversation—interrupted only once by Mrs. Weston, who came out, in her solicitude after her son-in-law, to inquire if he were come—and she was a little uneasy.—She had some fears of his horse.

Seats tolerably in the shade were found; and now Emma was obliged to overhear what Mrs. Elton and Jane Fairfax were talking of.— A situation, a most desirable situation, was in question. Mrs. Elton had received notice of it that morning, and was in raptures.

Sample question and model answer
(continued)

Text B

Strawberry Fields Forever

Posted by Sarah N on 19 June 2008

Recently I went strawberry picking in Thurstaston, up by White's Farm Shop. Now I'm not one for the great outdoors; trudging about in fields for fun is just not my cup of tea. But I tell you what, it was great fun! I love strawberries, but as a rule I'm use[d] to them coming pre-packed from the supermarket or from Colin Lunt's fruit and veg in West Kirby. And for me, the word "field" brings with it connotations of thousands of creepy crawlies and bees (in spite of my friend's assertions that bees are "like flying hamsters" I am petrified of them). So nothing could prepare me for the surprise that awaited me in the strawberry field. For once I was dressed appropriately...[.] well almost. I probably should have chosen to wear jeans over my lightweight combat pants, and maybe a pair of socks to protect my ankles from the thistles would have been a good idea, but it could have been so much worse. I could have worn the shorts/flip flops combo I stupidly decided to wear on a trip to Betws-y-coed last summer. (Well I didn't know we were going for a walk down by the extra muddy river bank!)

Thistles and insects aside, it was a lovely sunny day, and there were plenty of butterflies about (incidentally the only insect I do actually like). But to begin with, it didn't look to[o] promising for us. When we arrived at the field, we were informed by the man overseeing the strawberry picking that all of the ripe and ready strawberries had gone by the end of the morning, but that there "might be some by the conifers". So off to the conifers we went and in about half an hour he [we] had about 7 strawberries between us. It began to look like we were wasting our time, until the boyfriend's dad decided to go to the opposite side of the strawberry patch to the conifers, and lo and behold it was strawberry heaven!!

Our two plastic baskets which had looked too big for our initial haul were now becoming dangerously full, so we decided to quit while we were ahead. After paying for our strawberry loot and ensuring it was safe in the boot of the car, we wandered off to the farm shop for a bit of a nose about. I was pleased to see that the meat was completely fresh and free from all the rubbish additives you tend to get with supermarket fare, and also a damn sight cheaper, which, as you know from my quest for cheap, quality ingredients, was a major bonus. The sausages in particular, (as I found out the next day when cooking my tea) appeared to have very little fat in them, which saved the health grill a job.

On our return back to the boyfriend's house we made a jug full of a tasty strawberry smoothie (2 bananas, a sizeable quantity of strawberries and a splash of milk, all whizzed up in a blender) to go with our tea, and then I parked myself in the garden and painted a picture of a strawberry.

The following day I whipped up a quick strawberry crumble:
- Chop a sizeable quantity of strawberries in half (or into quarters depending on the size of the strawberry) and put into an ovenproof dish with 1tbsp sugar sprinkled over.
- Scoop 9tbsp self raising flour into a mixing bowl with a small amount of butter (no more than 25g) and rub them together to form breadcrumbs.
- Scoop the mixture over the strawberries and pat down, ensuring the strawberries are coated, and pop the dish into a preheated oven Gas Mark 6/200°C/400°F for about 20minutes until the strawberries are cooked and the crumble has browned.
- Allow to cool then serve with any additional dessert (cream, ice cream, fruit sorbet) or eat it on its own.

Sample question and model answer
(continued)

The following answer is only the beginning of this student's response, but it shows a confident grasp of appropriate terminology (AO1). The two texts are compared in terms of their mode, and reasonable arguments are deployed and backed up with appropriate evidence. Many modal features are identified, but some could have been analysed in more detail. This response would score well on AOs 1 and 3.

Good general opening statement.

Comments are made on the mode of *Emma* and how it has been achieved.

The blog mode is contrasted with the novel. Discourse features are identified, quoted and commented on, and there is commentary on authorial and reader positioning.

A variety of styles within the text are identified and commented on.

There is an analysis of the audience and the purpose of the text. The student comments on how the text creates meaning.

The student identifies the audience and possible purposes of the text. There is also commentary relating to how meaning is created.

Model answer

Both texts concern strawberry picking. The extract from *Emma* consists almost entirely of dialogue from one character, and the blog post falls into diary and recipe parts.

Both texts are in the written mode, but both make interesting use of spoken mode characteristics. After a general introduction from an omniscient third party narrator, the text from *Emma* consists simply of the spoken words of Mrs Elton, beginning with the phrase `The best fruit in England–'. Many of the snatches are not even complete sentences, and their total effect is almost like a stream of consciousness. Realistically, the recorded snatches could be just the parts of Mrs Elton's apparent monologue that Emma might have heard.

The blog also uses the language of ordinary speech in order to produce its noticeably chatty and colloquial tone. For instance, it uses spoken discourse markers like `Now I'm not one...' and `But I tell you what'. Several chatty comments and asides are enclosed in brackets, and there are familiar references forward and back in time as if the reader is someone known to the writer. Other aspects of the blog that reinforce this impression are references to `the boyfriend's dad' and indeed `the boyfriend', as if these people were already known. At one point, the author addresses the reader directly: `as you know from my quest for cheap, quality ingredients', again giving an impression of familiarity, or possibly a loyal and devoted readership.

On the other hand, it is quite conscious in its use of language, and even discusses the connotations of the word `field' for the author. In the final section on smoothies and strawberry crumble, the language changes to imperative instruction giving.

Text A is from a novel and so its main purpose is to entertain. A great deal of the entertainment in this section is at the expense of Mrs Elton, who the narrator clearly finds intolerable. Rather than stating this, Mrs Elton is condemned out of her own mouth. Her dialogue moves from enthusiastic to weary and shows off the inconsistencies of her opinions as it does so, e.g. `hautboy infinitely superior', `hautboys very scarce– Chili preferred–white wood finest flavour'. At the end of this section, Emma is `obliged' to hear more of Mrs Elton and this does not seem to give her much pleasure.

The blog appears on the Best of Wirral website, so at least part of its purpose is to convince people to go out and enjoy that part of the world. The entry certainly conveys enthusiasm, but hypertext links could have been used to advertise, say, the farm in question. The author has two further purposes – to share her experiences and her expertise at cooking. The second purpose takes up the latter part of the post and seems to be successful. The sharing of enthusiasm is clear, but the lexis chosen is rather formulaic, for instance `it was a lovely sunny day'.

Exam practice question

1 Language and technology

Read the text below.

R Xmas hols wr CWOT. Lst yr we wnt to LA 2C my sis, hr BF & thr 2 :-@ kids FTF. ILLA, it's a gr8 plc.

How has the language of this text been influenced by technology? **(48)**

_____

_____

_____

_____

_____

_____

_____

_____

_____

_____

_____

_____

_____

_____

_____

_____

_____

_____

_____

[Please continue your answer on separate paper if necessary.]

2 Grammar and lexis

The following topics are covered in this chapter:

- **How grammar is assessed**
- **Key grammatical terms**
- **How key grammatical terms relate to the study of linguistics**
- **How lexis and semantics affect meaning**

2.1 Assessment

LEARNING SUMMARY

After studying this section, you should be able to:

- explain the role of grammar in the English Language A-Level assessment
- understand how grammar is integrated into A-Level English Language
- appreciate the breadth of grammatical study required on the course

How grammar is assessed at A-Level

AQA	**A P1, B P1**
Edexcel	**P1**
OCR	**P1**
WJEC	**P1**

You cannot study the English language at an advanced level without some knowledge of grammar. This does not mean that you will be tested explicitly on grammar in your exam, but you will not be able to write sensibly about the key features of language without using grammatical terms. In this sense, grammar is a **metalanguage** that helps you to describe and discuss language in use.

Your ability to deploy knowledge of grammar will be assessed as part of AO1.

> **AO1: Select and apply a range of linguistic methods to communicate relevant knowledge using appropriate terminology and coherent, accurate written expression.**

Remember that this objective is present in almost **all** of the units that you study. As the most common objective, it will affect the way you are assessed in your entire course, whether this is in commentaries you write in your coursework, or in responses to your exam questions.

Your knowledge of grammar will also enable you to meet objective AO3.

> **AO3: Analyse and evaluate the influence of contextual factors on the production and reception of spoken and written language, showing knowledge of the key constituents of language.**

In both these areas, you will need to focus not on spotting grammatical features, but on detailing and analysing their effects.

In writing, you will most often be able to comment on:
- sentence and clause construction
- the variety of sentence types
- subordination and co-ordination
- authorial point of view.

In addition to the above factors, in speech you might also be able to discuss:
- uses and functions of minor sentences
- turn-taking conventions
- exclamative sentences.

Key grammatical terms

The grammatical terms you are expected to be familiar with are:
- **nouns** – proper/common; singular/plural; concrete/abstract
- **adjectives** – comparative/superlative; attributive/predicative
- **adverbs** – manner, place/direction, time, duration, frequency, degree, sentence
- **verbs** – infinitive; mood (imperative/interrogative/declarative/exclamative); main/auxiliary/modal auxiliaries; present and past participles; person; tense; voice; aspect (progressive/perfective)
- **pronouns** – personal (person, number and function); interrogative; demonstrative
- **prepositions** – indicates the relative position, e.g. 'at', 'by', 'on', 'to', 'for'
- **determiners** – definite/indefinite articles; demonstrative adjectives; numerals
- **conjunctions** – co-ordinating; subordinating
- **sentence functions** – statement; command; question; exclamations
- **sentence types** – minor; simple; compound; complex; compound-complex
- **clause types** – main; subordinate; co-ordinate
- **clause elements** – subject, verb, object, complement, adverbials.

Many of these terms should be familiar to you. However, as well as knowing grammatical terms, you must also demonstrate an ability to apply grammatical knowledge. For instance, you might point out that the alien nature of Yoda in *Star Wars* is reinforced by his tendency to place verbs at the end of his sentences instead of in the middle – in English unusual it is!

> **KEY POINT**
>
> You will not be studying grammar in the abstract. It will always be in the context of texts and how they make meaning.

You have probably already studied **parts of speech** such as nouns, verbs, adjectives and adverbs. You may even be able to say confidently that 'table' is an example of a noun and that 'run' is an example of a verb. You would only be partly right in both cases. **You can only tell what part of speech a word is when you see it in a sentence**.

For instance, **table** is a noun in the following sentence.

> Put the papers on the table.

However, **table** is a verb in the sentence below.

> The opposition was forced to table a motion to adjourn.

PROGRESS CHECK

1. In linguistic terms, what is grammar?
2. Which assessment objective does grammar appear under?
3. Is 'round' a noun or a verb?

3 This is a trick question. It can be both – you can only tell what part of speech it is when you see it in a sentence.
2 AO1.
1 A metalanguage.

2.2 Nouns

LEARNING SUMMARY

After studying this section, you should be able to:

- define – and understand about – the different types of nouns
- identify nouns
- understand the importance of choice in relation to nouns

Defining and identifying nouns

AQA **A P1, B P1**
Edexcel **P1**
OCR **P1**
WJEC **P1**

Nouns are often defined as 'naming words' in primary school, but at AS and A-Level it is probably better to say that nouns have a naming or 'pointing' function within a sentence and that they **can be preceded by determiners**. For instance, 'dog' could mean to follow someone, but if we put a determiner in front of it, 'the dog', we are certain that we are dealing with a noun.

Nouns can be either **singular** (e.g. cat) or **plural** (e.g. cats). The majority of nouns in English form their plural by adding 's' to the singular form. Irregular plural forms (e.g. child, children; sheep, sheep) are quite common, and can cause spelling problems for young writers.

Things such as cars, clouds and amusement are designated by **common** nouns.

Proper nouns are the names of particular people or places, for instance George Washington, the Thames or the Moon. Proper nouns start with a capital letter.

Choosing nouns

At AS and A-Level one of the most interesting properties of nouns is their level of abstraction. **Concrete** nouns refer to things that you can see, hear, smell, taste or touch. **Abstract** nouns refer to qualities such as love or determination.

The degree to which writers choose concrete or abstract qualities can give important clues about their intentions and purposes.

For instance, look at the following list:
- 'He was hit on the head with a hammer' – the object is named.
- 'He was hit on the head with a blunt instrument' – the object is vaguely referred to.
- 'He suffered head trauma' – the object is not mentioned at all.

Each sentence means more or less the same thing, but the further we get away from concrete language, the less disturbing the information is. Abstract language often plays a major part in **euphemism**.

Compare the experience of war in the following two poems.

> How does Brooke's use of non-specific nouns avoid offence?

If I should die, think only this of me;
That there's some corner of a foreign field
That is for ever England. There shall be
In that rich earth a richer dust concealed

Extract from The Soldier *by Rupert Brooke*

> How does Owen use concrete detail to highlight the horror of war?

If in some smothering dreams, you too could pace
Behind the wagon that we flung him in.
And watch the white eyes writhing in his face,
His hanging face, like a devil's sick of sin;
If you could hear, at every jolt, the blood
Come gargling from the froth-corrupted lungs

Extract from Dulce et Decorum Est *by Wilfred Owen*

KEY POINT

Although nouns in themselves are fascinating, you will normally be looking at a given speaker's or writer's **choice** of nouns.

PROGRESS CHECK

1. What can precede a noun?
2. How can you tell if a proper noun has been used?
3. Are army recruitment posters likely to use abstract or concrete language?

1 A determiner.
2 The presence of a capital letter.
3 Abstract.

2.3 Adjectives

LEARNING SUMMARY

After studying this section, you should be able to:

- identify the different types of adjective
- understand the role adjectives play in language
- appreciate how adjective and noun choice influences meaning

Different types of adjective

AQA **A P1, B P1**
Edexcel **P1**
OCR **P1**
WJEC **P1**

Adjectives modify nouns – they tell us more about nouns, and often provide insights into authorial attitudes and stances. Adjectives include words like 'green', 'difficult' and 'fast', and can usually be placed either in front of or after the noun they modify; for example, 'write in the **green** book' and 'that book is **green**'.

Adjectives placed before their nouns are known as **attributive** adjectives, and those placed after are called **predicative**. Some old-fashioned phrases, such as 'the governor general' or 'times past', feature **post-positional** adjectives.

Any **word** or **group of words** placed in front of a noun can have an adjectival function, as shown in the following examples:

- 'For a joke I bought an **exploding** cigar' – **exploding** would normally be a verb.
- 'I couldn't find the **nail** clippers' – **nail** is usually a noun.
- 'He was a **very-difficult-to-please** man' – **very-difficult-to-please** is an adjectival phrase.

The role of adjectives in language

AQA **A P1, B P1**
Edexcel **P1**
OCR **P1**
WJEC **P1**

A famous 1970s slogan for Pepsi Cola consisted simply of a string of adjectives modifying the noun Pepsi. The slogan has been reproduced below.

How have the advertisers made this drink seem energy giving in their choice of adjectives and adjectival phrases?

> Lip smacking, thirst quenching, ace tasting, motivating, good buzzing, cool talking, high walking, fast living, ever giving, cool fizzing, Pepsi!

Even when we don't understand them, adjectives can add powerfully to the atmosphere of a piece of writing.

What do the nonsense adjectives **brillig**, **slithy** and **mimsy** add to this description?

> Twas brillig, and the slithy toves
> Did gyre and gimble in the wabe:
> All mimsy were the borogoves,
> And the mome raths outgrabe
>
> *Extract from* Jabberwocky *by Lewis Carroll*

Is **mome** an adjective? How can you tell?

Adjectives are not 'necessary' in the way that nouns and verbs are, but they play a major role in controlling readers' responses, and in creating the 'feel' of a text.

Adjectives are not modified in any way by singular or plural nouns, for example 'a **blue** butterfly' and 'ten million **blue** butterflies'.

However, as shown in these examples, adjectives can be modified in comparatives and superlatives:

- 'This book is thinner than that one' – comparative form with 'er'.
- 'This book is more expensive than that one' – comparative form with 'more' or 'less'.
- 'This is the thickest book I've ever seen' – superlative form with 'est'.
- 'This is the least expensive book here' – superlative form with 'most' or 'least'.

How adjective and noun choice influences meaning

As might be expected, advertising often makes use of superlatives.

Cadbury's *Flake* used the slogan below for almost thirty years.

> What do the two superlatives suggest about a Flake bar as a whole?

Only the crumbliest, flakiest chocolate, tastes like chocolate never tasted before.

The national retailer and brewer, Carlsberg, has run many advertising campaigns. Their well-known slogan is below.

Probably the best beer in the world.

The adjective 'probably' seems to undermine the superlative 'best', but in fact it reinforces it. Readers and viewers of Carlsberg advertisements are likely to dismiss a straight claim to 'being the best' as boasting. By adding the word 'probably', the advertisers give the impression that this might be an honest and thoughtful claim.

1. What other part of speech do adjectives relate to?
2. How can other parts of speech become adjectives?
3. How can adjectives be modified?

3 In comparative and superlative forms.
2 By placing them in front of a noun.
1 Nouns.

2.4 Adverbs

LEARNING SUMMARY	**After studying this section, you should be able to:** ● identify the different functions of adverbs ● understand how adverbs work in sentences ● appreciate how adverb choice influences meaning

The different functions of adverbs

AQA **A P1, B P1**
Edexcel **P1**
OCR **P1**
WJEC **P1**

Just as adjectives modify nouns and give us more information about an object, adverbs modify verbs and give us more information about actions. Like adjectives, adverbs can be specific words or they can be adverbial phrases. Adverbs and adverbials are extremely flexible in terms of what they can do and where they can fit into a sentence.

Generally speaking, adverbs have the following functions:
● They add information about an event (this is their most common role), e.g. 'I waited **patiently**'.
● They link clauses together, e.g. 'The class was noisy. **However**, plenty of work was going on'.
● They comment on what is being said, e.g. '**Honestly**, I don't think it's going to happen'.

Adverbs are often said to have a range of specific functions, as shown in the table below.

Adverb of...	Function	Examples	Adverbial phrase
Manner	**How** something is done	Quickly, clearly	With care, at a snail's pace
Place / Direction	**Where** something happens or in what direction	Locally, backwards	In the garden, at work, closer to the door
Time	**When** something occurs	Yesterday, soon	In a moment
Duration	**How long** something takes	Continuously	All day, for a while
Frequency	**How often** an action occurs	Seldom, weekly	Every so often
Degree	**How intense** an action is	Fiercely, very	To some extent

Like adjectives, adverbs can have comparative and superlative forms, as shown in these examples:
● 'Is it possible to walk any slower?'; 'Can you walk more slowly?'
● 'He who laughs last laughs longest'; 'Which ball moved least?'

Single word adverbs often end in 'ly'. Recent research has shown that these kinds of adverbs are found more often in fiction than in other forms of writing.

How adverbs work in sentences

AQA   A P1, B P1
Edexcel   P1
OCR   P1
WJEC   P1

Charles Dickens draws attention to how adverbs can be used in conversation. Read the following exchange between Mrs Rouncewell and Lady Dedlock in *Bleak House*.

> In what way can one be 'charmingly' well?

> "My Lady is looking charmingly well," says Mrs. Rouncewell, with another curtsy.

> What attitude is expressed by Lady Dedlock's use of the phrase 'wearily well'?

> My Lady signifies, without profuse expenditure of words, that she is as *wearily well* as she can hope to be.
>
> *Extract from* Bleak House *by Charles Dickens (emphasis added)*

In more modern times, many commentators have objected to the use of the word 'hopefully' at the beginning of a sentence, largely because they do not understand the role of adverbs for commenting on as well as for modifying verbs.

Adverbs of manner are found in instructions, e.g. '**Carefully** remove the packaging'.

Adverbs of time feature in most narratives, e.g. 'We **quickly** unpacked and were down on the beach **by 10 o'clock**'.

KEY POINT

In **sentences**, adverbs can play a number of roles and appear in a very wide range of positions. There are no limits to the number of adverbial elements you can include in any given sentence.

Some simple sentences can be entirely adverbial, for example 'James walked **quickly backwards**' and 'We talked **all day**'.

In longer sentences, the placing of adverbs, adverbial phrases and even adverbial clauses (which contain their own verb) can be extremely flexible:
- Adverb – '**Suddenly** the bus overturned' / 'The bus overturned **suddenly**'.
- Adverbial phrase – '**Every Saturday** I go swimming' / 'I go swimming **every Saturday**'.
- Adverbial clause – '**When she was ten** her father died' / 'Her father died **when she was ten**'.

How adverb choice can influence meaning

> How does the placement of the adverbial change the emphasis of these sentences?

The ability to move adverbs and adverbials about in a sentence enables writers to direct a reader's attention with a great deal of subtlety. Here is an example:
- The car careered off the edge of the cliff at the very last moment.
- The car careered, at the very last moment, off the edge of the cliff.
- At the very last moment the car careered off the edge of the cliff.

2.5 Verbs

LEARNING SUMMARY

After studying this section, you should be able to:

- identify the moods, tenses and voices of verbs
- understand the importance of verbs in sentences
- appreciate how verb choice influences meaning

Understanding verbs

AQA **A P1, B P1**
Edexcel **P1**
OCR **P1**
WJEC **P1**

Along with nouns, verbs are the basic building blocks of sentences. In fact, a sentence is not a proper sentence unless it has a verb in it. Verbs describe actions, and also convey information about the timing and completeness of those actions. Just as nouns make sense with 'a' or 'the' in front of them, verbs can be recognised if we put 'to' in front of them, e.g. 'to be', 'to live', 'to work' and so on. This 'to' plus 'verb' form is known as the **infinitive**.

Verbs change their forms according to how they are used, and have different **moods**, **tenses** and **voices**.

Moods

The four common moods are **declarative**, **imperative**, **interrogative** and **exclamative**.

Declarative sentences are the most common – they state something is happening or that something is the case. Interrogative sentences ask questions, and imperatives give orders or instructions. Exclamative sentences are frequent in speech, and in writing they often end with an exclamation mark.

Identify the mood of the following sentences:
- 'Emma is such a good rider!'
- 'Please turn off your mobile phone'.
- 'The cake was delicious'.
- 'When will you be able to get here?'

At AS and A-Level you are most likely to notice verb moods when you are discussing different types of sentences. Conversation, for instance, is often marked by more interrogative and exclamative sentences, whilst things like instruction leaflets consist largely of imperatives.

Some people can get annoyed when declarative sentences are made to sound like interrogatives. This phenomenon is called uptalking, and it was identified by linguists in Australia in the mid 1960s. Experts refer to the uptalking style as high rising terminal (HRT) or high rising intonation (HRI). One view is that people (particularly young women) uptalk due to a lack of confidence, and that it is a way of trying to seek approval. However, uptalking is too widespread for that to tell the whole story.

> Have you noticed people uptalking? Why might some people find the habit tedious?

Auxiliary and modal verbs

A simple sentence might have one **main verb**, e.g. 'I lost my phone'.

This verb might be modified by **auxiliary verbs** such as 'have', 'be' or 'do':
- 'I am losing my phone' – 'Am I losing my phone?'
- 'I have lost my phone' – 'I had lost my phone.'
- 'I will lose my phone' – 'I will be losing my phone.'
- 'Did I lose my phone?' – 'Do I lose my phone often?'
- 'I did not lose my phone' – 'Will I have lost my phone by tomorrow?'

The function of auxiliary verbs is to change the tense, mood or **aspect** of the main verb, and to aid with negation.

The **aspect** of a verb is whether an action is:
- completed (**perfective**), e.g. 'I have eaten my dinner'; 'I had watched the programme', or
- ongoing (**progressive**), e.g. 'I am eating my dinner'; 'I was watching the programme'.

Auxiliary verbs are important for establishing order in narratives. Another group of 'helper' verbs are known as **modal auxiliaries**. In the present tense these are 'can', 'will', 'shall', 'ought to', 'must', 'need', 'may', and in the past tense they are 'could', 'would', 'should', 'might'.

Modal auxiliaries are used to express **certainty**, **necessity**, **obligation**, **possibility** and **probability**.

The following three statements show some examples:
- The government will improve school funding (**certainty**).
- The government ought to improve school funding (**obligation**).
- The government might improve school funding (**possibility**).

Modal verbs are particularly important in speech, as they allow users to negotiate or to explain their commitment to ideas or actions.

For instance, the following statements express decreasing levels of likelihood:
- 'I will meet you at seven.'
- 'I might meet you at seven.'
- 'I could meet you at seven.'

> **KEY POINT**
>
> Modal verbs are often key elements in polite statements. Subtle differences in the level of permission being sought are expressed by using 'may I?' instead of 'can I?'

Participles

We have already mentioned the infinitive form of verbs using 'to', for example 'to go'. Verbs also have a present and a past participle. The **present participle** is formed by adding 'ing' to the infinitive form, for instance 'going', 'talking' or 'being'. The **past participle** is usually formed by adding 'ed' to the infinitive form, for instance 'talked', 'believed' or 'disappeared'.

Although, statistically, most verbs take 'ed' past participles, irregular forms occur amongst common verbs. This can make learning past participles especially difficult for children, and speakers of other languages.

Examples of common verbs having irregular past participles include:
- am – was
- go – went
- eat – eaten
- ride – rode
- sing – sung.

The present participle:
- forms the progressive aspect, e.g. 'Sarah was listening'
- is the form a verb takes when it modifies a noun as an adjective, e.g. 'the missing jigsaw piece'
- is the form a verb takes when it modifies a verb or sentence in clauses, e.g. 'On current going, we should be there by Friday'.

The past participle:
- forms the perfect aspect, e.g. 'the library has closed'
- forms the passive voice, e.g. 'the window was broken'
- modifies a noun with an active sense, e.g. 'my confused friend'
- modifies a noun in the passive sense, e.g. 'the attached files'
- modifies a passive verb or sentence, e.g. 'looked at objectively, Peter should take the blame'.

Tenses

Actions are located in time by the tense of the verbs used to describe them.

The **simple present** tense indicates ongoing or habitual actions and takes the following form:
- 'I walk.'   • 'He listens.'   • 'They smile.'

The third person singular form using 'he', 'she', or 'it' adds an 's'.

The **continuous present** tense indicates ongoing actions in the following form:
- 'I am walking.'   • 'She is listening.'   • 'They are smiling.'

The **simple past** tense indicates completed actions and uses 'ed':
- 'I walked'; 'it snowed'; 'they smiled'.

However, there are many irregular forms:
- 'I ran'; 'I went'; 'they were'.

The **past perfect** tense shows when one thing has occurred before another:
- '**I had finished** my breakfast when you arrived.'

Grammatically speaking, there is **no future tense** in English. Future time is indicated by the use of the auxiliaries 'will' and 'shall', or by using time indicators with the present tense:

- 'I will be seeing you.'
- 'The film opens next Thursday.'

Most narrative and reportage writing is in the past tense, as the actions and scenes described are deemed to be over, but narration in the present tense is sometimes used. The following passage is from *The Siege* by Helen Dunmore and describes a moment of relief from near starvation.

> What tense is this written in? How does this affect your response?

> How would this passage be different in the past tense?

Anna comes back with four spoons, and twists the cap on the cloudberry jam. "We'll give Kolya his first. Here, open your mouth." He tips his head back, opens his mouth wide, and shuts his eyes. His foul, starved breath makes Anna's eyes sting as she carefully places the spoonful of jam in his mouth. "Don't swallow it all at once. Taste it."

The child's body shudders all over. He holds the jam in his mouth heroically, his eyes watering, then he gulps it down. He opens his eyes. "More."

"In a minute."

"More."

She spoons in more.

"Now wait. It's not good to have too much at once."

Extract from The Siege *by Helen Dunmore*

Person

The form of a verb is affected by the personal pronoun that applies to it; this is known as the **person** of the verb:

- First person singular – 'I walk'.
- Second person singular – 'You walk'.
- Third person singular – 'He walks', 'she walks' or 'it walks'.
- First person plural – 'We walk'.
- Second person plural – 'You walk'.
- Third person plural – 'They walk'.

In narrative fiction, the **point of view** of a narrative is the position that the author takes up in relation to its characters and events.

Three main types of viewpoint can be identified:

- In a **first person narrative**, the story is told by one of the characters in the novel, and ideally the impression created is that of sharing one person's view of the world. *David Copperfield* is an example of a first person narrative.
- A **third person omniscient** (**all knowing**) form of narration allows the author to travel freely from character to character, reporting on their thoughts and feelings, and giving information to the reader whenever necessary. The author is able to intersperse the narrative with his or her own comments and observations, but is also obliged to be completely honest, so that surprise and suspense are more difficult to achieve. *Tom Jones*, *Vanity Fair* and *Brave New World* all use this technique.

- A **third person 'centred'** form of narration involves a narrowing of the author's field of vision, since the story is told from the standpoint of one character only. In this way it is easier to maintain suspense, but obviously the story teller's options are more limited. Jane Austen, Henry James and George Orwell make extensive use of centred third person narratives.

Various combinations of these three techniques are possible, and in *Bleak House* Charles Dickens makes use of all three.

The novel opens with an extensive description.

> Notice how Dickens breaks rules. His first sentence has no verb.

> London. Michaelmas Term lately over, and the Lord Chancellor sitting in Lincoln's Inn Hall. Implacable November weather. As much mud in the streets as if the waters had but newly retired from the face of the earth, and it would not be wonderful to meet a *Megalosaurus*, forty feet long or so, waddling like an elephantine lizard up Holborn Hill.

Later, Dickens briefly looks at the world from the point of view of one of his characters.

> Dickens undermines pomposity with the use of slang, i.e. 'done up'.

> Sir Leicester Dedlock is only a baronet, but there is no mightier baronet than he. His family is as old as the hills, and infinitely more respectable. He has a general opinion that the world might get on without hills but would be done up without Dedlocks.

Another part of the narrative is written in the first person.

> I have a great deal of difficulty in beginning to write my portion of these pages, for I know I am not clever.

The first person narrative almost automatically puts us in sympathy with its writer, whereas Dickens's use of an omniscient narrator for his opening scene allows a panoramic overview. By showing the world through Sir Leicester Dedlock's eyes, Dickens is able to convey his pomposity and arrogance.

Some writers have made use of **second person narration**. This is difficult to sustain as it means that the reader is told what he or she is doing.

The technique is used chillingly in the 'crime' scenes of Iain Banks's *Complicity*, and, as shown below, for comic effect in Italo Calvino's *If on a Winter's Night a Traveler*.

> How does this compare or contrast with what you might be doing?

> You are about to begin reading Italo Calvino's new novel, *If on a winter's night a traveler*. Relax. Concentrate. Dispel every other thought. Let the world around you fade. Best to close the door; the TV is always on in the next room. Tell the others right away, "No, I don't want to watch TV!" Raise your voice – they won't hear you otherwise – "I'm reading! I don't want to be disturbed!" Maybe they haven't heard you, with all that racket; speak louder, yell: "I'm beginning to read Italo Calvino's new novel!" Or if you prefer, don't say anything; just hope they'll leave you alone.

Voice

Verbs can be in either an active or a passive voice. In the **active voice**, the person or thing performing the action is the subject of the verb. In the **passive voice**, the person or thing receiving the action is the subject of the verb.

The example below shows an active sentence.

Grace plays the guitar.

| Subject | Verb | Object |

The next example shows a passive sentence.

The guitar is played.

| Subject | Verb |

In the passive voice, the person or thing performing an action does not need to be mentioned. This can be very useful when an objective tone is required, or when the actor is unknown.

Here are a couple of examples:
- The experiment was started at 3.00pm.
- The wheel was invented during the Stone Age.

The passive voice can be seen in the phrase 'mistakes were made'. Why might a politician use these words?

> **KEY POINT**
>
> The active voice is usually clearer than the passive voice, but not all writers want to be clear.

> How would you re-write these two sentences in an active voice?

Over-using the passive voice can be tedious, and lead to dull-sounding writing:
- During your stay, the hotel swimming pool may be used. Access to the sports centre is free to guests.

> **PROGRESS CHECK**
>
> 1. What are the four moods of verbs?
> 2. What does a second person narrative involve?
> 3. What 'voices' can verbs have?
>
> 3 Active and passive.
> 2 A sentence using 'you'.
> 1 Declarative; imperative; interrogative; exclamative.

2.6 Other grammatical terms

LEARNING SUMMARY

After studying this section, you should be able to:

- identify a variety of other grammatical terms
- understand how these grammatical terms function in sentences
- appreciate how these grammatical terms help to create meaning

Pronouns, prepositions, determiners and conjunctions

AQA   **A P1, B P1**
Edexcel **P1**
OCR   **P1**
WJEC   **P1**

The meaning of nouns and verbs is usually clear, as they have real world equivalents. However, there are many grammatical terms that seem to only refer to other words, or co-ordinate words, or stand in the place of other words.

Pronouns

Pronouns take the place of proper or common nouns. **Personal pronouns** show such things as who or what is being referred to, how many, and their function as either subject or object in a sentence.

There are a number of other types of pronouns:
- **Subject pronouns** are 'I', 'you', 'he'/'she'/'it', 'we', 'you', 'they'.
- **Object pronouns** are 'me', 'you', 'him'/'her'/'it', 'us', 'you', 'them'.
- **Possessive pronouns** are 'mine', 'yours', 'his'/'hers'/'its', 'ours', 'yours', 'theirs'.
- **Possessive adjectives** are 'my', 'your', 'his'/'her'/'its', 'our', 'your', 'their'.
- **Interrogative pronouns** are used when asking questions. They are 'what', 'which', 'who', 'whom', 'whose'.
- **Demonstrative pronouns** are used to indicate particular nouns. They are especially important in discourse analysis when the things being referred to can be sensed by the speakers. The demonstrative pronouns are 'this', 'that', 'these', 'those'.

Until pronouns are grasped, young speakers are forced to repeat proper nouns. For instance, a child might say that 'Pala went to the zoo and Pala saw some lions and then Pala came home', instead of 'Pala went to the zoo and he saw some lions and then he came home'.

Writers who do not make appropriate use of pronouns can sound childish. On the other hand, excessive use of pronouns can be confusing:
- She gave it to her and she was like 'who's this from?' and she said she didn't know.

In discourse analysis, **deixis** or context may be necessary for full understanding of pronouns:
- 'I'll have that one' [points to green pen].

Lord Byron makes interesting use of nouns and pronouns in the opening of the poem *The Destruction of Sennacherib*, when his description moves from **Assyrian** to **his** to **their**.

> Notice how the shift from noun to determiner makes us focus on the number of invaders.

The **Assyrian** came down like the wolf on the fold,
And **his** cohorts were gleaming in purple and gold;
And the sheen of **their** spears was like stars on the sea

Extract from The Destruction of Sennacherib *by Lord Byron (emphasis added)*

Prepositions

The most common prepositions in English are 'of',' to', 'in', 'for', 'with' and 'on'. They indicate a relationship, usually in time or space, between things mentioned in a sentence. They can be single words or short phases.

Prepositions to do with **space** or **location** include 'above', 'at', 'behind', 'below', 'beside', 'between', 'by', 'from', 'in', 'in front of', 'in the middle of', 'on', 'onto', 'over', 'next to', 'to', 'under', 'with'.

Prepositions to do with **time** include 'after', 'at', 'before', 'by', 'during', 'for', 'from', 'in the middle of', 'on', 'since', 'until'.

John Donne uses prepositions in an interesting way in the following lines from his poem *On His Mistress Going to Bed*.

> Prepositions allow Donne's readers to imagine for themselves where his hands are wandering.

Licence my roving hands, and let them go
Before, behind, between, above, below.

You are unlikely to have to comment on a writer's use of prepositions in an exam question.

Determiners

There are several types of determiner in English. **Definite determiners** limit what is being referred to, whilst **indefinite determiners** broaden it.

For instance, the **definite article** (the) shows that the accompanying noun is a particular one. It may refer to something already mentioned, or it may be something unique.

Here are a couple of examples:
- I chose **a** book. I put **the** book in my bag.
- This is **the** best restaurant in town.

The **indefinite article** ('a', 'an' or 'some') shows that its noun is not yet a particular one. It is used when:
- a noun is first mentioned, e.g. 'Find yourself a chair'
- a noun's identity is irrelevant or hypothetical, e.g. 'An enemy might see you there'
- a general statement is being made, e.g. 'Some people don't know when to stop'.

Demonstrative adjectives ('this', 'that', 'these', and 'those') limit what is being referred to, and are often important in the analysis of speech. Cardinal **numbers** (one, two, fifty, etc.) are also determiners, as they limit the size of a group of nouns.

In speech, determiners can often be omitted:
- A: 'Do you want tea with that? Or cake?'
- B: 'No, I'm good.'

With determiners, i.e. 'Do you want **some** tea with that?', this conversation would be much more formal.

Conjunctions

There are two main types of conjunctions: co-ordinating and subordinating.

Co-ordinating conjunctions link words, phrases and clauses. They express ideas of joining, contrast, alternatives and logic. The main co-ordinating conjunctions are 'and', 'but', 'for', 'nor', 'or', 'so', 'yet'.

When co-ordinating conjunctions are used to join two clauses together, they have equal emphasis.

Here are a couple of examples:
- My sister lives in Manchester **and** my brother lives in Leeds.
- You can listen to the radio here **or** you can go out and play football.

In the examples above, each clause – on either side of the conjunction – can stand on its own and make sense.

Subordinating conjunctions link a dependent or subordinate clause to a main clause, as shown in the examples below.

I didn't buy a newspaper **because** you told me not to.

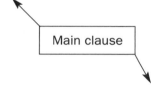

Main clause

Although it was summer already, he was wearing a pullover.

The main clause in each of these sentences makes sense on its own. The dependent clauses, that follow the subordinating conjunctions, do not make full sense on their own (see page 65, which discusses complex sentences).

Subordination can relate to time, reason, opposition and condition. Examples of each are shown in the table below.

Time	Reason	Opposition	Condition
After	As	Although	If
Before	Because	Even though	Even if
Since	In order that	Though	Only if
When	Now that	Whereas	Unless
While	Since	While	Whether or not
Until	So		

Co-ordinating and subordinating conjunctions are used to stitch together spoken and written texts, and they enable speakers to express complex and subtle sets of relationships. Younger speakers and writers tend to over-use simple co-ordinating conjunctions like 'and'.

2.7 Sentences

LEARNING SUMMARY

After studying this section, you should be able to:

- understand sentence functions
- identify sentence types
- discuss the impact of different types of sentence

Sentence functions

AQA **A P1, B P1**
Edexcel **P1**
OCR **P1**
WJEC **P1**

The four functions of sentences are:
- statement
- command
- question
- exclamation.

Most sentences are **statements** in that they describe a set of objections and actions:
- This sentence is a statement about this sentence.

Command or **imperative** sentences require an action. It can appear rude to simply tell someone to do something, and so most command sentences have ways of softening the command into a polite request. Command sentences can range from a single word, e.g. 'Stop!', to complicated constructions designed to make an order seem like a free choice for the listener – 'Would you mind moving to one side for a moment?'

Questions usually require information from the listener. There are many ways of forming questions. Here are a few examples:
- A simple statement – 'You live here?'
- Using 'do' – 'Do you live here?'
- Using a question tag – 'You live here, do you?'
- Using an interrogative pronoun – 'Where do you live? How long have you lived here?'

Exclamations are very common in speech, but less so in writing. They usually express a feeling or opinion in writing, but in speech they are frequently used as ways of backchannelling (as we mentioned in Chapter 1, this means providing feedback to the speaker).

An example of an exclamatory sentence is 'You'll never take me alive!' In conversation, listeners often use words or phrases that show they are paying attention, such as 'Really!', 'You don't say!', 'Yeah!'.

1 Make a recording of an informal conversation and identify the functions of the utterances in terms of statement, command, question and exclamation. In conversation, which is the most common sentence function?

2 Do the same for a formal classroom discussion. What differences do you notice?

The three main sentence types are:

- simple
- compound
- complex.

There are also minor sentences, although some grammarians refuse to call them sentences.

Simple sentences have a subject and a verb, and express complete thoughts:

- Jenna dances.
- Cows eat grass.
- The swings are painted green (auxiliary verbs and main verbs are counted as one).

Compound sentences consist of two main clauses (or simple sentences) joined by a co-ordinating conjunction:

- Freddy was reading a book and Stephanie was sending a text.
- Three people arrived on Thursday but four people left on Friday.

Complex sentences consist of a main clause, which makes sense on its own, and a clause that is subordinated to it. The subordinate clause is preceded by a subordinating conjunction:

- We ran home because it was raining.
- Although she was younger than me, my sister was usually better informed.

In theory, a sentence should contain a verb. In **minor sentences**, the verb is missing, usually because it is understood or implied. For instance, in the following exchange, 'at work' functions as a sentence:

- A: 'Where have you been?'
- B: 'At work.'

Minor sentences are common in speech and are frequently a source of backchannelling, e.g. 'Yes!', 'Wow!', 'Mary!', 'Really?'.

Different sentence types can be nested together to produce a **compound-complex sentence**. This type of sentence consists of at least two main clauses and at least one subordinate clause:

- My friend, who you met the other day, has arrived but I haven't talked to him yet.

The main clauses are:

- My friend has arrived
- I haven't talked to him yet.

The dependent clause is:

- who you met the other day.

There is considerable debate about how to define a sentence. In writing, a sentence is usually marked by a capital letter at the beginning and a full stop at the end. In speech, utterances that make sense on their own are usually treated as sentences.

An author's choice of sentence type can have a considerable effect on the reader. A series of short sharp sentences are easy to read and quite punchy. However, too many sentences like this might seem childish. Subordination allows very subtle relationships between ideas to be expressed, although too many complex sentences can be difficult to follow. Young writers frequently over-use co-ordinating conjunctions, so that their stories have a simple, often tedious, and... and... and... structure.

> **KEY POINT**
>
> Written sentences tend to be planned and make more use of subordination. Spontaneous spoken sentences tend to bolt one clause onto another in a loosely structured manner and make greater use of co-ordination.

Clause types

Just like a simple sentence, a clause must contain a single verb. Indeed, a simple sentence is identical to a clause. The term 'clause' is used when sentences are joined together.

The **main clause** of a sentence has both a subject and a verb and makes sense on its own, as shown in the example below.

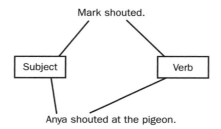

A **subordinate clause** is one that relates to a main clause in some way. Subordinate clauses are always preceded by subordinating conjunctions and do not always make sense on their own, as illustrated in the following example.

A **co-ordinate clause** is one that has been joined to a main clause by a co-ordinating conjunction such as 'and' or 'but'. Sometimes the conjunction can be omitted:

- Mark shouted but Anya shouted louder.
- Anya shouted at the pigeon; the pigeon flew off.

Clause elements

In a sentence or clause, we are told about things and actions. The simplest statement that can be made is that a thing acted, as shown in these examples:

- The dog ran.
- The tree grew.

The thing that the sentence is about is the **subject** of the sentence. If the subject acts on something else, we get sentences like the following:

- The dog chased the ball.
- The ball hit the tree.

The thing acted upon is the **object** of the sentence. Some sentences tell us more about the object, as in the following examples:

- The ball is red.
- The dog seems tired.

Extra information about the subject is known as a **complement**. Complements are adverbs or adverbials, and they always follow verbs like 'be', 'seems', 'looks' and 'sounds' (these are known as **copula verbs**).

Finally, some sentences tell us more about the verb. This element is extremely flexible and takes the form of **adverbs** or **adverbials**, as shown below:

- The dog ran **quickly**.
- The ball bounced **near the tree**.
- **Every day** the dog ran **round the tree**.

Identifying the different parts of a sentence is called **parsing**. You will never be required to do this as part of your assessment, but it is useful to know the different parts of clauses, in order to observe patterns and trends in language use. For instance, you might notice that some speakers over-use adverbs like 'really' to give emphasis to what they are saying, or you might notice that a writer frequently uses complement constructions to create an impression of how he or she felt.

PROGRESS CHECK

1. What are the three main types of sentence?
2. Name two clause types.
3. What is a minor sentence?

3 A sentence without a main verb.
2 **Any two from:** main; subordinate; co-ordinate.
1 Simple; complex; compound.

2.8 Lexis

After studying this section, you should be able to:

- understand the role of word choice in creating meaning
- consider denotational and connotational meaning
- understand the implications of corpus linguistics for language study

Words, words, words

AQA	**A P1, B P1**
Edexcel	**P1**
OCR	**P1**
WJEC	**P1**

Lexis is another word for 'word'. In linguistics it refers to the word choices that a speaker or writer makes from all the ones that are possible.

Word choice can be dictated by factors such as audience, genre, register and dialect, but consistent sets of choices place every text in particular **semantic fields**, such as economics or sailing. It has been argued, for instance, that you cannot understand the word 'sell' unless you have some knowledge of the semantic field of economic activity.

Denotational and connotational meaning

As even a cursory glance at a thesaurus will tell you, English has a very large number of words that mean approximately the same thing – **synonyms**. For instance, here are some of the words you might find in a thesaurus entry for the noun 'house'.

house (n)
abode, building, bungalow, domicile, dwelling, habitation, home, homestead, pad (slang), residence

This table shows the origin of – and notes about – each word.

Word	Origin	Notes
Abode	Middle English	A place where you abide
Building	Old English **byldan**	Related to bower
Bungalow	17th century Hindi	In the Bengali style
Domicile	Middle English via Old French	From the Latin 'domus' – 'home'
Dwelling	Old English **dwellan**	Delay, remain in a place
Habitation	Middle English via Old French	From Latin 'to live in'
Home	Old English	House – Germanic origin
Homestead	Old English	'House' + 'place'
Pad (slang)	16th century – bundle of straw to lie on	Popular in the 1950s and '60s
Residence	Middle English via Old French	Back formation from resident

Looking at even a single word in this manner tells you a great deal about the history of the English language and how it has been used. The presence of so many Latin words derived from Old French reminds us that the rulers of England spoke French for at least 200 years after the Norman Conquest in 1066. The Hindi word 'bungalow' came into English as a result of the British Empire, and the use of the word 'pad' to mean a house is an example of the kind of **metonymy** often used in slang.

As a speaker, you might choose to say 'house' or 'bungalow' or 'pad' or 'residence' when you want to talk about the place where you live. The word you choose will give your listeners a great deal of information about you, your attitudes and your social background. The Old French-derived Latin words sound formal and 'posh', whilst the Old English ones seem plainer and more ordinary – although the word 'abode' is perhaps rather old-fashioned. Describing your house as a 'pad' is very informal, and calling it a bungalow would probably be over precise outside of an estate agency.

> Words can have private connotations based on unique good and bad experiences, but linguistics considers only public ones.

All of these words, therefore, mean the same thing; lexically they have the same **denotation** – a place to live – but their **connotations** (how they might be understood by an audience) are very different.

Before he became president of Kenya, Jomo Kenyatta was described as a terrorist.

After he became president, he was described as a freedom fighter.

His actions did not change; only the **connotations** of the words used to describe them.

Word choice and register

A second important aspect of lexis is the way that the choice of one word affects the words nearby.

If you choose the word 'home' from the list above, you might find yourself writing 'I wanted to go home'. On the other hand, choosing 'residence' might lead to a sentence like, 'I wished to return to my residence'.

The choice of one lexical item often influences the words around it, so that a formal word for home seems to fit better in a more formal sentence. This coherent selection of words, level of formality, type of pronunciation and complexity of syntax establishes the **register** of the text.

> **KEY POINT**
>
> The register of speech or writing is also determined by its purpose – a note to a friend is much less formal than a letter of application.

Corpus linguistics

AQA   A P1, B P1
Edexcel P1
OCR   P1
WJEC   P1

Until quite recently, insights into which words go well together were largely confined to vague notions about style and appropriateness in the heads of linguists and lexicographers. However, the emergence of powerful computers, with the ability to store enormous amounts of data, has enabled thorough statistical analysis of which words **do** go together in real spoken and written texts. These bodies of data are called **corpora** (Latin for bodies – singular form corpus) and they form the basis of **corpus linguistics**.

It might seem that we are completely free to express ourselves as we like, as long we keep within certain rules for understanding. In practice, writers and speakers do not choose words one at a time, but rather stitch together pre-digested bits of language. With the help of computers, it is now possible to examine collections of over 400 million words to see how they are really written and spoken.

One of the key ideas in corpus linguistics is that certain words go together – in a process known as **collocation** – and certain words don't. It is as if each word has its own set of rules that experienced users of English are able to apply. For instance, there is no grammatical difference between 'strong' and 'powerful', but we tend to say '**strong** tea; **powerful** computers', rather than '**powerful** tea; **strong** computers'. It is very difficult to formulate a rule for when to use these two words so that they sound 'right', and people who are learning English often find this aspect of the language frustrating.

> In the exam, you might notice unusual collocations, produced by inexperienced speakers.

Words that constantly go together for no obvious reason, and which have developed a meaning of their own, are known as **idioms**. For instance, knowledge of the meaning of 'white' and 'noise' will not help you to understand the term 'white noise'. Collocates that have been over-used and have become annoying are called **clichés**.

Corpus linguistics also reveals interesting insights into the full meaning of a word or phrase. An example of this is the phrasal verb 'set in'. This looks as though it has neutral connotations, but analysis of the data shows that 'set in' is frequently collocated with words like 'rot' or 'rain'. It can therefore be seen to have a slightly negative set of associations.

Modern dictionaries are based on corpora, which enable lexicographers to analyse words in use for subtle shades of meaning and find out things such as which meaning of a word is most common. This means that modern dictionaries are **descriptivist** – interested in describing language – rather than **prescriptivist** – interested in imposing lexicographers' ideas of what is correct on others.

Spoken lexis – things and, like, stuff

Speaking to another person is a complex activity involving perception, comprehension, memory, advance planning, and many other tasks that make heavy demands on the brain. Speakers often do not have time to think of the exact word they want, and one characteristic of spoken lexis is the use of vague words like 'thing', 'stuff' and 'whatshisface'. **Inexactness** is also a feature of suffixes like '-ish' and '-y', which are more common in speech than in writing.

> **KEY POINT**
>
> Inexactness in speech is tolerable because there is often a chance to question the speaker. Inexactness in writing cannot be so easily remedied.

In order to give themselves time to think and not to give up their speaking turn, people use **fillers** such as 'like' and 'you know' that do not contribute significantly to the meaning of a statement. The end of a speaking turn is often signalled by **tails**, like 'or something' or 'or what-have-you'. As part of their politeness strategy, speakers will often soften what they are saying by using **hedges** to avoid offence. These include modals like 'might' and 'could', and words and phrases like 'possibly', 'sort of' and 'kind of'.

Even more so than with writing, speakers stitch together phrases and groups of words to express their meanings. This leads to common sets of **collocational pairs**, triplets and even larger groupings, as shown in the example below.

```
run out
run out on
run for it
run of bad luck
run for your money
```

These sorts of phrases occur again and again in different contexts. As with writing, if they are over-used they become clichés, which careful speakers then have to remember to avoid.

The beginnings and ends of stretches of writing can easily be indicated by punctuation and layout, but in speech, changes in the direction of speech need to be indicated by **discourse markers**, such as 'now', 'anyway' and 'as I was saying'. The choice of discourse marker will vary according to the register of the speech concerned and the characteristic personal preferences or **idiolect** of the person speaking.

Multimodal lexis

Electronic – and other – texts that share the interactivity of conversation, such as instant messaging, tend to share the lexical features of conversation, whereas more formal formats, such as e-mail and blogging, tend to adopt written lexical features.

One multimodal area – texting – has provoked a great deal of controversy because of its non-standard lexis. Commentators such as John Humphreys assert that text 'speech' will somehow spread to all forms of English. However, there is no evidence for this kind of cross-genre spread.

In contrast to face-to-face conversation, where extension and repetition are key features, texting – because of the restrictions of the text format and the mobile phone keyboards – values brevity and compression. Text messages can therefore look strange to an untutored eye. However, the strategies that text messages have adopted, such as **initialisms** (IMO), **deviant spellings** (woz) and **letter homophones** (CU) are far from new. According to David Crystal, the novelty of text language is only that it takes further processes that have been in use in English for hundreds of years.

> All conceivable types of feature can be juxtaposed – sequences of shortened and full words (hldmecls 'hold me close'), logograms and shortened words (2bctnd 'to be continued'), logograms and nonstandard spellings (cu2nite) and so on.
>
> *Extract from '2b or not 2b?' by David Crystal, guardian.co.uk*

PROGRESS CHECK

1. What is the denotational meaning of the word mansion?
2. What is the connotational meaning of the word mansion?
3. What is LOL an example of?

1 House.
2 A luxurious house.
3 Initialism.

2.9 Semantics

LEARNING SUMMARY

After studying this section, you should be able to:

- understand how groups of words form semantic fields
- appreciate the role of metaphors in communication
- contrast semantics with pragmatics

Semantic fields

AQA   A P1, B P1
Edexcel P1
OCR   P1
WJEC   P1

As the previous section explained, one word frequently leads to another, and all texts represent the world in a particular way – they employ at least one **semantic field**. There are some examples on the next page.

Text	Lexis	Semantic field
Shopping list	Tea, coffee, milk, newspaper, cough medicine	Things that can be bought in shops
Cookbook	Carrot, flour, slice, simmer	Food, and things you can do with it
Film magazine	Review, trailer, awful, great	Things to do with films and judgements about them
Moby Dick	Whales, whalers, captain, crew, shipwreck	Technical whaling terms and human relationships

> How do semantic fields affect responses to a text? Do you expect a science book to be more difficult to understand than a cookery book?

The role of metaphors in communication

The **primary semantic field** of a text is usually fairly obvious, but, as Lakoff[1] pointed out, human beings find it difficult to stick to a single semantic field for long. For instance, the semantic field of computers contains words like 'keyboard', 'mouse', 'monitor', 'desktop', 'file', 'folder', 'memory'. The term 'mouse' is a **metaphor** that compares a small computer-pointing device, usually with a wire attached, to a small rodent with a tail. Similarly, the way in which computers store data is metaphorically compared to the way that human beings physically store data in files and folders.

> Compare this with war as a 'game', sport as 'war', and health as a 'battle'.

For political journalists, the primary semantic field will be words to do with power and its distribution, but their writing consistently uses a **secondary semantic field** of the body, so that they speak of the **head** of government or the executive **arm**.

Even individual authors make similar choices consistently across their work. One critic, Caroline Spurgeon, observed the following.

> Just as [Francis] Bacon seems continually to see and reflect on human nature in the terms of light and shade, so Shakespeare seems to think most easily and naturally in the terms of a gardener. He visualises human beings as plants and trees, choked with weeds, or well pruned and trained and bearing ripe fruits, sweet smelling as a rose or noxious as a weed.

Some linguists have argued that metaphors and similes (comparisons involving 'as' or 'like') are at the core of all word creation, not just the kind of **figurative language** employed by Bacon and Shakespeare.

Society and semantics

Although the primary use of language is to communicate, it is also used from time to time to exclude people. The most obvious example of this is the use of criminal **cants** designed to confuse casual listeners, but many other groups of people use language to mark themselves off and to exclude strangers. Cockney rhyming slang began as a thieves' cant in the mid-nineteenth century – contemporary L33t speech used in some sections of the online community shows that the phenomenon is alive and well.

1 Lakoff, G. and M. Johnson. 1980. *Metaphors we live by*. University of Chicago Press.

The choice of words someone makes tells you a great deal about him or her. **Slang** words, for instance, are usually highly socially defined, so that using them either marks a person out as a member of a particular group, or shows some degree of respect or admiration for that group. Some groups use specialist vocabulary to help them to do their jobs more efficiently, but if they use it in front of non-specialists it becomes **jargon**, designed either to exclude or impress the non-specialist.

> **KEY POINT**
>
> Many metaphors are so embedded in English (such as the word embedded) that we scarcely notice that they are metaphors. For instance, the brow of a hill does not make us think of foreheads and we don't think of a tree when we go to a branch library! Such words and phrases are known as **dead metaphors**.

Beyond semantics – pragmatics

AQA **A P1, B P1**
Edexcel **P1**
OCR **P1**
WJEC **P1**

Semantics concerns itself with words and meanings, but there are many speech acts that are difficult to describe in such simple terms. So it is necessary to understand the **pragmatics**, the physical circumstance of texts.

Some utterances (such as 'I hereby grant …') are actions in themselves, whereas there are many acts of communication that feature few or no words (such as a referee holding up a yellow card). Other speech acts only make sense if certain external non-linguistic circumstances are true. For instance, 'Can you give me a lift?' is only meaningful if the person it is addressed to has a vehicle.

> It is always worth mentioning the pragmatic situation of a text in your analysis, even if you do not elaborate further.

The meaning of a verbal exchange may be implied rather than stated (often for reasons of politeness) in what is known as **conversational implicature**. A statement like 'Is there anything for tea?', for instance, is rarely a request for a list of the contents of a larder! The implied meaning is 'Have you made anything for me to eat?'. The hearer has to **infer** this meaning by reading between the lines of the first utterance using some basic assumptions.

Grice[2] proposed that understanding depended on:
- the usual linguistic meaning of what is said
- contextual information, based on shared or general knowledge
- the assumption that the speaker is not being deceitful.

Grice also formulated **four maxims of conversational co-operation** – maxims of quality, quantity, relevance and manner:
1. **Quality** – speakers should be truthful, avoiding what they know to be false or statements for which they have no evidence.
2. **Quantity** – contributions should be as informative as the conversation needs them to be; neither too little, nor too much.
3. **Relevance** – contributions should relate clearly to the exchange's purpose.
4. **Manner** – contributions should be clear, orderly and brief.

Grice offers these maxims as a set of conditions for satisfactory conversation rather than hard and fast rules, but it is clear that many of them go beyond exchanges of groups of words that make sense. Successful conversations also require consideration of what our listeners know, as well as what we want to tell them. If we assume they know more than they do, they will be confused, and if we over explain, they will feel patronised.

Spoken conversations frequently feature **deictic** expressions which refer to things that are obvious to the people talking, but which are not made explicit in speech acts. A statement like 'Is this yours?' will be immediately intelligible to the people concerned, but not to someone who does not know who 'you' or 'this' refers to. In written texts, deictic expressions sometimes also need to be interpreted by the reader, for example in advertising letters that begin 'Don't throw this away!'

PROGRESS CHECK

1. Name the primary and secondary semantic fields in these sentences:
   a) He struggled bravely against ill-health.
   b) As soon as she became queen, she began steering the ship of state on a new heading.
   c) My exam turned out to be very much a game of two halves.

1 a) primary – health; secondary – war
b) primary – politics; secondary – sailing
c) primary – education; secondary – sport.

Sample question and model answer

Text A is a news report concerning a prison break.

Text B is a script for a drama based on the incident.

- Identify and describe the main mode characteristics of the texts.
- Examine how the writer of Text A and the participants in Text B use language to achieve their purposes and create meanings.

In your answer you should consider:

- vocabulary and meanings
- grammatical features and their effects
- topics and how they are structured
- interactive features of language in Text A
- how the language of Text B addresses the reader and shapes their response.

(45 marks)

Text A

Prisoner escaped from ambulance after cutting off part of his ear

A criminal successfully escaped from prison by ambulance after slicing off part of his ear.

Michael O'Donnell, who was on remand for burglary and conspiracy to rob, was escorted from his cell by three officers after calling for help at around 1.30am on Sunday. The 28-year-old told staff he had been injured in an accident and they called an ambulance.

After it left Forest Bank prison in Salford it was forced to stop by four masked men in a stolen BMW. They smashed its windows and used bolt-cutters to reach O'Donnell in the back. He was handcuffed to a prison officer, but quickly released.

Ian Hopkins, the assistant chief constable of Greater Manchester, said today: "Officers from the major incident team, who usually investigate murders, are working round the clock now following up a number of lines of inquiry to try to find Michael O'Donnell, but we need the public's help too.

"This was a terrifying attack on an ambulance. O'Donnell had been warned by a judge that he was facing a long prison sentence."

O'Donnell, who has links to Brinnington, Stockport, was on remand at Forest Bank awaiting sentence after being found guilty at Manchester crown court of conspiracy to rob and commit burglary. Police believe he made a significant amount of money as the ringleader of a gang behind a string of vehicle thefts and house raids across Manchester over a two-year period.

He was due to be sentenced later this month and it is thought he was facing between eight to 10 years behind bars.

Police said the public should not approach O'Donnell, who is white, 6ft tall, and has short, fair hair.

Article by Martin Wainwright, guardian.co.uk

Sample question and model answer
(continued)

Text B

Filling out an eye witness report

PC318	So, where were you sitting?
W3	I was in the ambulance
PC318	At the back or at the front?
W3	At the back … I was handcuffed to the prisoner.
PC318	How did…?
W3	He was sitting up. I was sitting next to him. His head was bandaged.
PC318	So the van stopped and then what?
W3	There was a lot of shouting – don't move – stuff like that.
PC318	Did the prisoner say anything?
W3	No, seemed quite calm.
PC318	What about you?
W3	I was terrified – couldn't see a thing …broken glass everywhere … banging on the back door.
PC318	What do you do?
W3	Nothing I could do was there? Sat tight. Thought the door would hold, but they had bolt cutters.
PC318	So they got in?
W3	Yeah, they got in. Two of them. In masks.
PC318	Can you describe them further?
W3	They were both big blokes, I can tell you that. The one with the bolt cutters threatened to cut off my fingers if I didn't give him the key so I give him the key. I reckoned they'd get it in the end no matter what.
PC318	Did you notice anything about their clothing?
W3	Both had jeans, dark blue or black pullovers. The one with the bolt cutters smoked. But that's about it.
PC318	This is very helpful.

The following response is only part of the answer, but it shows a confident grasp of grammatical terms and how grammatical features are affected by the form and purpose of the text. Features are identified, and plausible explanations are offered for them. Some of the analysis could have been more extensive, but this response would score well on AO1 and AO3.

Good general opening statement.

Commentary on purpose of one of the texts, and constraints on it.

Identifies significant grammatical feature and comments on its purpose using appropriate vocabulary.

→ **Model answer**

→ These two texts concerning the same event are very different in their approaches and use very different linguistic strategies.

→ The newspaper article is a public document intended for a wide audience. *The Guardian* is a broadsheet newspaper and although it reports crime, it does not usually sensationalise it. This article is quite short, and it is structured to give the reader the maximum amount of information in the minimum of space.

→ Grammatically, the most noticeable feature of the text is the inclusion of subordinate clauses beginning with `who'. These are used by the journalist in paragraphs 2, 6 and 8. The advantage of this structure is that it allows extra information to be conveyed without interrupting the flow of the text. It is even used in the quotation from the deputy chief constable in paragraph 4.

Sample question and model answer
(continued)

The second feature is noticed and commented on. There is an understanding of purpose and context.

Identifies discourse structuring device.

Identifies and analyses grammatical feature.

Alternative explanations are offered.

This shows knowledge of the audience and purpose of the text.

The mode is identified.

As is normal in a newspaper article, the story is told in the past tense. This makes the present tense statements about what the police are doing and what the criminal looks like stand out. This was a crime, but its consequences are still going on and members of the public might even meet the criminal.

The interview script shows two people working on what will be an official legal statement. The officer is clearly trying to construct a narrative from the witness's account, as can be seen by his frequent use of the discourse marker `so..´ to move the conversation on to new topics. At the beginning of the transcript the witness's statements are well formed grammatically, but as he recalls more painful details, he tends to use `telegraphic´ sentences, with features such as the subject missing:

PC318   Did the prisoner say anything?

W3   No, seemed quite calm.

The subject of this sentence should be `he´, so perhaps its omission is intended to show that the witness did not wish to think of the criminal. In the most distressing part of the narrative, the witness's sentences break down into fragments, such as when he says `broken glass everywhere´, without using either a subject or a verb. When the witness says `I give him the key´, it is possible that he has shifted to the present tense to indicate that his memory of the moment is so vivid (although this phrase could also be dialectical).

The policeman makes few interventions and doesn't even use much backchannelling, apart from his final sentence. This may be because he was used to being recorded and wished to avoid being accused of `leading´ the witness in court.

The lack of features such as repetition and redundancies clearly mark this as a script rather than a transcript of a real conversation.

Exam practice question

1 Discuss the linguistic issues in the text below.

- Identify and describe the main mode characteristics of the text.
- Examine how the writer uses language to achieve a purpose and create meanings.

In your answer you should consider:
- vocabulary and meanings
- grammatical features
- lexis and semantic field.

(38)

Meaning of life

_____

_____

_____

_____

_____

_____

_____

_____

_____

_____

_____

_____

_____

[Please continue your answer on separate paper if necessary.]

3 Children's language

The following topics are covered in this chapter:

- **The function of children's language**
- **The development of linguistic competences**
- **The relationship between children's spoken and written language**
- **Theories about language development**

3.1 Language development

LEARNING SUMMARY

After studying this section, you should be able to:

- identify the different functions of children's language development
- give examples of pre-linguistic development
- understand how children prepare for language use

The functions of language

AQA   **A P1, B P1**
Edexcel   **P1**
OCR   **P1**

The linguist Michael Halliday[1] identified seven functions of language for young children. Each one motivates children to learn to speak because it serves an urgent purpose for them.

Language has the following functions for children:
1. **Instrumental** – expressing needs (e.g. 'Want nana').
2. **Regulatory** – telling others what to do (e.g. 'Get cat').
3. **Interactional** – making contact with others and forming relationships (e.g.'I see you!').
4. **Personal** – expressing feelings, opinions and individual identity (e.g. 'Me like').
5. **Heuristic** – gaining knowledge about the environment (e.g. 'What does duck say?').
6. **Imaginative** – telling stories and jokes; creating imaginary environments.
7. **Representational** – conveying facts and information.

The first four functions help children to satisfy physical, emotional and social needs, whilst the last three help them to come to terms with their environment.

> **KEY POINT**
>
> Learning a language from scratch is hard work, but children are very highly motivated in order to gain control of their lives.

1 Halliday, M.A.K. 1975. *Learning how to mean*. London: Edward Arnold.

Preparing for language learning

AQA	A P1, B P1
Edexcel	P1
OCR	P1

Before language learning can begin, children must be biologically, socially and psychologically mature enough. It is generally agreed that there is a 'critical period' in which children acquire language with great ease, so that, for instance, children in bilingual communities can learn two languages, without great effort, before the age of twelve. Learning a second language after that age can be very difficult.

Neurology suggests that the infant brain is only 40 percent developed at birth and does not achieve its final shape for 2 years. It has been argued that children's brains are not developed enough to cope with concepts like plurals and auxiliary verbs until that age. The fact that language develops in identical and predictable

ways in all speech communities suggests that **biological** factors have a major impact on language learning.

A simple game of peekaboo is a chance for social interaction, and teaches young children about turn taking during talking.

Language is a tool for **social interaction** and children must have the chance to interact socially if their language is to develop. Numerous studies have shown the importance of early and frequent social contact in language learning, and children's need for a social environment where they can share ideas. One study, for instance, showed that twins, who know each other well, feel less pressure to develop their abilities for talking to strangers.

Organisation and adaptation

The psychologist Jean Piaget posited that language learning was dependent on our ability to organise and adapt:

- The tendency towards **organisation** explains why children learn a new word ending – for instance, that '-ed' at the end of a verb means 'past time' – and then over-generalise it by saying things like 'I wented' or 'I goed'.
- **Adaptation** explains how new linguistic structures are incorporated into a child's existing knowledge and how a child might re-organise language patterns to fit evidence acquired in social interaction.

Language learning begins almost as soon as a baby is born. Research has shown that even the youngest children pay close attention to the facial expressions, body movements and gestures of others.

PROGRESS CHECK

1. What are the two **main** functions of language for children?
2. What are the necessary pre-conditions for language learning?
3. What three aspects of behaviour do young babies pay attention to?

3 Body movement; gestures; facial expressions.
2 Biological, social and psychological readiness.
1 Satisfying needs; coping with the environment.

3.2 Developing phonological competence

LEARNING SUMMARY

After studying this section, you should be able to:

- understand how children practise speaking
- identify the stages of sound production and development
- explain the transition from sounds to words

The stages of sound production and development

AQA **A P1, B P1**
Edexcel **P1**
OCR **P1**

Phonology refers to the sounds within a language. Linguists have identified around 55 individual sounds that can be used to mean something in human speech communities. For different languages, there is only a subset of this number – for instance, there are 44 meaningful sounds (or **phonemes**) used in most varieties of English. Phonemes are usually divided into vowels and consonants and, like everything else, children need to practise producing them. Before they can form words, babies go through three distinct phases – crying, cooing and babbling.

Crying, cooing and babbling

Many parents say that they can tell the difference between cries of hunger, pain and tiredness, but even with plenty of contextual clues, **crying** is not the most informative of noises.

Most babies begin **cooing** at between 8 to 12 weeks. They make a vowel-like gurgle, usually as their contribution to face-to-face conversations. Cooing sounds are acoustically similar to vowels and are often accompanied by rounding of the lips.

From around six months, children in all cultures begin to **babble**, producing long strings of consonant and vowel sounds. Although babbling is not speaking, it clearly exhibits a number of speech-like features:
- It takes place independently of physical needs, like hunger.
- It is articulated for its interactional social value.
- Babies babble for simple pleasure.
- Syllable structures found in adult language begin to develop.
- Adult intonational patterns appear.

Children experiment with sounds that do not appear in their mother tongue, e.g. clicks and trilled 'rs', which are not used in English.

Babbling has two major functions – as practice for later speech and to provide social interaction. Cooing and babbling provide children with their first taste of the pleasures of speech. It is important that parents pay close attention to babbling and encourage their children to continue talking. Several studies have shown that children neglected in the babbling stage make slower progress in learning.

The transition from sounds to words

AQA **A P1, B P1**
Edexcel **P1**
OCR **P1**

The apparently random nonsense syllables that children utter have a regular pattern, moving from vowels to increasingly complex combinations of consonants and vowels.

Children usually make steady progress in the complexity and meaning of their utterances during their first three years, as shown in the table below.

Children find final consonants more difficult to articulate and so final consonants develop more slowly.

Sound produced	Sound patterns made	Approximate age
Crying	A variety of crying sounds	0–4 months
Cooing	Vowel sounds, e.g. **ee oo uu**	2–6 months
Babbling	Consonant vowel sounds, e.g. **ma da ta**	5–9 months
	Vowel consonant vowel and vowel consonant sounds, e.g. **idi**, **aba**, **um**, **ab**	8–12 months
	Consonant vowel consonant vowel – some using re-duplication, e.g. **baba**, **gigi**, **tutu**, and some variegated, e.g. **baboo**, **gaba**	10–12 months
Single words	Usually re-duplicates, e.g. **mama dada**	9–18 months
Two words	The beginnings of syntax, e.g. **Doggie gone**	18–24 months
Telegraphic phase	Short phrases that gradually expand in length, e.g. **Bring doggie back**	24–36 months
Sentences	Usually short but grammatically correct, e.g. **Can I have some juice?**	36 months onwards

> **KEY POINT**
>
> The fact that children all over the world go through similar phonological stages is strong evidence for the in-built biological nature of our language-learning abilities.

In addition to developing the distinct sounds that they will need for talking, babbling children also practise the intonation patterns of adult speech – some babbles have a rising and falling tone like declarative sentences, and others have a rising tone like questions.

Children even explore the stress patterns within words. For instance, a child may use MAma (with stress on the first syllable) to call for his mother and maMA (with stress on the second syllable) to call his father.[2] In some languages, such as Mandarin Chinese, differences in stress can alter the meaning of a word, but babbling children in all language communities play with this sound pattern.

At about ten months, infants start to utter recognisable words; that is, they consistently make the same sound in the same context. Usually this is to do with naming things, states or situations. A child might say 'dog' when it sees the family pet, 'eat' at mealtimes and 'hot' at bath times.

Phonological development begins very early – newborn babies can tell the difference between speech and non-speech, and can also distinguish sounds like 't' and 'd'. By the time they are two months old, many infants react differently if they are spoken to in a language that is not their native one. However, it takes a long time for children to move from understanding to production.

How children cope with developing language production

This is now known as the **fis phenomenon**.

One famous incident reported by J. Berko and R. Brown[3] shows the difference between a child's perception and performance. A child who called his inflatable plastic fish a **fis** was asked by an adult 'Is this your **fis**?'. The child said 'no', but when he was asked, 'Is this your fish?' he replied, 'Yes, my fis'. This shows that although the child could not produce the phoneme 'sh', he could perceive it as different from an 's' sound.

So, children can hear the difference between sounds, but it takes a while for them to gain complete control of their own lips, tongues, teeth and vocal cords (see Figure 3.1 below).

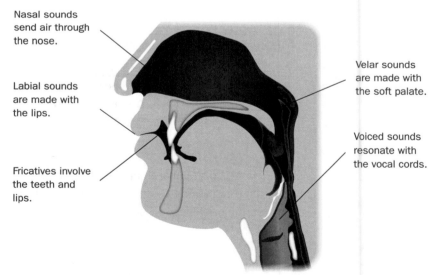

Nasal sounds send air through the nose.

Labial sounds are made with the lips.

Fricatives involve the teeth and lips.

Velar sounds are made with the soft palate.

Voiced sounds resonate with the vocal cords.

Figure 3.1 Speech sounds and where they are produced

2 Engel, W. v. R. 1973. 'An example of linguistic consciousness in the child', in *Studies of child language development*, pp.155–158, ed. by C. A. Ferguson and D. I. Slobin. New York: Holt, Rinehart and Winston.

3 Berko J. and R. Brown. 1960. 'Psycholinguistic research methods', in P. Mussen, *Handbook of research methods in child development*, pp.517–557. New York: John Wiley.

Some sounds require co-ordination of all of these things and small children simply cannot cope with the task. They therefore tend to **substitute** sounds that are 'easier' to pronounce in predictable patterns, as shown in the table below.

Phonological process	Example	Description
Context-sensitive voicing	'Pig' becomes 'big' 'Car' becomes 'gar'	A voiceless sound is replaced by a voiced sound.
Word-final devoicing	'Red' becomes 'ret' 'Bag' becomes 'bak'	A final voiced consonant in a word is replaced by a voiceless consonant.
Final consonant deletion	'Home' becomes 'hoe' 'Calf' becomes 'cah'	The final consonant in the word is omitted.
Velar fronting	'Kiss' becomes 'tiss' 'Give' becomes 'div' 'Wing' becomes 'win'	Sounds normally made with the middle of the tongue in contact with the palate towards the back of the mouth are replaced with front of mouth consonants.
Palatal fronting	'Ship' becomes 'sip' 'Measure' becomes 'mezza'	Consonants 'sh' and 'zh' are replaced by ones that are made further forward on the palate.
Consonant harmony	'Cupboard' becomes 'pubbed' 'Dog' becomes 'gog'	The pronunciation of the whole word is influenced by the presence of a particular sound in the word.
Weak syllable deletion	Telephone becomes 'teffone' 'Tidying' becomes 'tying'	In 'telephone' and 'tidying' the second syllable is 'weak' or unstressed. In this process, weak syllables are omitted.
Cluster reduction	'Spider' becomes 'pider' 'Ant' becomes 'at'	Consonant clusters of two or three consonants are reduced, and part of the cluster is omitted.
Gliding of liquids	'Real' becomes 'weal' 'Leg' becomes 'yeg'	The liquid consonants /l/ and /r/ are replaced by /w/ or 'y'.
Stopping	'Funny' becomes 'punny' 'Jump' becomes 'dump'	A fricative consonant like 'f' or 'v' is replaced by a stop consonant like 'p' 'b' or 'd'.

Table adapted from Bowen, C. 1998. *Developmental phonological disorders. A practical guide for families and teachers.* Melbourne: ACER Press.

It is not necessary for you to know the details of these processes, but as you study examples of how children speak, you will notice that these changes and substitutions are regular and predictable. They are not 'mistakes' that children make, but ways of coping with developing means of language production.

Although the sounds made by children are not the same as adults, they are usually sufficient for some form of social interaction between children and their carers, and sounds tend to be uttered in contexts that make them intelligible to the people involved. As children mature physically, their ability to reproduce adult sounds also increases, so that by the age of five most children can produce most sounds.

PROGRESS CHECK

1. How many phonemes are used in most varieties of English?
2. What does a rising tone usually indicate?
3. How long does it take most children to learn English phonology?

1 44.
2 A question.
3 About five years.

3.3 The transition from words to sentences

LEARNING SUMMARY

After studying this section, you should be able to:
- explain how children move from single words to sentences
- understand how syntax develops
- understand about the growth of grammar words

The one-word or holophrastic phase

AQA   **A P1, B P1**
Edexcel **P1**
OCR   **P1**

Children begin to talk at around 12 months old, although this may vary by up to 4 months in either direction. Children who have not begun to speak by about 18 months are tested for hearing loss or other developmental difficulties. As with phonology, there is a gap between understanding and performance, so children understand far more than they can say. One study that compared what children said with what they understood[4] showed that by the time they were saying 10 words they understood at least 60. The time taken from understanding 50 words to saying 50 words was on average about 5 months.

Every child's first words are unique, although there is some dependence on environment. For example, city children are likely to know about cars and buses whereas country children usually know about cows and tractors.

4 Benedict, H. 1979. 'Early lexical development: Comprehension and production', *Journal of Child Language*, 6, 183–200.

Here is a list of the first 50 words that appeared in the vocabulary of a boy named Will.

Notice his liking for repeated sounds.

Mama and daddy appear almost half way down the list.

Many early words refer to actions and social interaction.

1.	uh-oh	18.	keys	35.	meow
2.	alldone	19.	cycle	36.	sit
3.	light	20.	mama	37.	woof-woof
4.	down	21.	daddy	38.	bah-bah
5.	shoes	22.	siren sound	39.	hoo-hoo (owl)
6.	baby	23.	grrr	40.	bee
7.	don't throw	24.	more	41.	tree
8.	moo	25.	off	42.	mimi (ferry)
9.	bite	26.	tick tock	43.	s (snake)
10.	three	27.	ball	44.	ooh-ooh (monkey)
11.	hi	28.	go	45.	yack-yack (people talking)
12.	cheese	29.	bump	46.	hohoho (Santa)
13.	up	30.	pop-pop (fire)	47.	bye-bye
14.	quack-quack	31.	out	48.	doll
15.	oink-oink	32.	heehaw	49.	kite
16.	coat	33.	eat	50.	Muriel
17.	beep-beep	34.	neigh-neigh		

Taken from Stoel-Gammon, C. and J.A. Cooper. 1984. 'Patterns of early lexical and phonological development', *Journal of Child Language*, vol. 11, pp.247–271 (quoted in Crystal CEL).

Studies have shown that about 60 percent of children's words at this stage have a naming function and 20 percent refer to actions.

The typical words spoken by an 18-month old child can be divided into 4 categories. These are:
- entities, e.g. people, food, animals, clothes, toys, vehicles
- properties, e.g. 'hot', 'allgone', 'more', 'dirty', 'here', 'there'
- actions, e.g. 'up', 'sit', 'see', 'eat'
- personal–social, e.g. 'hello', 'bye', 'please'.

This early one-word-at-a-time stage is usually referred to as the **holophrastic phase**, as children are sometimes able to express whole sentences worth of meaning with a single word.

This economy of expression is often highly dependent on context, so that the word 'up' might be understood as 'lift me up', or 'coat' as a request to put on a coat and go outside. At other times, children will vary their intonation and stress patterns to convey meaning. For instance, 'shoes' with a rising tone might mean 'Where are my shoes?' 'Shoes!' stressed emphatically at the end might mean 'Look! I kicked my shoes off!'.

Underextensions and overextensions

An indication of how young children approach the world can be seen in the characteristic generalisations that they seem to make about language. Sometimes they will be too **narrow** in their assumptions and will only use 'hat' to mean one particular hat, or they may be too **broad** and use 'cat' as their word for all furry four-legged animals. The underextensions and overextensions that children use in their language change and develop over time.

A study in 1980[5] of children's lexical development suggested two sub-types of overextensions:

- A **categorical overextension** is when a word for one member of a category is extended to other members of that category; for example, using banana for all fruits.
- An **analogical overextension** is when a word for one object is extended to another object that is not in the same clear category, but which the child thinks is similar in some way. Similarities can be based on things like size, shape, taste, texture or sound (but oddly not on the basis of colour alone). For example, a child might refer to apples and tomatoes as 'balls' on the basis of their shape.

> **KEY POINT**
>
> Overextension in word production is not accompanied by overextension in comprehension. For example, children who call all furry four-legged animals 'doggy' can still pick out a picture of a dog from a set of animals.

The two-word stage

AQA **A P1, B P1**
Edexcel **P1**
OCR **P1**

The **two-word stage**, in which children purposefully combine separate words, can be observed from as early as 14 months. By 18 months, 11 percent of parents say that their child 'often' combines words and 46 percent say that their child 'sometimes' combines them. At 2 years old almost all children sometimes combine words, but around 20 percent still do not do so 'often'.

The development of syntax and grammar words

The earliest two-word utterances seem to be extensions of naming processes, such as 'Jack ball' or 'Mummy cup', and frequently show awareness of close association between two objects (if not yet ideas of ownership). In almost all

5 Rescorla, Leslie A. 1980. 'Overextension in early language development', *Journal of Child Language*, 7, 321–335.

cases, children reproduce the normal word order of their mother tongue – an English speaker would refer to a 'green tree' and a French child to 'abre vert'.

Typical 'sentences' at this stage might be as follows.

> 'Doggy gone'
> 'Good girl'
> 'Pat cat'

At this stage, some utterances are in fact subject-verb sentences, such as 'doggy gone', or verb-object sentences like 'get ball'.

Gradually, other grammatical features allow more and more sophisticated expressions, as shown below.

> 'Mommy sit, Anna play' (subject-verb sentence)
> 'That ball, big ball' (adjectival phrase)
> 'Daddy shoe' (possessive)
> 'Two spoon, allgone juice' (numbers and quantities)
> 'Gimme hat, again' (request)
> 'No bed, no keys' (negation)
> 'Mommy sock' – meaning 'Mummy get my sock' (subject-object sentence)
> 'Put book' – meaning 'Put the book here' (verb-object sentence)

Most of the constructions above involve nouns and verbs, but by their 24th month most children begin to use distinctly grammatical lexis. The phrases below are listed in the order in which they typically appear.

> 'I talking' (-ing form of verb)
> 'In cupboard, on table' (preposition)
> 'Two cats' (plural)
> 'It gone' (irregular past tense verb)
> 'Ed's ball' (possessive)
> 'There it is' (verb to be)
> 'A car, the sheep' (articles)
> 'Anna looked' (regular past tense verb)
> 'She looks' (third person singular verb)
> 'He has' (irregular third person singular)
> 'It is going' (progressive verb)
> 'It's here' (contraction)
> 'I'm eating' (complex verb)

The telegraphic phase

AQA	**A P1, B P1**
Edexcel	**P1**
OCR	**P1**

In the third phase of speech acquisition, children utter multi-word statements but frequently leave out 'unnecessary' things like determiners, auxiliary verbs, inflections and pronouns. In the days when people paid to send telegrams by the word, they would adopt similar strategies to keep costs down. This style of speaking is therefore known as the **telegraphic phase**.

Here are some examples.

> 'No like beans'
> 'Doggy gone bye byes'
> 'You go bed now'
> 'Where daddy put car?'

Progress is not always smooth, so adult and child forms sometimes exist in adjacent statements, However, progress is very rapid, so that by the time they are three years old, most children can form complete adult-style clauses and begin to use words to do things like tell stories (connectives such as 'and', 'cos', 'then' and 'so' play a significant role), and engage in other forms of imaginative play.

Mixed statements might be as follows.

> 'She's here. Her here now.'
> 'I asking you. I'm asking you.'
> 'Daddy haven't put the car away, has he?'

KEY POINT

Just because children use telegraphic sentences themselves, it does not mean that they accept them from adults. As is often the case, perception outpaces production.

PROGRESS CHECK

1. What are the three main phases of language acquisition?
2. What are the two main types of overextension?
3. At around what age is telegraphic speech common?

3 Between two and three years old.
2 Categorical; analogical.
1 Holophrastic; two-word; telegraphic.

3.4 Grammatical development

LEARNING SUMMARY	After studying this section, you should be able to:
	• explain how grammatical features are added to words
	• discuss how concepts and syntax develop together
	• understand what children's non-standard utterances reveal

Growing syntactic competence

AQA **A P1, B P1**
Edexcel **P1**
OCR **P1**

Once the multi-word stage has been reached, children develop more and more sophisticated grammatical resources. There is little doubt that such developments go hand in hand with increasing conceptual complexity.

Negation and questioning

Bloom[6] identified three stages of negation and showed that they were closely linked with the syntax a child might use.

The three types of negative meaning are as follows:
1. **Non-existence** – when something is absent, e.g. 'No ball', 'Mummy not here'.
2. **Rejection** – refusal to comply, e.g. 'Me not sleep', 'No want carrots'.
3. **Denial** – rejecting a proposition, e.g. 'Not naughty', 'Not said it'.

Non-existence is the easiest idea – and earliest negative idea – that children grasp. They tend to express it through individual words, or by adding 'no' or 'not' to other lexical items.

Rejection initially tends to be expressed by the single word 'no', but eventually children learn to place negative words in middle positions in sentences, for instance, 'I no want beans'.

Denial is a complex concept, as it often refers back to a previous statement, or possibly to non-verbal cues like an accusing look; for example, 'I didn't do it'.

David Crystal[7] identifies six stages of negation:
1. 'No' or 'not'.
2. Two-word combinations with 'no' or 'not'.
3. Mid-sentence negatives, e.g. 'Me not like'.
4. Use of more adult negative construction, e.g. 'I don't go there'.
5. Use of a range of negative constructions, e.g. 'I haven't got a pen'.
6. Implied negatives, or saying no without using negative expressions, e.g. 'I might go to bed'.

The same kind of growth in language and conceptual abilities can be seen in the way that questioning develops:
1. Children use rising intonation.
2. They use questioning words: 'what?', 'when?', 'where?', 'why?', 'who?', 'how?'
3. Children use more complex syntax to ask questions, e.g. 'What time do you think the bus will get here?'.

Morphological progress

Morphology is the way in which words change according to their grammatical function. In English, the most common **inflectional morpheme** is the letter 's', as it is used to show plurals, possessives and the third person singular form of regular verbs. Other morphemes include verb endings like 'ed' and 'ing', and the 'er' and 'est' modifiers for comparatives and superlatives.

Brown[8] defined two types of linguistic complexity:
- **Semantic complexity** or **conceptual complexity** refers to the difficulty of the ideas expressed.
- **Syntactic complexity** or **formal complexity** refers to how complex the expressions used to convey the ideas are.

6 Bloom, L. 1970. *Language development: form and function in emerging grammars*. Cambridge, Mass.: MIT Press.

7 Crystal, D. 1989. *Listen to your child: a parent's guide to children's language*. Penguin.

8 Brown. R. 1973. *A first language: the early stages*. Cambridge, MA: Harvard University Press.

Put simply, a child will not develop a grammatical structure until the necessary ideas have emerged. For instance, a child has to have the concept of number before he or she can start adding an 's' to the end of plural words. Adding an 's' for regular third-person verb forms requires ideas of both number (it is only used in the singular form) and time (it is used with the present but not the past tense). On the basis of increasing semantic complexity, Brown could predict that the plural 's' would be acquired before the third-person 's'.

These pictures test a child's ability to form plurals, possessives and past tenses.

Once children acquire morphemes, they begin to use them productively. They have little difficulty in inventing words they have never heard in line with pre-existing patterns. This is demonstrated in Berko's 1958 study,[9] in which children gave correct sounding plural, possessive and participle forms for creatures and actions that had been given invented names. The study suggested that children do not simply learn morphemes by heart; they develop their own morphological rules.

> **KEY POINT**
>
> Regularity and predictability make a language easy to learn. Irregularities have to be memorised one at a time.

Unfortunately, adult language is not as regular and as logical as many children assume, and a striking feature of the language of three- and four-year olds is that they say non-standard words that they almost certainly didn't hear from adults. They clearly have a fundamental understanding of how grammar and morphology work, and they have worked rules out for themselves, such as '-ed' at the end of a word indicates past time, or an 's' at the end of a word indicates a plural.

9 Berko, J. 1958. 'The child's learning of English morphology', *Word*, 14, 150–177.

Thus, a three-year old might say the following.

> 'The mouses wented to the fair.'
> 'He gived the hay to the sheeps.'

Such non-standard forms are actually more common at this age than with slightly younger children. Brown speculated that the earlier 'correct' uses were based on simple repetition of adult forms, whilst the non-standard forms showed understanding. By the time they are four or five, most children have built up enough linguistic experience to know the 'correct' forms and use them.

Children's spontaneous comments also show their expectation that words should be regular and rule bound. For instance, one four-year old saw a fork with three tines and said that it must be a 'threek'. Made-up words that children use reveal the patterns they have detected, as in the example of a child who went to a concert and remarked, 'We saw a drummist and a flutist too'.

The making of new words by changing their grammatical form is known as **derivational morphology** or **back-formation**. It is used by adults, for instance, whenever a noun becomes a verb, or vice versa:
- Sending a text becomes 'texting'.
- The job done by an editor becomes 'to edit'.

Children are often very inventive in applying and re-arranging morphological elements, as the table below shows.

Process	How it is achieved	Examples
Back formation	Shifting grammatical class to make a fresh word	• We **funeralled** the dead mouse. • I **hotted** the water. • Can you **biggen** my sweets?
Affixation	Adding new endings to words	• That's a Janey thing to say. • Get the litter picker-upper.
Compounding	Joining words together to make new ones	• Wolfcoat • Waterbag

PROGRESS CHECK

1. What do both progress in syntax and morphology show about children's language development?
2. If a three-tine fork is a threek, what would a two-tine fork be?
3. Why do children go backwards in some linguistic areas at about the age of three?

1 Ideas need to develop before linguistic competence can be acquired.
2 A twok.
3 They are shifting from repeating words to trying to understand them.

93

3.5 Pragmatics

After studying this section, you should be able to:

- explain how social awareness develops
- understand the nature of unspoken rules
- discuss the role of humour, implication and inference

The three main areas of pragmatics

AQA **A P1, B P1**
Edexcel **P1**
OCR **P1**

Communication is a complex social skill that involves many factors beyond the words actually spoken. Pragmatics deals with the role of such things as implied and inferred meanings, contextual awareness, humour and politeness in successful human communication. Parents often worry about their children being 'rude' or 'showing them up' because they have not fully come to terms with pragmatics.

There are three main areas of pragmatics:

1. Using language for different purposes and adopting appropriate strategies.
2. Being aware of the needs of a listener or situation.
3. Following rules for conversations and storytelling.

Here are some examples for the first area (using language for different purposes and adopting appropriate strategies).

Greeting – 'hello', 'goodbye'.
Informing – 'I'm going to bed now'.
Requesting – 'Can I have some toast?'.
Promising – 'I'll be there in a minute'.

Examples of the second area (being aware of the needs of a listener or situation) are:

- talking differently to a child than to an adult
- giving background information to an unfamiliar listener
- speaking differently in a classroom than in a playground.

In the third area (following rules for conversations and storytelling), examples are:

- conversational turn-taking
- introducing new topics of conversation
- staying on topic
- re-phrasing when misunderstood
- using, and responding to, verbal and non-verbal signals
- standing at an appropriate distance from others
- using facial expressions and eye contact.

For each of the areas, correct social interaction is dependent on more than simple information exchange. Children need to develop a sense of when it is acceptable to make a request, or when they are allowed to interrupt other people's conversations. Progress in pragmatics can only really be made through social interaction with other people. Lack of progress can often be a symptom of developmental disorders such as autism or Asperger's syndrome.

Jokes and implied meaning

A good example of pragmatic awareness is how younger children respond to jokes and riddles. The understanding that a joke is **meant to be** funny is present in many three-year olds, but the ability to see what makes it funny does not develop until later.

> Joe: Tell me a joke.
> Father: A man came yesterday and stole our gate... I didn't say anything in case he took offence (i.e. a fence).
> Joe: (Laughs) A man came yesterday and stole my hat... I didn't say anything in case he took a glove. (laughs)
> Father: Very funny, Joe.

Young children tend to like formulaic jokes that are clearly meant to be funny – adults do not.

In this example, the child thinks the situation is meant to be funny rather than the word play on offence / a fence. In responding to the child's attempt at a joke, the father could be encouraging a further example of pragmatic sophistication – irony.

Politeness theory (see pages 41–42) provides another reason why pragmatic communication is sometimes preferred to explicit demands and requests. Young children are taught explicitly to say 'please' and 'thank you' to soften demands and requests, as they are potentially face-threatening acts. Older children and adults will make statements like 'It's hot in here', as implied requests for someone to open a window. No face is lost on either side if such a subtle request is ignored.

PROGRESS CHECK

1 Why are pragmatics difficult to learn?
2 Why do children laugh at jokes that they don't understand?
3 Why do people sometimes make implicit rather than explicit requests?

1 Many of the rules are unspoken.
2 They learn the rule, 'laugh at jokes', but may not understand what is meant to be funny.
3 Implicit requests are less likely to cause offence.

3.6 Learning to read

LEARNING SUMMARY

After studying this section, you should be able to:

- explain how children move from speaking to reading
- understand some of the debates about reading
- understand some of the problems of phoneme grapheme mapping

The transition from speaking to reading

AQA **A P1, B P1**
Edexcel **P1**
OCR **P1**

The advantages of being able to speak must be immediately obvious to a small child – speaking allows social interaction, self-expression and the ability to control and manipulate one's environment.

Reading allows interaction with strangers or with friends who aren't around, but this is probably not apparent to younger learners who know about telephones and video cameras.

The impetus to read and write comes – as does the impetus to speak – from a child's environment. Writing in Western urbanised society is everywhere, and the ability to read words gives children access to plenty of things that they are interested in, for example stories in books, or what a character on the back of a cereal packet is saying. Children see their parents and older children reading and writing, and they want to engage in the same activities.

Figure 3.2

Literacy debates

Because the ability to read and write – **literacy** – is so important in modern society, a great deal of effort is put into ensuring that all children have access to it.

Unfortunately, there is a great deal of debate on how best to promote literacy:
- The traditionalist approach to reading focuses on appropriate levels of cognitive development. It usually involves a **phonics** system, which enables students to break down words into their component sounds.
- A second group argues that as adults read whole words, then children should learn whole words by building up a sight vocabulary of words using the **look and say** method.
- Advocates of social interaction believe that reading naturally emerges from encounters with **real reading** in everyday life. They argue that students should be exposed to text-rich environments that allow them to explore the writing system in their own way.

Countless studies investigating different approaches have failed to decide which approach is most effective, and most teachers of reading adopt some aspects of all three main schools of thought. They provide a 'text-rich' environment, for instance, but use a series of books like the *Oxford Reading Tree* to provide a guided and structured route to reading. A scheme like *Letterland* is used for phonic work.

Recently, politicians in the United Kingdom decided in favour of the **synthetic phonics** approach (which looks at the sounds that groups of letters make), and strongly recommended that it should be used in all state schools.

Understanding the writing system

Before young children can start to read, they need to understand how the writing system works. In some cultures, this is extremely difficult. For instance, in China full literacy in the Chinese language requires knowledge of between 3000 and 4000 characters (out of a possible total of 47 035). In English, students only have to cope with 26 letters, which are easy to learn, but are not terribly well suited to conveying the sounds of English.

As we mentioned in Section 3.2, English has 44 **phonemes** or sounds that can make a difference to the meaning of a word. A perfect spelling system for English would therefore have 44 letters, and reading would simply be a matter of converting marks on a page into their sound equivalents. However, for various historical reasons, there is a lack of sound and letter correspondence in English, as illustrated in the tables below.

Three of the alphabet's consonants are wasted.

Letter	Sounds	Example
C	'k' or a 's'	Cat, peace
Q	'Kw'	Quick
X	'eks' or 'z'	Extreme, Xerxes

Many vowel sounds are represented by the same letter.

Letter	Sounds	Example
a	ae	Cat
	a: aa	Car
	eɘ	Care
	ei	Case
	o:	Call
	o	Quality

The same sound is spelled in different ways.

Sound	Letters	Example
e	ea	Tea
	ee	See
	ey	Key
	e	Me
	ie	Siege
	ei	Seize

So, those learning to read are faced with many inconsistencies. It is therefore not surprising that people have been attempting to reform the English spelling system since modern English emerged in the fifteenth century. For instance, both George Bernard Shaw and Benjamin Franklin proposed new systems of spelling for English.

KEY POINT

It is difficult to talk about reading or writing in isolation, as children attempt both at the same time. Misconceptions in one skill – such as one letter, one sound – can have knock-on effects in the other.

Stages of reading

AQA   **A P1, B P1**
Edexcel **P1**
OCR   **P1**

Children learn to read in the same way as they learn to speak – by noticing other people using books and other texts, and deciding that they want to share a pleasurable or a profitable experience. Parents, for instance, will read bedtime stories and children will notice the unchanging nature of these texts – small children can get very annoyed if their parents try to alter familiar tales.

Pre-reading stage

In the earliest – **pre-reading** – stage, children mimic the reading process without actually reading. They will turn the pages of a book over and repeat the text as they remember it, or make up their own stories based on the pictures they see. They may observe moving fingers hovering over words and gather that texts in English run from the top to the bottom of the page and are read from left to right. Children will also make a connection between the marks a parent makes on paper and, for instance, a shopping list.

Beginning reading stage

In the **beginning reading** stage, English children have to get to grips with the spelling system and the links between **graphemes** – marks on paper – and phonemes. At this stage, almost all children's reading is reading aloud, as this reinforces the link between letters and sounds, and allows adults to monitor a child's progress. Children may make use of their sight vocabulary, their knowledge of phonics, or various contextual clues, such as illustrations, in order to read correctly.

Fluency

When they reach **fluency**, children can identify words easily and understand what they have read without too much difficulty. They will be paying attention to punctuation and other graphological features, and will be beginning to build up an understanding of the way texts are structured through features like alphabetical order or tables of contents.

Many children reach **adult competency** levels of reading whilst still in primary school, and can read silently and at length for personal pleasure, as well as using their reading skills in their school work.

PROGRESS CHECK

1 What are the three main approaches to learning to read?
2 Which three letters have no individual sounds?
3 What is a grapheme?

3 Any meaningful mark on a piece of paper.
2 Q: c: x.
1 Phonics; look and say; real reading.

3.7 Learning to write

LEARNING SUMMARY

After studying this section, you should be able to:

● explain how children move from speaking to writing
● understand how speaking and writing are interconnected
● identify the features of early writing

Moving onto writing

AQA **A P1, B P1**
Edexcel **P1**
OCR **P1**

Gentry[10] identified five distinct stages in the writing of young children:
1. The precommunicative stage.
2. The semiphonetic stage.
3. The phonetic spelling stage.
4. The transitional spelling stage.
5. The integration (or conventional) stage.

These are discussed in more detail below.

The precommunicative stage

In the **precommunicative stage**, most young children who have seen writing at home spontaneously begin to experiment with its forms. This will be simple mimicry, and although they may recognise letter forms and even know the names of some of the letters, children will not try to use them formally at this stage. Instead, their writing will tend to be impressionistic. Some attempt at letter formation may be evident and there may even be illustrations that imitate what children have seen in picture books.

Some children may make marks on pages from left to right, but there is unlikely to be any recognition that individual letters represent individual sounds.

Figure 3.3 An example from the precommunicative stage

The semiphonetic stage

In the **semiphonetic stage**, the child has begun to realise that there is a connection between letters and sounds. Typically children use a few letters, usually consonants, to capture words, syllables, initial letters, or parts of words.

10 Gentry, Richard. 1982. 'An analysis of developmental spelling in GNYS AT WRK', *The Reading Teacher*, 36(2), 192–199.

Strategies such as using the name of a letter appear at this stage, for example RUDF for 'Are you deaf?'.

Figure 3.4 An example of writing from the semiphonetic stage

The phonetic spelling stage

Most children reach the **phonetic spelling stage** in the early years of school when they have developed their awareness of speech sounds, sound–letter correspondences, and letter names.

As we mentioned earlier, children often use a 'one letter for one sound' policy, and usually all the sounds of a word are represented on paper. Children tend to use how a word feels in their mouths as a guide to spelling at this stage. Examples of children's 'invented' spellings might include COMPYUTA (computer) DA (Day) and LIK (like).

Further practice at this stage leads to longer stretches of conventional spelling. An example is shown below.

TANGK
THINGK
THINK

Figure 3.5 An example from the phonetic spelling stage

The transitional spelling stage

By the time children reach the **transitional spelling stage**, they will have looked at a large number of words in print and in writing and they will be receiving regular spelling lessons. Children at this stage have begun to understand that most sounds are represented by letter combinations and they realise that syllables are spelt in predictable ways. Spellings exhibit the conventions of English orthography, like vowels in every syllable, e-markers and vowel digraph patterns. Inflectional endings ('ing', 'ed') are correctly spelt, and frequent English letter sequences are common. Below are some examples of the sorts of spelling errors that are likely to occur.

HAVEING (having) – both parts spelt correctly, but not the combination
SRING (spring) – simplification of a consonantal cluster
LHITE (light) – wrong model, white used

On Thursday my Grandma and Grandad came. They came to our house, When they got here they said 'hello Isaac and me went on the trampoilen It Was really fun. I gigled, we bounced, when It was 4.30 pm we wathed a Dvd. I had pasta With Isaac. It Was yummy. Grandma and Grandad went to there hotel at 6 o'clock The next day I went swimming, at the

Figure 3.6 An example from the transitional spelling stage

KEY POINT

Spelling errors are almost never random. Writers tend to misapply rules or choose the wrong model for a way of writing a sound down.

The integration (or conventional) stage

Children of around eight or nine years old tend to be at the **integration stage** (sometimes known as the conventional stage) and have become **conventional spellers**. They break words up into syllables rather than sounds, and have acquired a reliable number of spellings based on the meaningful parts of words like roots, prefixes and suffixes. They have learnt how to deal with homophones, like 'be' and 'bee', that show that a word's meaning can decide its spelling.

I went to lapland it was the best holiday in the world.

First we went sleging and it was very fun, then I went to have a skiing leson for the first time and I realy enjoyed it so I kept having the lesons.

My skiing teacher gave me a test, I completed it and he bought me a hot chocolate. It was yummy. I had a great time in lapland, a week I will never forget.

Figure 3.7 An example from the integration stage

Spelling development

In his *Monster Spelling Test*, Gentry provides the following table to illustrate spelling development.

WORDS		Precommunicative stage	Semiphonetic stage	Phonetic stage	Transitional stage	Conventional stage
1.	monster	Random letters	mtr	mostr	monstur	monster
2.	united	Random letters	u	unitd	younighted	united
3.	dress	Random letters	jrs	jras	dres	dress
4.	bottom	Random letters	bt	bodm	bottum	bottom
5.	hiked	Random letters	h	hikt	hicked	hiked
6.	human	Random letters	um	humm	humum	human
7.	eagle	Random letters	el	egl	egul	eagle
8.	closed	Random letters	kd	klosd	clossed	closed
9.	bumped	Random letters	b	bopt	bumpped	bumped
10.	type	Random letters	tp	tip	tipe	type

PROGRESS CHECK

1. Identify the spelling stage of the following three graphemes.
   a) rayulway
   b) (�environment symbol)
   c) ka (meaning 'car')

1 a) transitional b) precommunicative c) semiphonetic.

3.8 Theories of language development

LEARNING SUMMARY

After studying this section, you should be able to:

- identify key theories about language development
- relate these theories to your own knowledge about language acquisition
- enter into the debate on the main theories of language development

Background to the language development debate

AQA   **A P1, B P1**
Edexcel   **P1**
OCR   **P1**

The fact that babies and young children are able to learn to speak fluently in a comparatively short space of time is little short of miraculous, and scientists are still in disagreement about how the language acquisition process works. As far as we know, human language is unique – other large primates with similar bodies and sensory equipment can communicate effectively with each other, but they do not use a system that allows such things as abstract thought or invented narratives. Because we have language and can write it down, we can know the thoughts of people who died thousands of years ago, and we can enjoy the benefits of the technology developed and shared through language.

The sophisticated grammatical language we employ today probably evolved as a way of sharing the tasks of **a community** – as in 'I'll chip this arrow head if you'll go and hunt me some food'. Some evolutionary biologists argue that the development of our language can only be understood as part of a communal response to evolutionary pressures. Certainly, human beings who are not raised in human communities (as in the case of feral children) do not develop language fully.

Probably around 50 000 years ago, the first people with the right combination of brains and voice boxes appeared, and the evolutionary advantages of language are clear. There has been a great deal of debate, however, about whether language abilities have been 'hard wired' into our brains since then, or if they have been acquired as part of our life in communities.

> **KEY POINT**
>
> Whether built in or acquired, our ability to use language is a key factor in both our social and psychological development.

The key theories and the debates surrounding them

AQA	A P1, B P1
Edexcel	P1
OCR	P1

The rest of this section identifies the key theories of language development and looks at the debates surrounding them.

Cognitive development

If language does not grow in isolation, it seems logical to argue that children's language will grow with their ability to think. This leads to a sort of chicken and egg argument about whether language leads to ideas or whether ideas lead to language.

Jean Piaget was a Swiss psychologist who did a great deal of early and influential work on children's development. He argued that maturation – the simple process of growing up – was the key factor in children's increasing capacity to make sense of their world. However, the process is not continuous, and Piaget outlined various key developmental stages – taking place at about 2 years, 7 years and 11 years – in which children's thought processes made significant leaps forward. According to Piaget, there was no point in teaching a child something until the child had reached the right mental stage.

Figure 3.8, on the next page, illustrates Piaget's stages of cognitive development.

From the point of view of language development, the leap forward at the age of two is the most significant. Children cannot form sentences about themselves until they know that they are separate from everything else, and they cannot talk about abstract ideas until they realise that things continue to exist when they are not perceived.

For Piaget, thought came before language, but Sapir and Whorf claimed that language shapes thought. The Sapir-Whorf hypothesis states that languages affect the way people think, so that speakers of different languages think and behave differently. It was based on their observations of the Hopi people who, they claimed, had a completely different attitude to time as a result of the way they constructed grammatical verb tenses. More recent research has cast doubt on their conclusions, but there is a persistent suspicion that constant use of a particular kind of language – overtly sexist for instance – may distort people's perceptions.

Stage	Characteristics	Language
Sensori-motor (Birth–2 years)	Differentiates self from objects	'Anna ball'
	Recognises self as agent of action and begins to act intentionally	'Get ball'
	Achieves object permanence — things exist even when not present to the sense	'Where ball?'
Pre-operational (2–7 years)	Using language representing objects by images and words	From single word to full grammar
	Egocentric thinking – difficulties with the viewpoint of others	'I' and 'me' very common
	Classifies objects by a single feature, e.g. all red blocks regardless of shape, or all square blocks regardless of colour	Overextension
Concrete operational (7–11 years)	Thinks logically about objects and events	Development of clause structures
	Conservation of number (age 6), mass (age 7), and weight (age 9)	Tenses mastered
	Objects classified by several features and can be ordered by a single dimension such as size	Non-chronological writing
Formal operational (11 years and up)	Logical and abstract thinking	Formal arguments
	Concerned with the hypothetical, the future, and ideology	Writing in a full range of genres

Figure 3.8 Piaget's stages of cognitive development

Another influential child psychologist has been Lev Vygotsky, who saw language as the child's tool for exploring, understanding and controlling the world. In a famous example, he says a young child might cry because he does not have a horse, but an older child can pick up a stick and use language to call it a horse. In another, he mentions two sisters who would pretend to be 'sisters'; by making sisterhood a game, they could explore the rules of sisterly behaviour more fully.

Vygotsky believed that collaborative play was essential for the development of learners. He argued that new skills are acquired in a **zone of proximal development**, in which tasks that are too difficult for a child to master can be successfully completed with the help and guidance of adults or more skilled children. According to Vygotsky, the role of the teacher is to assess a child's level of conceptual development and provide 'scaffolding' so that a task can be completed successfully. As the learner's confidence grows, scaffolding is gradually withdrawn until full independence is reached.

Vygotsky made the following comment.

> What children can do with the assistance of others might be in some sense even more indicative of their mental development than what they can do alone.
>
> *Extract from* Mind in Society *by L.S. Vygotsky*

KEY POINT

Language is above all an aspect of social interaction. Other animals can signal the location of food, and even share it, but only human beings have dinner parties or write restaurant reviews.

Behaviourism

Both Piaget and Vygotsky took language itself as a given, but the behaviourist psychologist B. F. Skinner[11] attempted to explain how language developed from the beginning. He argued that language emerged as a result of 'operant conditioning' in which young children appear to copy their parents' language behaviour. Their success is reinforced by **praise**, just as their 'mistakes' are discouraged by **correction**.

The strength of this approach is that it conforms to many observations of language interactions – children listen to parents and repeat what they hear, as shown in the example below.

Parent: Look! A dog!
Child: Dog!
Parent: Yes! A dog!

A parent's positive response to their child's utterance, according to Skinner, acts as a **reward**, and encourages him or her to make similar identification in future. Children certainly do learn in this way, but the behaviourist approach does not give any insight into the processing of information that goes on in children's minds. For instance, as we have already touched on, many small children, having been rewarded for identifying a four-legged furry thing as a dog, go on to label cats and sheep in the same way.

The behaviourist approach works best when vocabulary is the focus. It is less successful at explaining how children learn grammar and other aspects of language. In the first place, parents do not speak in full sentences themselves, and when they 'correct' children they tend to focus on things like politeness and truth rather than, say, proper use of plurals.

Child: Look. Sheeps!
Parent: No, that's horse.
Child: Can I have a sheeps?
Parent: Can I have one, please.

11 Skinner, B.F. 1957. *Verbal behavior*. Acton, Massachusetts: Copley Publishing Group.

Furthermore, parents who do attempt to correct grammatical errors tend to be ignored, particularly if their corrections are in advance of a child's developmental stage.

See, for example, the following exchange, which is quoted by McNeil.[12]

> Child: Nobody don't like me.
> Mother: No, say, 'Nobody likes me'.
> Child: Nobody don't like me.
> **(Eight repetitions of this dialogue)**
> Mother: No, now listen carefully. Say, 'Nobody likes me'.
> Child: Oh! Nobody don't **likes** me.

Research has also shown that 'correcting' rather than encouraging children's speech can impede language development, as children are made to feel unduly self-conscious about making errors.

Behaviourism finds it difficult to explain why all children all over the world go through the same linguistic stages at approximately the same time. Those who agree with the behaviourist theory would presumably expect children who had a great deal of language input from their parents to make much faster progress, and vice versa, but even comparative neglect from adults does not seem to impede language development. However, as mentioned earlier, feral children who are completely ignored do not seem to be able to get back their language if they missed input in the critical early years of their lives.

> **KEY POINT**
>
> Behaviourism is useful as a way of understanding how we acquire and correct language through positive and negative feedback, but it cannot explain the creative processes that are involved in language acquisition.

Social interactionism

Social interactionism attempts a more complex description of language development by placing it in a wider behavioural context. Language acquisition is not just about picking up sounds from parents, but of learning such skills as turn-taking in conversations, maintaining eye contact, and other aspects of body language.

Social interactionists like Brunner take their cue from Vygotsky's cognitive theory and suggest that parents and carers provide infants with the social 'scaffolding' to allow them to successfully enter into spoken communication. In their view, games such as peekaboo help even tiny babies to learn the rules of conversational turn-taking.

Brunner coined the term 'Language Acquisition Support System' (LASS) to emphasise the role of parents and carers in language development, and claims that adults involved with small children adopt a number of strategies to help them learn.

12 McNeil, D. 1966. 'Developmental psycholinguistics', in F. Smith and G. A. Miller (eds.) *The genesis of language. A psycholinguistic approach*. Cambridge, Massachusetts: The MIT Press.

These strategies of **child-directed speech**, or 'parentese', include:

- simpler vocabulary
- shorter utterances, allowing for less complex grammar
- the use of tag questions to encourage turn-taking
- grammatical frames that draw attention to change and variation, e.g. 'I went to the zoo and bought me a ... (name of animal)'
- pronunciation that draws attention to morphemes and lexemes
- non-verbal elements – such as smiling, nodding, pointing – that encourage speech
- exaggerated lip and mouth movements to help children to form their own words
- higher pitch, slower speed, more pauses (particularly between phrases), and clearer, more 'distinct' pronunciation
- exaggerated intonation – heavily emphasising some words, and using a very prominent rising tone for questions.

Rather than the behaviourists' 'correcting' strategy, social interactionists point to the way that parents can expand and re-cast their children's utterances, to provide them with better models of communication.

Child: Want lollipop!
Parent: You want a lollipop, do you? Do you want a red one or a green one?
Child: Red one.
Parent: A red one it is then.

The implications of social interactionism are wide ranging, and even affect whether classroom desks are arranged in rows or groups. Many studies in western societies have shown that children who grow up in environments where there is a great deal of interaction do better in school than those who do not. However, some societies do not appear to adopt child-directed speech, with little apparent effect on adult competencies.

> **KEY POINT**
>
> No single theory about language development provides a full explanation – each major theory illuminates different aspects of the problem.

Chomsky and universal grammar

Skinner's behaviourist theories were strongly challenged by Chomsky.[13] He first of all pointed out that children become fluent and grammatical speakers without an adequate stimulus from the language users around them. This **poverty of stimulus** argument was based on a number of factors, including the theoretical impossibility of learning any language that features recursion from positive evidence alone. All known human languages do in fact feature recursion – that is, the ability to embed one idea inside another – as in 'I saw the man you saw yesterday today'.

A second and more striking argument was the fact that children routinely produce language that they could not possibly have heard from an adult, for example, 'I

13 Chomsky, N. 1959. 'Review of verbal behavior by B.F. Skinner', *Language*, 35, 26–58 (A critique of behaviourist approaches to learning).

wented to town'. Rather than being a mistake, such utterances are evidence that children formulate for themselves the grammar rules of any language they are exposed to. Subsequent research has shown that all children 'create' their own grammar, ranging from variations in sign language between deaf children to fully functioning creoles.

Chomsky argued that children must have an innate language acquisition device (or LAD), which he termed a 'universal grammar'. The device has to be 'activated' by stimulus from a language community, but once set going almost all children acquire knowledge of the world in similar ways. Chomsky's **nativist** arguments are compelling, but many thinkers do not like the idea of innate knowledge and have sought to challenge universal grammar by finding languages that do not obey its rules. Recently, for instance, it was claimed that the Pirana people, who live in the Amazon rainforest, have a mother tongue without recursion.

Pinker,[14] on the other hand, has attempted to deepen Chomsky's insights and has proposed a set of innate linguistic **principles and parameters** that are switched on or off by encounters with real languages. Verbs in English, for instance, tend to take a position in the middle of a sentence, whereas in German or Latin they are placed at the end. Children learning languages absorb these rules and are then able to apply them in new and creative ways.

Further support for Chomsky has come from **neuroscience**, which has identified Broca's area and Wernicke's area in the brain as sites of **specifically** linguistic activity.

Recent research has shown that children's brains are extremely flexible in terms of the connections they can make, but this flexibility is **time constrained**. This means, for instance, that if a child is not exposed to language stimulus in his or her early years, language development is severely impaired. As we have already mentioned, this insight has been borne out by instances of feral children finding it very difficult to learn to speak when they return to human society.

Chomsky's ideas were mostly concerned with the generation of complex grammatical rules, and he did not study how real children operate in real environments, with their carers and other children. No account is given of either interaction or what motivates children to learn to speak. In 1977, Bard and Sachs[15] described how the hearing son of deaf parents made little progress in his speech, in spite of being exposed to environmental sound from the radio and television. They concluded that simply being exposed to language was not enough. Without the right kind of interaction, there is little incentive to work out its meaning.

PROGRESS CHECK

1 Which thinker(s) do you identify with each of the following theories?
  a) Social interactionism
  b) Nativism
  c) Behaviourism

1 a) Brunner b) Chomsky; Pinker c) Skinner

---

14 Pinker, S. 1994. *The language instinct*. New York: Morrow.

15 Bard, P. and J. Sachs. 1977. 'Language acquisition patterns in two normal children of deaf parents', Paper presented at the Second Annual Boston University Conference on language development.

Sample question and model answer

Read the text below. Comment linguistically on five features of language use that you find of interest.

(10 marks)

> 5 Smith Drive
> Norwich
> NR12 2AB
>
> Dear Mrs Wilkinson,
> Although I am not sure everyone will agree so I beleive sweets shoud be ban because they are very bad if you eat to many.
>
> Firstly, some sweets are very very sticky and so very very bad for your teeth, and so when you do good things at school pleaes change from giving sweets to giving helfier snaxs.
>
> Furthermore if you keep eating sweets you might need to have lots of filings at the dentist and that may be inbarrison.
>
> Finally so it would be very very very good if everyone had a dbaete.

This response is very strong and would achieve the 10 marks.

The genre conventions have been noted.

The theory of children's language is mentioned and appropriate technical terms are used.

The student has closely observed the text and made reference to it to back up points.

Technical language is used in analysis.

The student recognises the language development process.

Audience, format and purpose are recognised.

Model answer

This letter has clearly been written by someone with a developing idea of the conventions of letter writing. He/she has included an address and a salutation, but there is no date or sign off at the end.

The structuring of words at the beginning of each paragraph - `although´, `firstly´, `furthermore´ and `finally´ - do not seem natural for someone who appears to be at a transitional stage of writing and spelling, and are probably the result of the teacher providing a Vygotskian scaffolding or template.

The writer usually uses correct sentences. However, cohesion is sometimes lost, as in the first sentence when `so´ intrudes. Only one sentence per paragraph is used.

The lexis is generally appropriate for the subject matter, but register can drift slightly. For example, the sentence about sweets being bad for your teeth changes into a plea to `pleaes change´ them.

Spelling is transitional, and difficult words like embarrassing (`inbarrison´) are spelled out phonetically. However, most common words are spelt correctly.

`Very´ is repeated as a rhetorical device, indicating that the writer is aware of his/her audience.

Exam practice question

1 How far do children acquire their language skills by imitating adults?

In your answer you should:
- refer to particular linguistic features and contexts
- refer to appropriate linguistic research and theory
- present a clear line of argument.

(35)

_____

_____

_____

_____

_____

_____

_____

_____

_____

_____

_____

_____

_____

_____

_____

_____

_____

_____

_____

_____

_____

[Please continue your answer on separate paper if necessary.]

4 Language and representation

The following topics are covered in this chapter:

- **How texts produce and maintain social values**
- **Representation of social groups, individuals, events, issues and institutions**
- **Language as a site of debate and conflict**

4.1 Language in context

LEARNING SUMMARY

After studying this section, you should be able to:

- understand the importance of context in texts
- understand how language and society influence each other
- understand the concept of representation

The influence of context

AQA	A P2
AQA	B P1
Edexcel	P1 and P2
OCR	P3
WJEC	P3

All language happens somewhere. This means that who is speaking or writing, who the audience is, and where the exchange is taking place will have a profound effect on what is said or written.

Language use will reflect:
- the purpose of the text
- the relative power between producer and receiver
- gender, ethnicity, disability, sexuality, age and class
- the events surrounding the text
- the institutional framework in which the text exists
- the text genre.

For instance, you are reading this book because you want to know more about A-Level English (purpose). It is written by someone with expertise in that field (relative power). You are probably studying it in the context of a school (institution) with a view to gaining an A-Level qualification (surrounding events). When you selected the book, you recognised it as a revision guide (genre). You may have noticed that it uses constructions like 'he or she' in order to be gender neutral (gender).

As expert language users, we automatically register such issues when we respond to texts, and we usually try to control these issues when we produce texts. In this chapter, we will be looking at the question of whether language is simply a reflection of its context, or whether it determines human social contexts in the most basic and fundamental ways.

How language and society may influence each other

The Sapir-Whorf hypothesis (see page 103) argues that the language we use actually defines the way that we look at the world, but the hypothesis cannot be tested experimentally because all humans have the same basic biological make-up.

Would space aliens or computers with artificial intelligence see the world differently, or are, for instance, nouns and verbs part of the basic fabric of reality?

The concept of representation

Another philosophical issue is the question of **representation**. It is clear that the word 'dog' is not the same thing as the thing dog – in using language at all, we **re-present** the world to ourselves. To what extent does the language people choose to do this affect their thoughts and feelings? For instance, in war or other conflicts, soldiers sometimes refer to their enemies using insulting, de-humanising nicknames. Does this make killing them easier?

The issue of how language (certainly) reflects and (possibly) creates society is at the centre of many debates about, for instance, gender, power and, more recently, technologies.

4.2 Language and gender

<table>
<tr><td rowspan="2">LEARNING SUMMARY</td><td>After studying this section, you should be able to:</td></tr>
<tr><td>

- understand some of the theories about language and gender
- understand how talk can be 'gendered'
- understand how sexism in writing is expressed and avoided

</td></tr>
</table>

The representation of women in texts and speech

AQA   **A P2**
AQA   **B P1**
Edexcel **P1 and P2**
OCR   **P3**
WJEC   **P2**

The way that women are represented in texts has been a controversial topic for some time. In the past, it was assumed that women were inferior to men and that they were 'the weaker sex'. In the seventeenth century, John Milton described the difference between Adam and Eve – and by extension between all women and men – in the following way.

> For contemplation he and valour formed,
> For softness she and sweet attractive grace;
> He for God only, she for God in him.
>
> *Extract from* Paradise Lost *(IV.296–298) by John Milton*

VATICAN SAYS 'NO' TO WOMEN PRIESTS

Men, it seemed, like to think and fight, whereas women were more interested in softer things. It was best, thought Milton, for women to approach God through a man.

In the twentieth century, Robin Lakoff[1] proposed that women's speech can be distinguished from men's speech in a number of ways, including the features shown in the table on the next page. Do you think that these features are representative of women's language in the twenty first century?

1 Lakoff, R.1975. *Language and woman's place.* New York: Oxford University Press.

Feature	Example
Empty adjectives	'divine', 'adorable', 'gorgeous'
Excessively polite forms	'Is it OK if...?', 'Would you mind...?'
More apologies than men	'I'm sorry, but I think...'
Speak less frequently	...
Avoid swear words and coarse language	... 'oh dear'
Hyper-correct grammar and pronunciation	Speak more clearly and with better grammar than men
Requests made indirectly	'You don't mind me sitting here, do you?'
Speaking in italics	'I'm *so* not going to that party'
Tag questions	'That's right, isn't it?'

How far do Milton and Lakoff agree? Are women 'softer' in some senses than men?

Some doubt has been cast on tag questions by researchers – can you think of ways of testing the others?

The key issue here is whether these perceived differences are 'natural', or whether they are imposed by societal conditioning. One study[2] of the language used in courtrooms noted that the characteristics mentioned above were the result of lack of power rather than gender – the women with the fewest of these features were well-educated professionals. This would fit in with theories of dominance and difference.

KEY POINT

One recent large scale study showed that men and women speak an average of 16 000 words per day. However, women are perceived to speak more than men.

Theoretical perspectives

AQA   **A P2**
AQA   **B P1**
Edexcel **P1 and P2**
OCR   **P3**
WJEC   **P3**

A great deal of work has been done on the language of women since Lakoff's proposals, and many of her insights have been supported. This section looks at some of the key contributions to the debate.

Spender

Dale Spender[3] takes the view that language is constructed by men as a way of embodying and sustaining male dominance in society.

> One semantic rule which we can see in operation in the language is that of the male-as-norm. At the outset it may appear to be a relatively innocuous rule for classifying the objects and events of the world, but closer examination exposes it as one of the most pervasive and pernicious rules that has been encoded.
>
> *Extract from* Man made language *by Dale Spender*

2 O'Barr, William and Bowman Atkins. 1980. "'Women's language' or 'powerless language'?", in McConnell-Ginet et al. (eds) *Women and languages in literature and society*, pp.93–110. New York: Praeger.

3 Spender, D. 1980. *Man made language*. Routledge & Kegan Paul.

The fact of male dominance makes it difficult, first of all, to maintain awareness of it (because it is the 'norm'), and secondly to change it.

> The crux of our difficulties lies in being able to identify and transform the rules which govern our behaviour and which bring patriarchal order into existence. Yet the tools we have for doing this are part of that patriarchal order.
>
> *Extract from* Man made language *by Dale Spender*

What does it say about the norms of our society if we have to qualify nurse with 'male' and firefighter with 'female'?

Tannen

Tannen's[4] best-selling book, *You just don't understand*, contrasted male and female language, and identified six major areas of difference:

1. **Status versus support** – this contrast emphasises male competitiveness and status seeking as opposed to female giving of confirmation and support. Men seek status; women seek consensus.
2. **Independence versus intimacy** – male competitiveness means that men use language to assert their freedom, whereas women are more inclined to use it for sharing and relationship building.
3. **Advice versus understanding** – men focus on solutions, whereas women focus on processes. This means that men tend to find solutions to a problem rather than trying to understand its cause, or give comfort and sympathy to the person with the problem.
4. **Information versus feelings** – men use speech to exchange information; women use it to express and share feelings.
5. **Orders versus proposals** – women tend to be indirect when seeking co-operation, and make suggestions rather than give commands. Men tend to use, and are more comfortable dealing with, explicit orders.
6. **Conflict versus compromise** – women are reluctant to engage in open conflict and are more willing to explore compromises; men are more likely to engage in direct confrontation.

The contrasts in areas 2 and 3 are easily testable as part of a language research project.

4 Tannen. D. 1992. *You just don't understand*. Virago Press.

In terms of conversational goals, Tannen argues that men have a **report style**, which prioritises and values factual information, whilst women have a **rapport style**, which is more concerned with establishing and maintaining relationships. Such differences can be found in all aspects of communication – from face-to-face conversations to the way male and female media presenters interact with their audiences.

Do you agree with Tannen's observations?

Results of other recent studies on male and female language

Here are some other differences that have been noted in recent studies:

- **Accommodation** – gender differences are most pronounced in single-gender groups, possibly because people moderate or accommodate their language style in the presence of members of the opposite sex. An example of this would be the strong taboo that used to exist against men swearing in the presence of women.
- **Changing the topic** – according to one study of same-sex friend interactions, males tend to change subject more frequently than females. This difference could account for the idea that women chatter more than men.
- **Minimal responses** – men make less use of backchannelling than women (i.e. supportive remarks like 'yeah' and 'OK'), and if they do so, it is usually to show agreement.
- **Questions** – men use questions to request information, whereas for women questions can simply be a way of showing engagement with a conversational partner; thus, women use questions more frequently.
- **Self-disclosure** – women share details about themselves, often to offer sympathy, e.g. 'I know how you feel, that happened to me…'; men tend to be more impersonal.
- **Turn-taking** – women are usually happy to take turns in conversation; men like to be the centre of talk, or remain silent when turns are offered implicitly through hedges such as, 'you know?'
- **Verbal aggression** – men make more use of threats, swear words, shouting and name calling than women, and are more likely to engage in direct confrontation. Women are likely to see this behaviour as a disruption to conversation, whereas men tend to view it as a way of showing status in a social group.
- **Listening and attentiveness** – women think listening is important and value the role of confidante of the speaker. They therefore interrupt less than men.
- **Dominance versus subjection** – male experts speak at greater length than their female counterparts, and male teachers gain more attention from their students. Perhaps this is why men predominate in scientific and technical subjects.
- **Politeness** – women are more concerned with preserving both positive and negative face than men (see pages 41–42); they are more polite.

What are your views on the differences noted in these studies? Have you noticed any of these differences in your day-to-day activities?

Jones

Jones[5] explored talk in women-only groups and identified four distinct sorts of gossip. These are:

- house-talk
- scandal
- bitching
- chatting.

5 Jones, D. 1980. 'Gossip: notes on women's oral culture', *Women's Studies International Quarterly*, Vol.3, Issues 2–3, 193–198.

House-talk relates to being a housewife and commonly includes tips, tricks and information on new products. House-talk, and its male equivalent, shop-talk, are very popular in social media where things like 'How to' videos are common.

The 'considered judging of the behaviour of others' defines **scandal** as a method of social policing. It often reinforces traditional male hierarchical ideas, for instance by disapproving of perceived sexual promiscuity.

Bitching involves expressing anger at women's restricted social role and low status. The purpose is not to change the situation, but to evoke sympathy.

Chatting is a form of communal recreation, where women tell personal stories that share underlying emotions.

Cameron

Cameron[6] argues that one function of language is to regulate the behaviour of both men and women as a measure of 'verbal hygiene'. She points out that many cultures have different standards of speech for the different genders and that appropriate speech is taught in a variety of ways. She then examines how such things as editors' style guides, grammar teaching in English schools and explicit advice given to women on how to speak operate to impose social norms. In discussing advice to women, Cameron wonders whether paying too much attention to a phenomenon actually makes it worse. She comments as follows.

> …a rash of articles on the problem of women's speech might lead people who had never noticed it was a problem to become anxious about it. The question of women's alleged 'indirectness' is a classic example of a non-problem turned into a crisis by constant reference to it in advice texts. There is little evidence that it exists in the relevant contexts…
>
> *Extract from* Verbal hygiene *by Deborah Cameron*

Russell

Russell[7] argues that women are frequently controlled by the use of insulting language. Of the insulting terms for a woman, a large number refer to sexual promiscuity (such as 'slag' or 'tart'). Words referring to male sexual promiscuity are far less insulting. Similarly, a bachelor is someone to be envied, whereas a spinster is to be pitied. This last imbalance is known as **lack of lexical symmetry** and can also be seen in the relative prestige of terms like 'witch' and 'wizard' or 'master' and 'mistress'.

Objectifying women

Many commentators have remarked on the way in which women are frequently **objectified**, that is, described in terms that do not see them as fully rounded human beings. Often this is a piece of metonymy where some aspect of a woman is taken for the whole, as in 'a bit of skirt', or it might be a metaphor such as 'tart', 'baby', 'sweetie pie'.

6 Cameron, D. 1995. *Verbal hygiene*. London: Routledge.

7 Russell, S. 2001. *Grammar, structure and style*. Oxford: OUP.

> **KEY POINT**
>
> It is often argued that men are more at home with objects (magazines aimed at men often focus on things like music, computers or motor bikes), whereas magazines aimed at women often focus on people and relationships.

Gender in writing

AQA   **A P2**
AQA   **B P1**
Edexcel **P1 and P2**
OCR   **P3**
WJEC   **P3**

Gendered talk is a fascinating area of study, but it is often difficult to capture all the nuances of human interaction and account for them consistently.

Neil Armstrong's first words on the moon were 'One small step for man, one giant leap for mankind'. He insists that he said 'a man', but this did not come out in the radio transmission.

Writing is usually much more public and much more consciously controlled; consequently it is much easier to police.

Since concerns about gender have been raised, many institutions have formulated guidelines on avoiding sexism in written communication.

Guidelines are likely to include the following advice:

- **Avoid 'man' as generic** as this implies that man is either the norm, or superior – for example, 'ordinary people' not 'the man on the street'; 'humanity' rather than 'mankind'.
- **Do not use male pronouns as the default** – use 'he or she', 's/he', 'him or her', or plural forms.
- **Avoid old-fashioned phrases that are framed in masculine language** – for example, 'Politeness produceth persons' rather than 'Manners maketh man'.
- **Use balanced titles.** Miss and Mrs indicate a person's sex and marital status, while Mr indicates sex only. It is unbalanced and unnecessary to specify the marital status of women but not of men. Use 'Mr' and 'Ms'.
- **Avoid the terms 'ladies' and 'girls'.** Adult males are usually referred to as men. To refer to an adult woman as a 'girl' or a 'lady' implies that she is either immature or that she ought to act in a particular way. Use woman or female instead.
- **Make sure that there is equality of address.** There is a tendency to include first names when referring to women. If a woman's first name is included, a man's should be as well, and vice versa – for instance, Ms J Smith and Mr D Jones; Ms Jennifer Smith and Mr David Jones.
- **Avoid 'terms of endearment'.** Men do not call each other 'love' and 'dear', and so it is patronising for men to address women in this way.
- **Avoid certain job titles.** Titles like fireman and cleaning lady should be avoided, as should titles that imply one sex or the other is the norm – do not say 'male nurse' or 'female electrician'. Also avoid sex-based diminutives such as actress and waitress.
- **Avoid biased and stereotyped assumptions.** Do not say, 'Lecturers and their wives are invited to attend', as this assumes that lecturers are male, heterosexual and married. Instead say, 'Lecturers and their partners are invited to attend'.
- **Avoid sex-role stereotyping** that assumes particular behaviours for each gender – for example, 'She's an adventurous/daring girl', rather than 'She's a tomboy'; 'He's a sensitive/caring boy', rather than 'He's a sissy'.

It could be argued that this guidance is over simplified, because women sometimes use the same sorts of terms to address men. What is your view? Do you think that, generally speaking, women object to men's 'terms of endearment', and vice versa?

Other advice might include the following:

- Be balanced in using female and male names in examples.
- Do not refer to ships as 'she'.
- Use the term 'women and men', as well as 'men and women'.

In 2003, the *Letterland* characters were given new names, as illustrated in the table below.

New name	Old name
Firefighter Fred	Fireman Fred
Harry Hat Man	Hairy Hat Man
Lucy Lamp Light	Lucy Lamp Lady
Noisy Nick	Naughty Nick
Peter Puppy	Poor Peter
Red Robot	Robber Red
Talking Tess	Ticking Tess / Ticking Tom
Vicky Violet	Vase of Violets
Walter Walrus	Wicked Water Witch
Fix-it Max	Max and Maxine
Yellow Yo-Yo Man	Yo-Yo Man

How many of these changes were motivated by concerns about sexism?

Gendered writing styles

Electronic versions of texts make them much more amenable to statistical analysis, and some linguists have attempted to use computer programming algorithms to tell whether a text is written by a man or a woman. One such algorithm[8] is based on the assumption that women are more likely than men to use personal pronouns, especially 'I,' 'you' and 'she'. Men seem to prefer so-called determiners like 'a,' 'the,' 'that,' 'these', along with numbers and quantifiers like 'more' and 'some'. This suggests that women are more comfortable talking or thinking about people and relationships, while men prefer to contemplate things, which leads us back to the start of this section and John Milton.

> **PROGRESS CHECK**
>
> 1 Name three types of gossip identified by Jones.
> 2 How did the missing 'a' change the meaning of Neil Armstrong's speech?
> 3 What does shouting and swearing do for men, according to recent studies?
>
> **1 Any three from:** house-talk; scandal; bitching; chatting.
> **2** Without 'a', man is being used as a generic term.
> **3** Show their status within a group.

8 Argamon, S., M. Koppel, J. Fine, A. R. Shimony. 2003. 'Gender, genre, and writing style in formal written texts', *Interdisciplinary Journal for the Study of Discourse*, Vol.23, Issue 3, 321–346.

4.3 Political correctness

LEARNING SUMMARY	**After studying this section, you should be able to:**
	• understand how texts shape thought and action
	• examine the debate on political correctness
	• discuss how language 'positions' its users

The debate on political correctness

AQA   **A P2**
AQA   **B P1**
Edexcel **P1 and P2**
OCR   **P3**
WJEC   **P3**

The arguments over avoiding sexist language can be seen as part of a broader movement in recent years to eliminate bias from public discourse. In the past, language has been biased on the basis of gender, sexuality, ethnicity, disability and social class, and the attempt to redress the balance in language terms is known as political correctness (PC). Politically this has been left-inspired, and PC language is frequently criticised in the right-wing media.

'Political correctness gone mad' stories usually involve a government agency being over-zealous in trying to avoid causing offence to minority groups. The agency typically 'bans' a word or phrase in a remarkable display of power over the English language.

Recent examples in the *Daily Mail* include:
- 'gingerbread man' biscuits having to be called 'gingerbread person' biscuits to avoid offence to women
- a primary school cancelling Halloween to avoid offence to religious parents
- 'Baa, baa, black sheep' being replaced by 'Baa, baa, rainbow sheep' to avoid offence to black people.

Many of these stories are based on single incidents and even misinterpretations of guidelines, and some are urban legends with almost no basis in fact. However, the debate over PC language shows that both left- and right-wing thinkers consider that the way ideas are expressed are important.

Sexuality

Reflecting the PC debate in newspapers are regular letters to the editor bemoaning the loss of the word 'gay', meaning happy. These letters assume that a word's original meaning is somehow its 'real' meaning, and therefore object to what are usually referred to as the 'political correctness brigade' imposing the new meaning on people who simply wish to express the idea of being carefree.

In fact, the word 'gay' has been associated with homosexuality for over 150 years, but it was not until the 1970s that the word entered common usage. Since that time, 'gay' has started to acquire a pejorative meaning, in some contexts, of 'lame' or 'rubbish'. The DJ Chris Moyles was cautioned by the BBC governors in 2006 for describing a ring tone he did not like in this manner.

Should outsiders accept the judgement of members of a group? If 'gay' is used by homosexual people, is this the 'correct' term?

In contrast to 'gay' is the word 'queer'. The general connotations of 'gay' are positive, as mentioned above, but the word 'queer' implies strange or unnatural. Many homosexual men and women have objected to being referred to in this way, but some have attempted to 'reclaim' the word and make it positive through widespread use. The UK TV series, *Queer as Folk*, about a group of gay men (broadcast from 1999 to 2000), is an example of this tendency.

Ethnicity

Words for groups of people clearly carry a great deal of emotional power, and this is especially true when the group belongs to a recognisable ethnic community. Insulting words for foreigners probably go back to pre-history, given language's role in cementing group identity. The word barbarian, for instance, comes from the Greeks, who thought that the language of foreigners sounded like the 'baa baa' of sheep. In multicultural societies, however, respect for all groups is the goal, and to refer to an ethnic group by a derogatory name can be described as 'hate speech'. The fact that there are laws against hate speech in this country is evidence of the power of language to translate into action.

> Do all words for foreigners have negative connotations? Can you think of any positive ones?

The word 'negro' originally meant 'black', but during the period of the trans-Atlantic slave trade it came to mean anyone from sub-Saharan Africa. When the civil rights movement began to be successful in America, activists rejected this colonialist and slave–owner label and preferred the word 'black' (older people in their turn disliked this new label). In Britain, 'black' was sometimes used in distinction to the word 'brown', meaning people from Asia, but now it is the generally accepted term for people of African and Afro-Caribbean descent. 'Brown' is no longer used as a description of ethnicity, and the informal form of negro, 'nigger', is completely taboo outside the black community. The word is illegal in New York, and in 2007, Emily Parr, a contestant on *Big Brother*, was evicted from the show for using it to describe another contestant.

The word for negative feelings about foreigners is xenophobia – meaning literally 'fear of strangers'. Some words are used deliberately to stir up xenophobia. In England in the 1930s, Sir Oswald Moseley attempted to stir up racial hatred against Jewish people in the East End of London using the slogan 'The Yids, the Yids, we are going to get rid of the Yids'. At the battle of Cable Street, working people banded together to prevent a fascist march into the East End. Today, both Jewish and non-Jewish supporters of Tottenham Hotspur refer to themselves as 'Yids' in an example of **reclamation**.

> **KEY POINT**
>
> The context in which a word is used can be misunderstood. For instance, the profoundly anti-racist book *To Kill a Mockingbird* is often criticised because it contains the word 'nigger'.

People with disabilities

There have been numerous debates about the appropriate language for discussing disability. One major area of discussion is the overarching term itself. Is it meaningful to use the same term to talk about someone with a learning difficulty and someone who has lost the use of his or her limbs? If we see the 'label', the argument is that we fail to see the person behind it. To counter this, it is now recommended by experts working in the field that at the very least the word order in discussions should put people first, as in 'people with disabilities'.

Another discussion centres on the **lexical gap**, which means that there is no neutral way to talk about disability in English. Words that feature negative elements, like 'dis' and 'non', focus on what people cannot do rather than what they can.

In a process known as **pejoration**, words that began as scientific descriptions, like 'spastic' or 'mongoloid', are adopted as insults. The latest example of this is the insulting use of the word 'special', because of its association with special needs departments in schools. In 1994, the Spastics Society charity changed its name to Scope because of this process.

Social class

Social class has a significant effect on the way people speak – in large cities like London, there may be three or four social dialects being spoken within a square mile or so. Bernstein[9] introduced the idea of **elaborated** and **restricted language codes** as a way of accounting for differences in educational performance between working-class and middle-class children.

As illustrated in the example below, it could be argued that middle-class people tend to use elaborated codes; that is, they tend to spell things out and explain what they mean. Working-class people assume a great deal of shared knowledge and they speak with much greater economy.

> **Elaborated:** If you go to town, could you buy me some Pinot Grigio from Austen's near the Metro?
> **Restricted:** Get me some wine if you're going to the shops.

Neither code is better than the other, but the restricted code is more suited to talk in small, familiar communities (almost everyone uses a restricted code in their own family), whereas the elaborated code is more suited to communication with wider audiences of relative strangers. Needless to say, the elaborated code is the one which gains the best marks in school.

Other interesting aspects of the impact of social class on language include studies of accent and sociolects, and attitudes to particular regional and social accents. Would you trust a working-class man from London more than a 'posh' person from Devon?

Subcultures

Groups that are associated with music-based subcultures are self-defining – they represent a choice that members of groups like pensioners cannot make. This self-consciousness may well result in a particular language choice and type of display. For instance, to what extent do members of a music-based group quote from the lyrics of their favourite bands? Are there linguistic **shibboleths** in play to exclude non-group members?

From the other side, linguists may be interested in how group members are perceived by outsiders. Why are 'emo' children the subject of more jokes than children who like heavy metal or hip hop? Membership of a subculture is a classic method of representing and positioning oneself.

9 Bernstein, B. 1971. *Theoretical studies towards a sociology of language*. Routledge.

Age

Much of people's concern over language in society is that it obscures rather than reveals. If we think of someone as a 'chav', or an 'OAP', or 'emo', we will not see an individual, but a collection of pre-conceived ideas, and even prejudices.

This is particularly a problem for older age-based divisions of society because, in the end, simply being the same age as someone else does not mean that you have much in common.

There are clear developmental stages of language use, but once language competence is achieved, does everybody go their separate ways? Do shared events like living through a war or a period of social change affect how people use slang, for instance?

As with subcultures, it is interesting to look at how older people are positioned by the media. Sigourney Weaver, for instance, is over sixty, but is never referred to as a pensioner. Do newspapers present older people as 'beleaguered' veterans eking out their winter fuel payments, or as adventurous, sprightly people, making the most of their retirement?

Figure 4.1 Two different presentations of older people

KEY POINT

Different colours are often used in phrases that describe older people. Affluent people using the Internet might be called 'silver surfers' in their 'golden years'. The 'blue rinse' brigade might fill up public transport, and the 'grey pound' might inflate the price of bungalows.

PROGRESS CHECK

1 Identify which parts of the following statements are politically correct/incorrect.
   a) Women firefighters needed.
   b) The person in charge should use his skeleton key to open the door.
   c) All the children in the class will take part in the nativity play.

1 a) Firefighters is PC; women in this context is not.
b) Person and skeleton (not master) key are PC; using generic 'his' is not.
c) Using 'all' is PC; assuming they are all Christian is not.

4.4 Language and the individual

After studying this section, you should be able to:

- appreciate how people are positioned by language
- understand how powerful narratives shape responses to others
- discuss the way in which celebrity is represented

Individuality and the media

AQA   **A P2**
AQA   **B P1**
Edexcel **P1 and P2**
OCR   **P3**
WJEC   **P3**

One of the main difficulties outlined in the previous sections of this chapter is getting to see people for what they are, rather than seeing them as some sort of **stereotype** defined by a label. This difficulty persists at an individual level when people are being presented by the media. It is as if there are only a limited number of personality templates available, and the main job of media writers and presenters is to sort people into appropriate categories.

Categories include:

- troubled teen
- battling granny
- plucky British sportsperson (who never quite wins)
- social security 'scrounger'
- celebrity with a secret sorrow.

Some categories shift from time to time. For example, single mothers are now – usually – independent and self-sufficient, whereas in the 1980s they seemed to be the cause of all society's ills. However, most categories seem to go on from generation to generation, as pop stars, politicians and other people in the public eye are presented for popular consumption.

Fame

AQA   **A P2**
AQA   **B P1**
Edexcel **P1 and P2**
OCR   **P3**
WJEC   **P3**

In 1968, the artist Andy Warhol famously said that in the future, everyone would have 15 minutes of worldwide fame. Recent developments in social media and television programming have meant that many people have come to see Warhol's remark as a prophecy. Anecdotal evidence suggests that many children now simply want to be famous, rather than being famous for, say, curing the common cold or travelling to Mars. The modern cult of celebrity, it has been argued, celebrates people for 'being' (on a reality TV show, for example), rather than for 'doing'.

People who are famous for solid and worthwhile achievements are often described as A-list celebrities, and people who are merely famous for being famous might be on the B- or even the Z-list. So there is an implied **hierarchy** amongst famous people. This is amusingly satirised in an article by Schulman,[10] which looks at what kinds of magazine or other media source might be interested in a particular celebrity.

10 Schulman, E. 2006. Measuring fame qualitatively (3): What does it take to make the "A" list?, *Annals of Improbable Research*, Vol.12, No. 1, January/February, 11.

These media sources are specific to the USA. Can you think of comparable UK-based examples for each 'level' of celebrity?

… an 'A' List Celebrity might be the subject of a cover story in *Time*, the picture of a 'B' List Celebrity might appear on the cover of *People Magazine*, the money troubles of a 'C' List Celebrity might be discussed in the pages of *The National Enquirer*, and a 'D' List Celebrity might be mentioned briefly on *National Public Radio*.

Extract from 'Measuring fame qualitatively (3):
What does it take to make the "A" list?' by E. Schulman

This is rejected by Schulman as being too impressionistic, and a way of measuring a level of fame based on search engine hits is suggested. This article may be tongue-in-cheek, but it does suggest two interesting ways of looking at how celebrity is constructed.

One of the paradoxes of celebrity culture is that it values – and at the same time condemns – intrusions into the private lives of famous people. The most notorious case in this context is the death of Princess Diana and Dodi Fayed as their car attempted to avoid a group of **paparazzi** (photographers who specialise in taking pictures of famous people). There have been numerous debates about the morality of using photographs obtained without their subjects' consent in newspapers and magazines. Some celebrities co-operate with the media and earn large fees for selling such things as their wedding photographs to magazines like *Heat* and *Hello*. When stars don't co-operate, editors frequently use the excuse that the printed or broadcast images are in the **public interest**.

However, you could comment that public interest is not the same as something that is 'interesting' to the public. For example, it is in the public interest to expose a crime, or an issue such as MPs' expenses, but it is 'interesting' to the public if a sports person or celebrity has an affair.

The price of fame

The case of Madeleine McCann presents some interesting insights into the way the media responds to a tragedy, and how stories are **constructed**. When the daughter of Kate and Gerry McCann disappeared from a holiday apartment in Portugal in May 2007, there was intense media interest.

The search for Madeleine occupied newspaper attention for several months afterwards, and the *Daily Express* in particular became noted for its excessive coverage. Apparently the paper received around 10 000 messages a day about the story, and its sales increased each time an article about Madeleine appeared on the front page. The paper's hunger for material led it to print some questionable accusations, and eventually it was successfully sued by the McCann family for defamation of character. The editor, Peter Hill, admitted that the story was certainly of interest to the public, but wasn't in the public interest. At the time, *The Sun* also had sympathetic coverage of the case. Words like 'Mummy' and 'Our Maddie' were used in headlines and strap lines.

What impact did this language tend to have on readers?

The McCann parents justified feeding stories to the media as a way of keeping their daughter's image in the public eye, in the hope of finding her. But in some quarters they were criticised for exploiting their daughter's disappearance for personal gain, or even as a cover-up for a crime. Some critics pointed out that thousands of children disappear every year and the only reason Madeleine McCann made so many headlines was because she was white, middle class, and had articulate, professional parents. When the backlash against the parents was at its height, Boris Johnson, the future Mayor of London, made this comment.

> We want the story to end, of course. It has been the most wretched event of a wretched summer, and we want it to climax one way or another, even if the denouement exceeds even the ghastliest Channel Five real-life family murder drama.
>
> *Extract from 'Madeleine McCann saga reflects our society' by Boris Johnson, telegraph.co.uk*

> What other framing devices do people use? For instance, who might be described as having a 'fairy tale romance'?

The tragic disappearance of a small girl is here being **framed** in terms of popular drama. The problem with such an approach is that it makes people look for facts that will confirm the pre-formed story.

In the article, Boris Johnson also referred to an Aristotelian approach to tragedy, in which strong feelings come from placing yourself in the position of the sufferer. He said that people's grief and anger was real, but to a large extent they would also be thinking about themselves. This view is perhaps confirmed by the tendency to speak about 'our' Madeleine in many responses to the story.

Political celebrities and celebrity politicians

AQA	**A P2**
AQA	**B P1**
Edexcel	**P1 and P2**
OCR	**P3**
WJEC	**P3**

One noticeable development in recent years has been the merging of previously separate aspects of public life. In 2003, the prime minister, Tony Blair, was pictured holding a guitar (with the home secretary on drums!), and over the past 25 years, one of the leading campaigners against poverty in Africa has been the pop star Bob Geldof. Going even further in this direction, a former actor became President of the United States, and an actress, Glenda Jackson, became a Member of Parliament in the UK.

Street[11] distinguishes two types of celebrity politician:

- The first type use celebrity to promote and endorse their policies – for instance, by appearing in photo opportunities with film stars, appearing on light entertainment programmes like *Have I Got News For You?*, or playing the saxophone with a jazz group, as President Bill Clinton did.
- The second type is a celebrity in a non-political field who decides to use his or her status with the public to promote a good cause. Examples of this type of celebrity are Brad Pitt, who has raised money and campaigned for the re-building of New Orleans, and Bono, who campaigns to reduce the debt of developing countries.

Constructing narratives

Some critics are alarmed by the apparent influence of unelected spokespeople on political and social issues, but Street argues that the fact that a celebrity is supporting a cause does not seem to short circuit people's ability to assess it, and give their own time or money. Equally, representative politicians are also masters of **re-presentation**, and political campaigning is, and to some extent always has been, a marketing exercise involving ideas.

11 Street, J. 2004. 'Celebrity politicians: popular culture and political representation', *BJPIR*, Vol.6, 435–452.

One example is the way in which the telegenic John F. Kennedy defeated his more experienced, but less media-conscious rival, Richard Nixon, in a television debate. A great deal of energy is spent on **constructing narratives** for politicians so that, for instance, Gordon Brown triumphed as a 'prudent' chancellor, but failed to inspire as a leader with vision and experience. Furthermore, this kind of marketing is nothing new, as the statues, paintings, carefully posed photographs, and even nicknames – from 'Richard the Lionheart' to 'Charles the Bold' – of historical figures tell us.

> The 'Iron Lady', the 'Iron Chancellor' and the 'Man of Steel' – what do the adjectives applied to politicians imply?

Figure 4.2 Margaret Thatcher – the 'Iron Lady'   **Figure 4.3 Otto von Bismarck – the 'Iron Chancellor'**   **Figure 4.4 Joseph Stalin – the 'Man of Steel'**

The life stories of politicians and celebrities are as much a part of how they are presented to the world as their policies or latest works of art. Much was made of the fact that Margaret Thatcher grew up in a grocer's shop. The classic example of this in American politics is Abraham Lincoln's rise from living in a lowly log cabin to the White House, and parallels between Lincoln and Barack Obama are frequently drawn. Pop and football stars often have their **biographies** published when they are still in their teens and early twenties, and lucrative book deals are a feature of top politicians' retirements. Again, the focus is on constructing familiar narratives, such as overcoming early hardships or enduring (hitherto) secret sorrows. Celebrities frequently detail their 'battle' against drug addiction or their 'fight' against disease, and some even use their celebrity status to raise public awareness. For instance, Michael Landon, the star of the TV series *Little House on the Prairie*, revealed the problems he had as a child with bed wetting in his biography, *Michael Landon: His Triumph and Tragedy*.

> **KEY POINT**
>
> The 'secret sorrow' narrative is particularly attractive to celebrities, as it forestalls potential jealousy of their privileged lifestyles.

When celebrities 'go bad'

AQA   **A P2**
AQA   **B P1**
Edexcel **P1 and P2**
OCR   **P3**
WJEC   **P3**

Some people become famous for good reasons and then remain famous for bad ones. There is a noticeable gender difference in this particular narrative, as young men are frequently admired, or at least given the benefit of the doubt as they 'sow their wild oats', whereas young women are usually roundly condemned. Male celebrities like Russell Brand and Robert Downey Junior seem to be able to put their troubles behind them, whereas females like Lindsay Lohan and Amy Winehouse are held up as examples of how not to behave. 'Bad girls' eventually seem to disappear from the public eye, but controversial men seem to be able to trade on their former notoriety. For example, John Lydon of the Sex Pistols now advertises margarine, and Ozzy Osbourne – who once bit the head off a bat on stage – had a successful reality TV show.

The article below, which discusses 'bad girl' celebrities, is typical of the sort of article you may see in a 'gossip' magazine. In Deborah Jones's terms (see page 116), it falls under the 'scandal' heading.

Notice the use of 'we' to justify public interest.

A big part of the reason why some of these celebrities are so well known.

The Brit Award success gets very little coverage in the article, compared to Winehouse's misdemeanours.

Winehouse is frequently condemned out of her own mouth. Is she consciously collaborating in creating her 'bad girl' image?

'A spot of light vomiting' – this bad behaviour is made to seem trivial and amusing.

Why do we all love a bad girl?

The concept of the 'bad boy' has been around for years, and we all secretly love them, don't we? The concept of 'bad girls' is newer, but no less exciting! No matter their indiscretions, nothing seems to keep a bad girl down – they bounce back faster than a bungee rope.

But why are we so fascinated with 'bad girls'? They are often seen drunk, being loud mouthed, frequently dabbling in illicit substances, and not infrequently being arrested. Hardly a typical female 'role model'. Yet, in spite of all the 'bad' stuff that propels media interest in these 'bad girls', the fact is that they are pretty damn good at what they do. Take Amy Winehouse. Despite her many booze-related misdemeanours, her tattoos, and her 'did my eye make-up and hair in a moving car' look, she is a very talented musician. Not surprising then that, among her other awards, she was crowned Best British Female at the Brit Awards in 2007.

But she has been described, in her own words, as 'an ugly dickhead drunk'. Boozing, blacking out and fighting seem, for her, to be the norm. She recently confessed to having 'smacked' a girl who came up to her after a gig. During one performance she left the stage halfway through her first song for a 'spot of light vomiting', and never returned! Talented performer yes, someone you might want to get too close to of an evening? Maybe not.

There are not only 'bad girls' in the music industry. You might have thought that Kate Moss's career was all over after her alleged dabble with cocaine, but it emerged she was earning more a while after the incident than before. Kerry Katona is never off the telly these days, despite her alleged long-standing drug problem. And Winona Ryder and Lindsay Lohan have both had spells in prison.

Will these kinds of 'bad girls' continue to surprise us with their antics, or will they go the way of one of the 'bad boys' of rock, Iggy Pop, and end up advertising car insurance one day? Only time will tell.

An informal tone runs through this article, and the language can be described as informal – even slangy in places. It includes commentary about 'colourful' celebrities – Kate Moss, Kerry Katona and Amy Winehouse.

Although the article appears to be light-hearted in tone and seems to think that the audience will enjoy hearing about drunkenness, there are implied criticisms of self-injury, unreliability and casual violence. A very small percentage of the article is devoted to the talent of the women. The rest re-tells old news about their unconventional lifestyles.

Some of Winehouse's bad behaviour is made to seem trivial and amusing. Transgressive words are used – for example, Amy Winehouse uses the word 'dickhead' to describe herself. The apparent purpose of articles such as this one is to leave readers shaking their heads in sadness rather than moral outrage.

Re-presenting yourself

AQA	A P2
AQA	B P1
Edexcel	P1 and P2
OCR	P3
WJEC	P3

Until recently, only a very small number of people had what might be called a 'public' profile. In the 1970s, the only information you could easily look up about other people was their phone number in the telephone directory. Today, most people keep their mobile numbers private, but over 400 million people have Facebook accounts, and a surprising amount of data is publicly available about most individuals. The noun Google has become a verb, and people regularly google new acquaintances to get to know them electronically.

This situation is fascinating for linguists, who have huge new opportunities for studying real language, but it is more problematic for other people. To begin with, which photograph of yourself should you use as your profile picture – the one of you at a party with your friends, the one of you on a mountain top on holiday, the one that makes you look older? Whichever one you choose, you will be constructing a narrative about yourself – as fun loving, or adventurous, or serious, or any one of countless other possibilities.

In the 'about you' section, should you list all the bands you like, or only the popular ones, or only the very obscure ones? Again, your choices will reflect you in some way, but the **purpose** of your choices will be to manage your public image in a way that was scarcely imaginable a few years ago. In an electronically connected world, the number of strangers you can meet via Bebo, MySpace, Facebook, Twitter, and even YouTube, is truly astronomical.

If you decide to write something about yourself, the way that you express your ideas will be open to interpretation. What **register** should you use? Should you worry about a general **audience**, or just your intimate friends? Should you keep your status updates short and to the point, or would the world benefit from your considered opinion on the benefits of bananas for breakfast!?

Some social networking is highly managed, for instance on dating sites, whilst other parts of it are frighteningly public. A photograph of you might be picked up by an online community and turned into an Internet meme. Or you might become as popular as Charlie and his brother. 'Charlie bit my finger – again!' has been viewed over 200 million times on YouTube.

Ghyslain Raza was not pleased by his Internet fame as 'the Star Wars Kid' and sued the students who uploaded a video of him onto the Internet. He had become depressed, and dropped out of school as a result of the attention the clip of him received. Cyber bullying has been added to the difficulties of growing up.

4.5 Representing institutions

LEARNING SUMMARY	**After studying this section, you should be able to:**
	• understand how institutions present themselves to the public
	• discuss the importance of iconography
	• appreciate how institutions are shaped by language

Corporate identity

AQA **A P2**
AQA **B P1**
Edexcel **P1 and P2**
OCR **P3**
WJEC **P3**

Institutions such as schools, hospitals, churches and prisons are self-defining collections of people, so one of the first things these groupings do is try to provide a sense of **group identity**.

Schools usually insist that only the students wear uniforms; in prisons the inmates and staff wear different uniforms; in hospitals and churches only the staff wear distinctive clothing; and in the armed forces, where group identity is a matter of life and death, everyone wears a uniform.

Graphology

Along with the sense of identity provided by clothing, institutions also adopt language-based strategies. At the **graphological** level, there is a school badge, a company logo or a regimental flag that is meant to be instantly recognisable. Commercial companies sometimes spend millions on getting their visual presentation right, from logo to corporate font. In the past, schools and regiments had **mottos** – short, pithy statements of what the institution believed in – and today, most institutions have slightly longer **mission statements**, which perform the same function.

Do you know the motto and mission statement for your school/college?

Figure 4.5 The Manchester Grammar School's Coat of Arms and the modern logo

The Manchester Grammar School's Coat of Arms uses heraldic owls to show wisdom, and a Latin motto that translates as 'Dare To Be Wise'. The modern logo uses lower-case initials – showing a willingness to be unconventional – and includes a date that emphasises success over time.

The badges for the French and English Special Air Services (SAS) are also 'daring'. They both use the motto 'Who Dares Wins', and employ icons that sum up the unit's purpose – flying or dropping into an area, and fighting.

Iconography

A particular image drawn in a fixed and conventional way is known as an icon. Icons are familiar today because of their use on computers, but in the past they were associated with religion – illiterate worshippers were able to quickly and easily identify a particular saint or bible story because of the iconography used. For instance, the four writers of the gospels, Matthew, Mark, Luke and John, were frequently represented with a lion, an angel, an ox and an eagle. In Hindu art, gods can often be distinguished by their blue, green or red skin.

Figure 4.6 An example of religious iconography

The iconography chosen by a particular institution can have a powerful impact. For example, the suggestion of solar energy, and even flowers, in the BP company logo is intended to signal the company's interest in alternative forms of sustainable energy.

Essentially, iconography plays with associations and tries to link corporate bodies with particularly pleasant ideas. It is difficult nowadays to see a Golden Labrador puppy without thinking of Andrex toilet tissues, and a few years ago Old English Sheepdogs were frequently called Dulux dogs because of a long-running advertising campaign.

> **KEY POINT**
>
> Some companies go to great lengths to avoid meaning. For example, Esso was renamed Exxon to avoid naming conflicts with other oil companies – Enco was rejected because it sounded like the word for 'stalled car' in Japanese, and Exon was rejected because it was a politician's name.

Corporate language – embodying values

AQA   **A P2**
AQA   **B P1**
Edexcel **P1 and P2**
OCR   **P3**
WJEC   **P3**

When institutions speak to the public through advertisements or other publicity material, they are careful to manage their language use so that the values of the institution are clear. A recent trend in corporate language is the inclusion of concern for the environment, whereas in the past other values have prevailed.

For example, the Andrex® website now has a 'sustainability zone'. Consumers can buy 'Longer Lasting' tissue, which has 50 percent more sheets but is only 10 percent larger in size. Andrex® has put the onus back on to consumers through the language they use to promote this product – 'Longer Lasting toilet tissue helps **you** to take one more step towards doing **your** bit for the environment' (emphasis added). Andrex® argues that if everyone bought Longer Lasting tissue rather than normal length tissue, fewer transport trucks would be needed (because the Longer Lasting tissue takes up less space). Andrex® has also introduced the Forest Stewardship Council (FSC) logo on packs of toilet tissues, which is a visual reminder to consumers of the brand's environmental efforts.

Figure 4.7 'It's the little things' – the image of a Labrador puppy is synonymous with Andrex®, but sustainability is also a key selling point for the brand today

Institutions such as churches develop **specialist vocabulary**, which is meaningful to believers but opaque to the outside world. For example, only Roman Catholics come face to face with the meaning of the word transubstantiation when they eat the 'real' body of Christ in Holy Communion. Where people work together, many institutions develop job-related **jargon**.

Job-related jargon can be useful within an industry because terms do not need to be explained to people who already understand the concepts.

For example...
- 'Section 5 of the Public Order Act' is a term used by people working in law enforcement
- talking about 'risers' and 'balusters' is understood by someone who works in the joinery trade
- 'mass spectrometry machines' and 'linear ions Q-traps' is familiar terminology to a Chemistry teacher
- the term *mens rea* is known to people working in the legal profession.

However, sometimes jargon can confuse and patronise the listener. The 'office-speak' sometimes used by managerial staff has been discussed in newspaper articles and was famously parodied by Ricky Gervais in the BBC comedy, *The Office*.

Here is a typical example:

> Going forwards, if we all put our thinking caps on we can employ some blue sky thinking to respond to the external challenges, and produce some improvement levers to bring to the table. We can facilitate our fellow employees to climb their mountain of pessimism.

Notice the use of mixed metaphors in this example (see page 213 for more information on mixed metaphors). In the above instance, jargon clearly hasn't been used in a positive way. It would have been much better to say this:

> If we all think clearly about the problems we are facing with suppliers, we will be able to produce some helpful ideas. This should help our colleagues feel more positive.

PROGRESS CHECK

1. What do you think the Salvation Army's motto, 'Blood and Fire', suggests?
2. What is the iconography of the Nike 'tick'?
3. Google's corporate motto is 'Don't be evil'. What does this suggest about the company's values?

1 That the organisation is willing to struggle for its beliefs.
2 Approval; the right answer.
3 That it is well meaning.

4.6 Representing events and issues

LEARNING SUMMARY	**After studying this section, you should be able to:**
	• understand how news events are positioned by language
	• discuss how media bias may be manifested
	• appreciate how different voices may be heard

Selling wars

AQA	**A P2**
AQA	**B P1**
Edexcel	**P1 and P2**
OCR	**P3**
WJEC	**P3**

There is probably nothing more serious than war as a subject for the media but, as in all areas of human endeavour, the way it is represented can vary enormously. In modern democracies, it is impossible to go to war without convincing the public that the conflict is justified, and so the prelude to many armed struggles is a war of words and propaganda.

A famous example of this is the 'Rape of Belgium', a term that describes a series of German war crimes that took place shortly before Britain's entry into the First World War. A number of war crimes were committed, including the death of civilians, the burning of libraries and the looting of industrial equipment, but this was presented in the British press as the sexual violation of an innocent and neutral population. The 'Huns' (the name of a savage Germanic tribe) were depicted in dehumanised forms, as gorillas or monsters, with babies on their bayonets.

Atrocity stories are in themselves a problem in war. They motivate soldiers to fight, but if they are believed they may lead to fresh atrocities in revenge. For example, soldiers – having heard that the enemy takes no prisoners – will take no prisoners themselves.

All wars have a 'cause' that people can believe in. Whether it is fighting for freedom or for survival, the cause has to be expressed to the public through a combination of official and media channels.

Media bias

In order to go to war, governments have to convince people that the war is worth fighting, and to stay in the war, news has to be managed to prevent loss of morale.

In the First World War, the British government simply appointed a newspaper proprietor, Lord Beaverbrook, to be head of propaganda, and although people in Dover could sometimes hear the guns on the Somme, all news about the progress of the war was strictly controlled. It is generally agreed that the American public lost its appetite for the war in Vietnam because of what they saw on television. Nowadays, the Internet, mobile phones and satellite technology can bring news of wars directly from the participants. Journalists do not sit back and wait for press releases, but are 'embedded' with the armed forces.

Some wars are more controversial than others. The recent war on Iraq has provoked strong and contrasting views from different areas of the media regarding its justification. The polemic shown below was written by the campaigning journalist, John Pilger. In the extract, he says that much of the information made available to the public about the war was simply untrue. Read it now, and then take a few moments to consider how biased you think it is.

> The public have to be convinced of the threat.

> He accuses journalists of collaborating with politicians.

On 24 August last year [2005], a *New York Times* editorial declared: "If we had all known then what we know now, the invasion [of Iraq] would have been stopped by a popular outcry." This amazing admission was saying, in effect, that the invasion would never have happened if journalists had not betrayed the public by accepting and amplifying and echoing the lies of Bush and Blair, instead of challenging and exposing them.

> Pilger is shocked that a journalist should take a politician's word at face value.

> He criticises the BBC's unduly mild language.

We now know that the BBC and other British media were used by MI6, the secret intelligence service. In what was called "Operation Mass Appeal", MI6 agents planted stories about Saddam Hussein's weapons of mass destruction – such as weapons hidden in his palaces and in secret underground bunkers. All these stories were fake. But this is not the point. The point is that the dark deeds of MI6 were quite unnecessary. Recently, the BBC's director of news, Helen Boaden, was asked to explain how one of her "embedded" reporters in Iraq, having accepted US denials of the use of chemical weapons against civilians, could possibly describe the aim of the Anglo-American invasion as to "bring democracy and human rights" to Iraq. She replied with quotations from Blair that this was indeed the aim, as if Blair's utterances and the truth were in any way related. On the third anniversary of the invasion, a BBC newsreader described this illegal, unprovoked act, based on lies, as a "miscalculation". Thus, to use Edward Herman's memorable phrase, the unthinkable was normalised.

> A general point that the media serve the status quo.

> A counter assertion is backed up by a quotation from a respectable source.

> He is aligning himself on the side of the victim.

Such servility to state power is hotly denied, yet routine. Almost the entire British media has omitted the true figure of Iraqi civilian casualties, wilfully ignoring or attempting to discredit respectable studies. "Making conservative assumptions," wrote the researchers from the eminent Johns Hopkins Bloomberg School of Public Health, working with Iraqi scholars, "we think that about 100,000 excess deaths, or more, have happened since the 2003 invasion of Iraq . . . which were primarily the result of military actions by coalition forces. Most of those killed by coalition forces were women and children..." That was 29 October 2004. Today, the figure has doubled.

Extract from 'The real first casualty of war' by John Pilger, New Statesman.com

Euphemism

The reporting of war is never pleasant. In bringing such events into people's homes via their newspapers, televisions and computers, most journalists take some care not to be too horrific. This includes not showing body parts in news programmes, and deploying euphemistic language to describe unthinkable events.

In addition to the media's self-censorship, military spokespeople are well known for their use of non-specific terms. A retreat becomes a 'strategic withdrawal', and the death of civilians is known as 'collateral damage'. Many of these words and phrases are borrowed from outside the semantic field of warfare, such as 'mopping up' or 'surgical' strike, whilst others turn traditional meanings on their head, as in 'pacifying' missions that involve heavy casualties. The phrase 'blue on blue', meaning killing soldiers from your own side, is actually borrowed from war gaming.

PROGRESS CHECK

1. How has the war in Afghanistan been sold to the British public?
2. What is implied by the phrase 'the fog of war'?
3. How has modern technology changed war reporting?

3 Mobile phones and the Internet give uncensored access.
2 That war is natural, like the weather.
1 As part of the war on 'terror'.

Sample question and model answer

AQA students This topic is covered via coursework and you will normally be required to compare different examples of representation across time or space. See Chapter 8, Language investigations and other coursework tasks (page 242), for help on preparing your investigation.

Below is a sample question for students of all other exam boards.

Read texts A and B and answer the following question.

Analyse and compare the ways in which each writer presents himself.

In your response you should include reference to any relevant theories and research. (50 marks)

Text A

Text A is from the introduction of *My Booky Wook*, written by the comedian and actor Russell Brand. It is an autobiographical account of his early life and various addictions. The American edition was published in 2010.

Author's Note

Dear American reader,

Jolly well done, you have purchased this book in spite of 1. Its seemingly childish title, and 2. The photo of me on the cover, thus proving that you are: 1. Prepared to take risks, and 2. A sexy, adventurous outsider. Congratulations, you are in for a giddy, wild ride through language, hedonism and amusing despair. Unless you bought the book(y wook) for a relative, and are now perusing it only to ascertain its suitability, or worse still, you are a shoplifter pretending to read before committing your crime.

If either scenario is true, then, be assured, it is suitable for your relative—unless they are crushingly naive or small-minded. And if you are a shoplifter, I'm in no position to complain as I, myself, have stolen many books. I'm not condoning it, I just understand that you must be desperate, and at least you're stealing a good book(y wook). Good luck.

Now, assuming that all who remain are good, honest consumers, I'd like to thank you. This book is mine, it's all true, I wrote it, and while I'm proud of the book(y wook), I'm not proud of some of the chaos within. I am an Englishman and, as such, reserve the right to talk, and write, in a manner that may strike you as macabre or bonkers or crackers, nuts or weird; to avoid possible confusion, I have included a glossary so that you can understand what I have written. I only pray you can understand why I wrote it.

Long live the Queen, God Bless America.

Ta ta

Russell

Extract from My Booky Wook *by Russell Brand (American edition, published in 2010)*

Sample question and model answer
(continued)

Text B

Text B is from *Confessions of an English Opium Eater* by Thomas De Quincey. In it he records his early life of extreme poverty and eventual addiction to opium. De Quincey was a writer and journalist working at the beginning of the nineteenth century.

To the Reader

I here present you, courteous reader, with the record of a remarkable period in my life: according to my application of it, I trust that it will prove not merely an interesting record, but in a considerable degree useful and instructive. In *that* hope it is that I have drawn it up; and *that* must be my apology for breaking through that delicate and honourable reserve which, for the most part, restrains us from the public exposure of our own errors and infirmities. Nothing, indeed, is more revolting to English feelings than the spectacle of a human being obtruding on our notice his moral ulcers or scars, and tearing away that "decent drapery" which time or indulgence to human frailty may have drawn over them; accordingly, the greater part of *our* confessions (that is, spontaneous and extra-judicial confessions) proceed from demireps, adventurers, or swindlers: and for any such acts of gratuitous self-humiliation from those who can be supposed in sympathy with the decent and self-respecting part of society, we must look to French literature.... All this I feel so forcibly, and so nervously am I alive to reproach of this tendency, that I have for many months hesitated about the propriety of allowing this or any part of my narrative to come before the public eye until after my death (when, for many reasons, the whole will be published); and it is not without an anxious review of the reasons for and against this step that I have at last concluded on taking it.

Guilt and misery shrink, by a natural instinct, from public notice: they court privacy and solitude: and even in their choice of a grave will sometimes sequester themselves from the general population of the churchyard, as if declining to claim fellowship with the great family of man, and wishing (in the affecting language of Mr. Wordsworth)

Humbly to express
A penitential loneliness.

It is well, upon the whole, and for the interest of us all, that it should be so: nor would I willingly in my own person manifest a disregard of such salutary feelings, nor in act or word do anything to weaken them; but, on the one hand, as my self-accusation does not amount to a confession of guilt, so, on the other, it is possible that, if it did, the benefit resulting to others from the record of an experience purchased at so heavy a price might compensate, by a vast overbalance, for any violence done to the feelings I have noticed, and justify a breach of the general rule.

Extract from Confessions of an English Opium Eater *by Thomas de Quincey (published in 1820)*

Sample question and model answer
(continued)

This is a competent response that has taken into account the methods that both writers have used to position themselves and their audience. There is plenty of close reference to the text in a variety of modes, and there is a sustained comparison throughout. This work would achieve a high grade.

The genre is identified.

A clear and close comparison is made, and a discourse level.

Semantic differences are noted, compared and commented on.

Author positioning is compared.

The lexis is discussed.

Reader positioning is compared.

Social and cultural context is commented on. Varieties of English are noted.

Grammar and punctuation are discussed, including the choice of pronouns.

The sentence structure is analysed.

The overall purpose is identified.

The theoretical perspective is covered well.

Model answer

Both authors are presenting confessions, and they are both aware that the pictures that they are about to present of their own behaviour might be less than flattering. The writers pursue similar strategies to disarm the reader's criticism, firstly by claiming honesty - De Quincey is not a `demirep´ or `swindler´, and Brand says `it's all true´ and then admits shame. Brand is `not proud´ of everything in his book and De Quincey is very clear about his feelings of `guilt and misery´.

The two strategies differ in what they promise the reader. Brand offers a `wild ride through language, hedonism and amusing despair´. De Quincey - after reassuring readers that they are not in for a pack of lies or French style `gratuitous self-humiliation´ - offers to let his readers learn from the exposure of his `moral ulcers or scars´. Brand uses the language of fairgrounds, or possibly white-water rafting, to indicate that his narrative will be frightening, but fun. De Quincey compares his confession to a sort of medical examination that might make you feel sick, but that will do you good in the long run

So we can see that both authors are positioning themselves as outsiders. Brand does this at a lexical level by giving his book a childish title. He admits that the title is childish, but persists in using it as a sort of distinguishing mark of his eccentricity in the body of the introduction. Most of Brand's lexis is, however, sophisticated, and at a reasonably high register, containing words like `scenario´, `macabre´ and `hedonism´. De Quincey takes the feeling of being an outsider to extreme lengths, even suggesting that he will be buried in a separate part of the cemetery from normal human beings. This is far more macabre than anything Brand mentions. For Brand, being an outsider is `sexy´ and `adventurous´, whilst for De Quincey it is lonely and melancholic.

Both authors flatter their readers by making assumptions about them. Brand's ideal reader is a risk taker and not naïve or small minded. De Quincey's average reader is a `courteous´ Englishman who is normally revolted by confessions that put aside the veil of decency. He is only going to do so on this occasion because De Quincey assures him that he will learn something.

Oddly, both authors make use of their Englishness. De Quincey equates Englishness with manliness (or at least not being French and self-indulgent), and Brand clearly thinks that the sort of American who would pick up his book would associate Englishness with wackiness and eccentricity. Helpfully, Brand follows two English words for mad - `bonkers or crackers´ - with two American terms - `nuts or weird´.

De Quincey's text is almost 200 years old, and is fairly typical of literary writing of the period. There are many long and complex sentences, with a sophisticated use of subordinated clauses. His punctuation is light. De Quincey seems to be aiming for an informal tone, with his use of italics for emphasis and in the small conversational asides he makes. He also attempts to draw the reader in by using `our´ to refer to the English in general.

Brand uses much shorter sentences, and even numbered lists to make himself clear. At times he uses heavy punctuation for emphasis, for instance `as I, myself, have stolen many books´. He is playful in his use of language, using long lists at one point and even a balanced period (`understand why I wrote it´ rather than `understand what I have written´) at the end. He uses clichéd English markers at the beginning (`Jolly well done´) and in his sign off (`ta ta´). Generally speaking, Brand uses far more consciously clever devices than De Quincey, who is striving for an informal, conversational tone.

Both writers attempt to make their readers feel indulgent towards them by constructing a sympathetic persona. In terms of Brown and Levinson's politeness theory, they are trying to maintain positive face in a potentially negative face situation. They both admit to being bad, but they both suggest that the reader will get something other than mere voyeuristic pleasure from continuing to read their texts. The greatest difference between the two texts is time. De Quincey and Brand are clearly two intelligent men with sorry tales to tell. The shift in registers, and the change in formal tone that has taken place between the writing of the two texts, accounts for many of their differences.

Exam practice questions

Read texts A and B and answer the following question.

Analyse and compare the ways in which each writer presents themselves.

In your response you should include reference to any relevant theories and research.

Text A is an extract from *Bleak House* by Charles Dickens. It is the beginning of the narration of the novel by the character Esther Summerson. Other parts of the novel have a third person narrator. Bleak House was published in 1853. **(50)**

Text A

I have a great deal of difficulty in beginning to write my portion of these pages, for I know I am not clever. I always knew that. I can remember, when I was a very little girl indeed, I used to say to my doll when we were alone together, "Now, Dolly, I am not clever, you know very well, and you must be patient with me, like a dear!" And so she used to sit propped up in a great arm-chair, with her beautiful complexion and rosy lips, staring at me—or not so much at me, I think, as at nothing—while I busily stitched away and told her every one of my secrets.

My dear old doll! I was such a shy little thing that I seldom dared to open my lips, and never dared to open my heart, to anybody else. It almost makes me cry to think what a relief it used to be to me when I came home from school of a day to run upstairs to my room and say, "Oh, you dear faithful Dolly, I knew you would be expecting me!" and then to sit down on the floor, leaning on the elbow of her great chair, and tell her all I had noticed since we parted. I had always rather a noticing way—not a quick way, oh, no!—a silent way of noticing what passed before me and thinking I should like to understand it better. I have not by any means a quick understanding. When I love a person very tenderly indeed, it seems to brighten. But even that may be my vanity.

I was brought up, from my earliest remembrance – like some of the princesses in the fairy stories, only I was not charming – by my godmother. At least, I only knew her as such. She was a good, good woman! She went to church three times every Sunday, and to morning prayers on Wednesdays and Fridays, and to lectures whenever there were lectures; and never missed. She was handsome; and if she had ever smiled, would have been (I used to think) like an angel—but she never smiled. She was always grave and strict. She was so very good herself, I thought, that the badness of other people made her frown all her life. I felt so different from her, even making every allowance for the differences between a child and a woman; I felt so poor, so trifling, and so far off that I never could be unrestrained with her—no, could never even love her as I wished. It made me very sorry to consider how good she was and how unworthy of her I was, and I used ardently to hope that I might have a better heart; and I talked it over very often with the dear old doll, but I never loved my godmother as I ought to have loved her and as I felt I must have loved her if I had been a better girl.

Exam practice question (continued)

Text B is based on personal accounts from a web-based dating service in 2010.

Text B

Why should you get to know Phoenix26?

I am warm, down to earth and have a dry sense of humour. I love a good intellectual debate, not to say argument, and I love to be with people who see the world in new and interesting ways. I am intelligent and confident, outgoing and friendly, and have a varied social life.

I like to keep fit but I'm not a fanatic. I am a member of a gym and have done a few fun runs, but I won't be signing up for a marathon anytime soon. I bike to work and I like hill walking when I can get away from the city. I like meeting new people, keeping up with old friends and going out for drinks, or for meals, or for movies, or just hanging out in the park on a nice day. I would like to get to the theatre more often, but I draw the line at ballet and opera.

I've travelled a little, having lived in China for a year and Australia for two, as well as the usual jaunts around Europe. I'd love to do more of this with someone who likes getting to know local culture, as much as exploring beaches, mountains and monuments.

Here is how she describes her ideal match:
Someone who's confident, intelligent, honest and has a good sense of humour. They should be able to laugh at themselves and not care too much about winning or losing in games or arguments.

5 Language production

The following topics are covered in this chapter:

- Types of original writing
- Researching your written task
- Planning a written task
- Writing commentary

5.1 Types of original writing

LEARNING SUMMARY

After studying this section, you should be able to:

- describe the original writing task you will be undertaking
- understand your coursework requirements
- start developing ideas on audience, format and purpose

Your own writing

AQA **A P2** OCR **P2**
AQA **B P2** WJEC **P2**
Edexcel **P2**

As part of your AS course, you will have the opportunity to produce your own writing and reflect on it in some way. In some courses you will be writing parts of novels and short stories; in some you will be writing to instruct or explain; and in others you may be producing a multimodal text, or adapting a text from one genre to another.

Whatever task you are involved in, there are certain basic principles that you will need to consider and be able to comment on:

- **Who you are** – that is, how will you position yourself with regards to your audience?
- **Who your audience is and what your attitude to them is.**
- **What genre you are writing in** – is it a film script or an instruction leaflet? What is its format?
- **The purpose of your writing** – is it to inform, to entertain, to persuade? Or all of these?

In your commentary, you will need to:

- reflect on the writing process, and in some cases provide evidence of the process itself
- use your knowledge of mode, lexis, grammar, and other stylistic features, to accurately describe your writing and its achievements.

What you will write

Please read this information if you are studying the **AQA A** specification.

For the **AQA A** specification, your writing can be in any literary or non-literary genre other than an academic essay. It should look at or question the particular way in which a social group, individual, event or institution is represented. You also have to specify a clear audience, purpose and place of publication.

Your 600-word text should be accompanied by a 400-word commentary, which gives reasons for choosing the representation, and explains how your aims have been achieved.

Please read this information if you are studying the **AQA B** specification.

The **AQA B** specification requires two pieces of original writing for two different audiences, purposes and genres.

Examples of purposes and formats include:
- **writing to entertain** – e.g. a soap opera script, autobiography, dramatic monologue
- **writing to persuade** – e.g. an editorial, a speech delivered as a football captain
- **writing to inform** – e.g. travel journalism, health leaflet, maintenance manual
- **writing to advise** – e.g. text on choosing a university, guide to texting for novices.

Two commentaries are required that examine the writing process and analyse the success of the two pieces.

The writing should be between 1500 and 2500 words, and the two commentaries should total 1000 words.

Please read this information if you are studying the **Edexcel** specification.

For the **Edexcel** specification, you are asked to produce two pieces – one for a reading audience and one for a listening audience. Both pieces must be accompanied by commentaries.

For the **reading audience**, you can complete a **journalism interview**. This should be based on an actual transcribed interview and written up in a way that consciously shapes the readers' response. The commentary should explain what techniques you used to convey desired effects. Alternatively, you can compose **narrative writing**. This should be based on audience research, a recording of the story, and at least two written drafts that experiment with different narrative techniques. The assessment will be of the final version of the narrative and the commentary explaining the techniques you used to convey desired effects.

For **listening audiences**, you can produce a **scripted presentation on a topical issue in language already introduced in the course**. Work should be based on audience research and a study of various live and recorded spoken presentations. Assessment is based on the full script of the presentation, any presentational aids or handouts used, and a technical commentary. Alternatively, you can write and present a **dramatic monologue** based on audience research and pragmatic theories about implied meaning. Assessment consists of the monologue and commentary.

The reading audience task should be between 1000 and 1500 words long, and the listening audience task from 500 to 1000 words.

Please read this information if you are studying the **OCR** specification.

Coursework for the **OCR** specification consists of two tasks.

The first task is a **text study**, in which you write an analytical essay on two chosen texts – one written and one multimodal. Your analysis should show awareness of audience and purpose, and social and cultural context, and deal with the texts' meaning and their phonological, lexical, morphological and grammatical features.

The second task, **adaptive writing and commentary**, allows you to choose the texts from the first task and adapt them for a different audience and/or purpose. The adapted texts can be spoken, written or multimodal – that is, in the same format as, or different to, the original texts. The commentary should discuss the choices you made, and demonstrate appropriate subject knowledge.

Your choice of **written texts** might include:

- poetry
- prose
- fiction
- drama
- tabloid and broadsheet journalism
- travel writing
- biography

- advertising material
- music or film reviews
- magazine articles
- leaflets
- letters
- diaries.

Your choice of **multimodal texts** might include:

- TV presentations
- illustrated books
- films
- music videos

- cartoons
- illustrated talks
- computer games
- web-based texts.

The total word count for both tasks is 3000 words.

Please read this information if you are studying the **WJEC** specification.

For the **WJEC** specification, you are asked to complete an original writing task and explore spoken language.

For the first task, you complete one long piece of creative, original writing, which is in a fictional, literary mode. You cannot submit poetry, or any writing that is simply informative, factual, or vaguely descriptive.

Examples of suitable texts are:
- a short story
- a novel extract (e.g. the opening or concluding chapter)
- an extract from a piece of genre fiction (e.g. romance, crime, horror, science-fiction, detective, fantasy, etc.)
- a dramatic monologue
- a play script for stage, radio, or TV
- a satire or parody.

The original writing should be approximately 1000 words and it should be accompanied by a commentary of about 500 to 750 words.

The second task focuses on spoken language of the media, in terms of variations in language according to mode and critical listening.

You can choose to discuss:
- spoken commentaries
- interviews
- chat shows
- TV or radio advertisements
- film dialogue

- reporting
- soap operas
- stand-up comics
- phone-ins
- voice-overs.

You are required to write an analytical study and discussion of your area of investigation of about 1500 words, and you will also need to make a transcript of the speech you have studied.

> **KEY POINT**
>
> Even in the research stage, you should be thinking about your final commentary. Cut and paste ideas you like into a clippings file, or use a research tool like Microsoft OneNote to organise your ideas.

> **PROGRESS CHECK**
>
> 1 In what part of your coursework will you need to reflect on the writing process?
> 2 Why should you keep track of your research?
>
> 1. The commentary.
> 2. In your commentary, it will help explain how your ideas developed over time, and you will need to reference the sources of your research in the bibliography.

5.2 Getting started

LEARNING SUMMARY	**After studying this section, you should be able to:**
	• better understand what writing tasks involve
	• reflect on different aspects of the writing process
	• further develop ideas for your own writing task

Preparing to find your voice

AQA **A P2** OCR **P2**
AQA **B P2** WJEC **P2**
Edexcel **P2**

Before you can begin to write in a particular way, you need to have read extensively. If you are planning to write a speech or carry out an interview, you need to watch and listen to as many examples of the genre as you can. In carrying out your research, you will need to split your attention between, for instance, the content of the novel or the speech you are focusing on, and the techniques that are used to create them. Ask yourself what your favourite comedy sketch or newspaper article is, and then try to break down the elements that make it stand out from all the rest.

Once you have absorbed enough of your chosen type of text, you will be in a position to plan your own. In this section, we will look at a number of approaches to speaking and writing tasks.

Biographical writing

AQA **A P2** OCR **P2**
AQA **B P2** WJEC **P2**
Edexcel **P2**

Establishing yourself in a piece of writing can be difficult to achieve. In biographical writing, there is a tendency to allow stories to progress from beginning to end without a great deal of shape. As the article on the next page shows, choosing a theme is often a good idea.

Thematic approach

The theme of lack of cheerfulness is presented immediately in the headline and strapline.

There is a dramatic use of quotation at the start of the article, and a well-known situation to establish the scene.

The focus shifts to the writer's inner life.

The writer uses a second example and makes a pop cultural reference.

There is a play on words to do with the theme.

The writer compares herself with others. She uses a short sentence to define the problem.

A quotation is used to provide evidence and other people's perspectives.

The writer returns to the theme.

Cheer up, it might never happen

Growing up with a naturally scowling face is even less fun than it looks, says **Lotte Jeffs**

Hollered from scaffolding platforms across town, the builder's favourite catchphrase "Cheer up love, it might never happen" has been the soundtrack to my adult life. For years I've obsessed over what my witty comeback should be, and still I never manage to think of anything quite in time to retaliate with acerbic nonchalance, before flashing a winning grin and striding away. Instead the furrows on my brow deepen and the corners of my mouth droop as I scurry off, cursing my thin lips and natural pallor.

Even as a baby I had trouble cracking a smile – a mangy Snoopy puppet was the only thing that would stop me scowling. As I got older, I cultivated the sullen features of Wednesday from the Addams Family. Then Goth got cool, and I was laughing – except I wasn't. Only on the inside, anyway.

I've never suffered a prolonged malaise. Even when my teenage peers were busy slamming doors and painting their bedrooms black, my biggest angst was that I might be anaemic. I just find it hard to grin at will. My neutral facial expression, thanks in the most part to the turned-down mouth I inherited from my grandmother, has been described by those close to me as at best "intense" and at worst "a little threatening". But no matter how hard I try, unless I'm particularly happy or amused by something specific, smiling doesn't come easy.

Extract from 'Cheer up, it might never happen' by Lotte Jeffs, guardian.co.uk

In the short space that you have available to you for your coursework, positioning yourself and establishing your credentials as a writer will be very important. The example above is a **confessional** style, in which the writer tells something of herself in order to establish the trust of the audience. Rather than tell one story, however, small details such as encounters on the street, a favourite toy, and conversations with relatives and friends, are all used to build up a **thematic picture**.

The lexis chosen is also important in establishing character. In this extract, phrases such as 'acerbic nonchalance' and 'prolonged malaise' show that the writer has an extensive vocabulary, but any hint of pretentiousness is undermined by playfulness, as shown in the following example.

> Then Goth got cool, and I was laughing – except I wasn't. Only on the inside, anyway.

The simple monosyllables at the beginning set up the word play on the colloquial use of the word 'laughing' to mean 'in a good position'. This is followed by an instant contradiction of the surface meaning, and further play on cultural attitudes to laughing – or crying – on the inside.

> **KEY POINT**
>
> When writing a commentary you should always be clear about **why** a device or technique is used. It is not enough just to list it.

Interiors and exteriors

A different approach to biographical writing is revealed in the following text, which relates a single incident.

The opening is in a journalistic style – who, where, what, when.	
More details and reported dialogue rather than direct speech.	
An aside about language.	
Concrete details and minimal dialogue, followed by authorial comment.	
Moving forward in time – this is a significant event – also note the socio-linguistic comment.	
Confessional details about attitudes at that time.	
Detailed direct speech dialogue giving the episode an immediate feel.	

I met Simon Goldman in 1960 when I was 16 and he was – he said – 27, but was probably in his late 30s. I was waiting for a bus home to Twickenham after a rehearsal at Richmond Little Theatre, when a sleek maroon car drew up and a man with a big cigar in his mouth leant over to the passenger window and said, "Want a lift?" Of course my parents had told me, my teachers had told me, everyone had told me, never to accept lifts from strange men, but at that stage he didn't seem strange, and I hopped in. I liked the smell of his cigar and the leather seats. He asked where I wanted to go and I said Clifden Road, and he said fine. I told him I had never seen a car like this before, and he said it was a Bristol, and very few were made. He told me lots of facts about Bristols as we cruised – Bristols always cruised – towards Twickenham. He had a funny accent – later, when I knew him better, I realised it was the accent he used for posh – but I asked if he was foreign. He said: "Only if you count Jews as foreign." Well of course I did. I had never consciously met a Jew; I didn't think we had them at my school. But I said politely: "Are you Jewish? I never would have guessed." (I meant he didn't have the hooked nose, the greasy ringlets, the straggly beard of Shylock in the school play.) He said he had lived in Israel when he was "your age". I wondered what he thought my age was: I hoped he thought 19. But then when he said, "Fancy a coffee?" I foolishly answered, "No – my father will kill me if I'm late." "School tomorrow?" he asked, and, speechless with mortification, I could only nod. So then he drove me to my house, and asked: "Can I take you out for coffee another evening?"

Extract from 'My harsh lesson in love and life' by Lynn Barber

This piece of biographical writing recounts a single episode in great detail, and with one exception, maintains a single time line. It packs in a great deal of detail, and the fact that so much has been remembered is in itself a comment on the significance of the event for the author.

There is a good mixture of detailed physical description and authorial comment. The foolishness of accepting a lift from a stranger, the author's responses to the car and the driver's cigar, and reflections for modern readers on the author's 1960s attitude to Jews are integrated within a simple **chronological** framework. The significance of the chance meeting is announced in the opening sentence, and we are explicitly told that Lynn Barber would get to know Simon Goldman better about half-way through the extract.

The language used is straightforward, using colloquialisms like 'hopped in' and 'funny accent', and there is even some self-consciousness about choosing the word 'cruised'. Elsewhere, words like 'sleek' and 'mortification' reveal an extensive and precise vocabulary.

The scene described by Lynn Barber later became part of the film *An Education*. The script for this was written by the novelist, Nick Hornby.

> The rain is used to express the oppressive and dreary aspects of Jenny's life – David represents escape.

> These aspects will inform the choice of actor and will be fully realised in period detail.

> Another example of domestic tedium.

> Jenny is seen from the exterior – the audience can see what David likes about her.

> These were Lynn Barber's reflections – they are given to David to make him seem mature and worldly.

> This is a long way from 'hopped in'. The scene establishes that David is charming, and that Jenny is cautious and not stupid – via her actions rather than her thoughts.

6   EXT. BUS STOP. DAY

The rain has begun. Jenny attempts to cover herself. A mother and two children cross the road in front of her, and a beautiful, sleek red sports car – a Bristol – stops to let them across. David, possibly in his mid-thirties, dapper, and almost but not quite handsome, is driving the car. David, distracted, impatient, spots Jenny at the bus stop.

In front of the car a small wellington boot drops off the foot of one of the children, further slowing down their painfully slow progress across the road.

Jenny is wet. David makes eye contact. Jenny smiles ruefully, and enchantingly. David sighs, and then hesitates for a moment. The window of the Bristol slowly rolls down.

           DAVID
  Hello.

Jenny ignores him.

           DAVID
  Listen. If you've got any sense,
  you wouldn't take a lift from a
  strange man.

Jenny smiles thinly.

           DAVID
  I am, however, a music lover, and
  I'm worried about your cello. So
  what I propose is, you put it in
  the car and walk alongside me.

           JENNY
  How do I know you won't just
  drive off with the cello?

           DAVID
  Ah. Good point.

He winds down the other window and waves on the cars that have stopped behind him.

           DAVID
  How much does a new cello cost?
  Twenty pounds? Thirty? I don't
  know. Let's say thirty.

> Along with the car, this establishes David's wealth. £30 would have been over a month's wages in this period.

He pulls out a wallet, takes out three ten-pound notes, hands them to her.

> DAVID
> There. Security.

Jenny laughs and waves the money away.

7   EXT. STREET. NEAR SCHOOL. DAY.

Later. The cello is in the back seat of the Bristol. Jenny is trotting alongside the car, while David leans nonchalantly across the passenger seat to talk to her while driving.

> DAVID
> I'm David, by the way.

She says nothing.

> DAVID
> And you are...?

> JENNY
> Jenny. (Beat) I've never seen a
> car like this before. C'est tres chic.

> Jenny attempts to use language to show her own sophistication.

> DAVID
> It's a Bristol. Not many of 'em made.

Jenny nods, but doesn't know how to respond.

> DAVID
> How did the concert go?

> JENNY
> It was a rehearsal. The concert's
> next Thursday.

> DAVID
> What are you playing?

> JENNY
>   (making a face)
> Elgar.

> David's comments on Elgar show that he too has some sophistication beyond money and cars.

> DAVID
> Ah, Elgar. I often think it's a
> shame he spent so much time in
> Worcester, don't you? Worcester's
> too near Birmingham. And you can
> hear that in the music. There's a
> horrible Brummy accent in there,
> if you listen hard enough.

Jenny looks at him and smiles. She hadn't expected him to be able to make Elgar jokes.

> The 'Jewish' theme is only touched on in this scene, but discomfort about it is established.

DAVID

Anyway, I'm not sure Elgar and
Jews mix very well.

JENNY

I'm not a Jew!

DAVID

(smiling)
No. I am. I wasn't...*accusing*
you.

JENNY

Oh. (She smiles awkwardly.) Can I
sit in the car with my cello?

David stops the car.

DAVID

Jump in.

8   INT. CAR. DAY

> Jenny's approval will have to be demonstrated by the actress playing her, rather than relayed as a simple authorial comment.

Jenny shuts the door and sinks approvingly into the white
leather seat. David regards the dripping girl with amusement.

JENNY

It's even nicer on the inside.

DAVID

Where to, madam?

> In this scene David does not have a cigar in his mouth. Would this have made his lines more difficult to deliver?

Jenny makes a face.

JENNY

I only live round the corner.

DAVID

What a shame. We'll just make it
last as long as we can.

Extract from An Education by Nick Hornby, adapted from the article

Extract from An Education *by Nick Hornby, adapted from the article 'An Education'*
by Lynn Barber

The changes between biographical script and screenplay are indicative of the strengths and weaknesses of the two media. Autobiographical writing can move smoothly from inner thoughts to events, whereas film has to express inner thoughts through exterior details.

Written scripts – even ones by Shakespeare – are always partial documents, in that they are not meant to be finished statements, more a set of recommendations to the actors and director who will produce the film or play.

Some film scripts contain elaborate details of the kinds of shots that may be needed, but Nick Hornby's script confines itself to physical detail and dialogue. In the dialogue, more is said than in Lynn Barber's original piece – partly because of the need to dramatise Jenny's initial reluctance. This may reflect the fact that 'stranger danger' advice is much more emphatic than it was in the 1960s, and a modern audience might judge her harshly for hopping into a strange man's car.

The level of language in the screenplay is more colloquial than in the biographical piece, and so sophistication of taste has to be demonstrated in explicit conversations about the classical musician Elgar.

Playing with genre conventions

AQA **A P2** OCR **P2**
AQA **B P2** WJEC **P2**
Edexcel **P2**

The following extract is from a short piece of **humorous writing**.

This assumes that readers will have had a similar maths education.

The author re-casts maths problems as short stories.

If they are short stories, what other genre conventions – plot, character and so on – do they obey?

Examples of the genre.

How the genre has developed in terms of plot detail.

Genre language conventions are quoted.

Typical plots and typical character interactions are delineated.

A style point – there is a short, emphatic sentence after a long list.

THE HUMAN ELEMENT IN MATHEMATICS

The student of arithmetic who has mastered the first four rules of his art, and successfully striven with money sums and fractions, finds himself confronted by an unbroken expanse of questions known as problems. These are short stories of adventure and industry with the end omitted, and though betraying a strong family resemblance, are not without a certain element of romance.

The characters in the plot of a problem are three people called A, B, and C. The form of the question is generally of this sort:

"A, B, and C do a certain piece of work. A can do as much work in one hour as B in two, or C in four. Find how long they work at it."

Or thus:

"A, B, and C are employed to dig a ditch. A can dig as much in one hour as B can dig in two, and B can dig twice as fast as C. Find how long, etc. etc."

Or after this wise:

"A lays a wager that he can walk faster than B or C. A can walk half as fast again as B, and C is only an indifferent walker. Find how far, and so forth."

The occupations of A, B, and C are many and varied. In the older arithmetics they contented themselves with doing "a certain piece of work." This statement of the case however, was found too sly and mysterious, or possibly lacking in romantic charm. It became the fashion to define the job more clearly and to set them at walking matches, ditch-digging, regattas, and piling cord wood. At times, they became commercial and entered into partnership, having with their old mystery a "certain" capital. Above all they revel in motion. When they tire of walking-matches – A rides on horseback, or borrows a bicycle and competes with his weaker-minded associates on foot. Now they race on locomotives; now they row; or again they become historical and engage stage-coaches; or at times they are aquatic and swim. If their occupation is actual work they prefer to pump water into cisterns, two of which leak through holes in the bottom and one of which is water-tight. A, of course, has the good one; he also takes the bicycle, and the best locomotive, and the right of swimming with the current. Whatever they do they put money on it, being all three sports. A always wins.

> Note the genre naming conventions – younger children are given familiar names; older ones 'Christian' names.

> This establishes the author's credentials as an expert.

> This establishes sympathy for A, B and C.

> This is a reminder of A's role in mathematical problems.

> This is an extrapolation of the results of A, B and C's actions.

> The language of mathematics is turned into a character judgement.

In the early chapters of the arithmetic, their identity is concealed under the names John, William, and Henry, and they wrangle over the division of marbles. In algebra they are often called X, Y, Z. But these are only their Christian names, and they are really the same people.

Now to one who has followed the history of these men through countless pages of problems, watched them in their leisure hours dallying with cord wood, and seen their panting sides heave in the full frenzy of filling a cistern with a leak in it, they become something more than mere symbols. They appear as creatures of flesh and blood, living men with their own passions, ambitions, and aspirations like the rest of us. Let us view them in turn. A is a full-blooded blustering fellow, of energetic temperament, hot-headed and strong-willed. It is he who proposes everything, challenges B to work, makes the bets, and bends the others to his will. He is a man of great physical strength and phenomenal endurance. He has been known to walk forty-eight hours at a stretch, and to pump ninety-six. His life is arduous and full of peril. A mistake in the working of a sum may keep him digging a fortnight without sleep. A repeating decimal in the answer might kill him.

B is a quiet, easy-going fellow, afraid of A and bullied by him, but very gentle and brotherly to little C, the weakling. He is quite in A's power, having lost all his money in bets.

Poor C is an undersized, frail man, with a plaintive face. Constant walking, digging, and pumping has broken his health and ruined his nervous system. His joyless life has driven him to drink and smoke more than is good for him, and his hand often shakes as he digs ditches. He has not the strength to work as the others can, in fact, as Hamlin Smith has said, "A can do more work in one hour than C in four."

Extract from A, B and C, The Human element in mathematics, by Stephen Leacock, published in the collection Literary lapses (1910).

This piece of writing establishes a set of genre conventions in an inappropriate context for humorous effect.

This is quite a common technique in humorous writing. Other examples include:
- the Armstrong and Miller sketches, where RAF officers use street slang
- Ali G using street slang to interview 'serious' subjects
- the Newman and Baddiel sketches, where historians use 'your mum' insults
- Monty Python's philosophy department/sheep farm sketches.

In the above extract, the chosen 'genre' is mathematical problems, which the author treats as human dramas rather than ways of making calculations relevant to the real world.

There is humour in the disparity between the source material and Leacock's interpretation of it, and, by treating the source problems as if they were stories of real human endeavours, the absurdity of the mathematical world of calculation is revealed.

Choosing words carefully

AQA   **A P2**   OCR   **P2**
AQA   **B P2**   WJEC   **P2**
Edexcel **P2**

Below is the transcript of part of a news briefing given by the then Secretary of Defense, Donald Rumsfeld, in the run-up to the invasion of Iraq.

> **'This building' means the Pentagon – an example of metonymy.**
>
> **'Jumping on' is a euphemism for starting a war with.**

DoD News briefing – Secretary Rumsfeld and Gen. Myers

Rumsfeld: This building has always been attentive, for at least more than a decade now, 10, 12 years, to Iraq. We've had Northern no-fly zones and Southern no-fly zones; been flying flights there attempting to contain that country and prevent them from jumping on one of their neighbours.

Yes?

Q: Could I follow up, Mr. Secretary, on what you just said, please? In regard to Iraq weapons of mass destruction and terrorists, is there any evidence to indicate that Iraq has attempted to or is willing to supply terrorists with weapons of mass destruction? Because there are reports that there is no evidence of a direct link between Baghdad and some of these terrorist organizations.

> **Weapons of mass destruction is the standard formula meaning nuclear and chemical arms.**
>
> **'Reports that there is no evidence...' – has someone proved a negative?**

Rumsfeld: Reports that say that something hasn't happened are always interesting to me, because as we know, there are known knowns; there are things we know we know. We also know there are known unknowns; that is to say we know there are some things we do not know. But there are also unknown unknowns – the ones we don't know we don't know. And if one looks throughout the history of our country and other free countries, it is the latter category that tend to be the difficult ones.

> **Rumsfeld outlines types of knowledge – it is possible that weapons of mass destruction count as 'unknown unknowns'.**
>
> **Rumsfeld reinforces the point about the impossibility of certainty, and criticises people who are certain.**

And so people who have the omniscience that they can say with high certainty that something has not happened or is not being tried, have capabilities that are – what was the word you used, Pam, earlier?

Q: Free associate? (laughs)

Rumsfeld: Yeah. They can – (chuckles) – they can do things I can't do. (laughter)

Q: Excuse me. But is this an unknown unknown?

Rumsfeld: I'm not –

Q: Because you said several unknowns, and I'm just wondering if this is an unknown unknown.

Rumsfeld: I'm not going to say which it is.

Q: Mr. Secretary, if you believe something –

> **He assumes humility by saying that he cannot know, whereas others claim they can.**
>
> **The journalist challenges his agnosticism.**
>
> **The journalist accuses him of knowing, but not saying.**

Extract from a Department of Defense News Briefing, presented by Donald H. Rumsfeld, February 12, 2002

In the real world, it is always difficult to tell what people really mean, and we cannot always interpret what is said by reading between the lines.

In this interview, the Secretary of Defense is scrupulously honest about his level of knowledge. He does not claim to know that the Iraqis have weapons of mass destruction (WMDs), but on the other hand he is careful to keep open the idea that they might have them, but that he and his allies might not actually know about them at the time of the interview.

At the core of Mr Rumsfeld's strategy is the impossibility of proving a negative – there is no evidence for WMDs, but they might still exist. Cleverly, Mr Rumsfeld positions himself as more intellectually honest than those people who have the 'omniscience' to know that there definitely are no WMDs. The word 'omniscience' is usually only applied to God in Christian countries, and so Mr Rumsfeld also implies a certain lack of piety in his critics.

This is how a journalist in favour of invading Iraq might report this briefing.

> **Rumsfeld tight-lipped about WMDs**
> Donald Rumsfeld today admitted that there was, as yet, no positive evidence of Iraqi weapons of mass destruction, but he remained tight-lipped about the possibility of their existence. He also reminded today's press conference of Iraq's aggression toward its neighbours over the past twelve years.

An anti-war journalist might choose a different approach.

> **Rumsfeld admits complete ignorance on WMDs**
> Donald Rumsfeld today admitted that he had no knowledge of the existence of weapons of mass destruction in Iraq. He stated that even though Iraq had been the subject of constant attention by the United States for at least the last twelve years, there was currently no knowledge of weapons of mass destruction. If there were any, he admitted, he didn't know about them, as they were 'unknown unknowns'.

The first account uses 'Iraq's aggression' to subtly suggest that the weapons do exist, whilst the second account uses the idea that WMDs are unlikely, because they have not been found in Iraq despite 'constant attention' by the United States for at least twelve years. In the pro-war article, the words 'as yet' suggest that evidence is on its way.

Expressing opinions

AQA **A P2**   OCR **P2**
AQA **B P2**   WJEC **P2**
Edexcel **P2**

The article below relates to news that the latest editions of Enid Blyton's 'Famous Five' books are to have their language updated.

The headline reflects the old-fashioned language of the books.

The strapline shifts from an outdated idiom to a modern one.

This establishes the author's credentials as an 'expert'.

The quotations and examples are presumably from a publisher's press release.

I say, chaps, the queerest thing has happened...

The jolly old Famous Five are to have their language, like, updated, yeah?

As the Guardian's special (albeit self-appointed) Enid Blyton correspondent, it falls to me to break the latest news. Publisher Hodder Children's Books has announced that the Famous Five adventures are to have their language "subtly" updated so it does not alienate today's children. Thus in the books being reissued next month, "mother and father" become "mum and dad", "school tunic" becomes "school uniform" and, "She must be jolly lonely all by herself" reads, "She must get lonely all by herself."

Obviously the heart cries out against it. Obviously the head swiftly follows with the thought that if a child reader cannot discern the meaning of "school tunic" from its context, said child reader shouldn't be left unsupervised on the sofa with a book anyway, lest it accidentally suffocate itself in the cushions or blind itself with its own thumbs.

...

... [Enid Blyton] survives because she serves perfectly the purely narrative appetite of a child that precedes more sophisticated tastes – and which must be stimulated and satisfied if those tastes are ever to develop. If the increasing gap between her written and our modern idiom is denying children this, perhaps changes are needed.

But against this possible benefit must be weighed the possible losses. First, a constant updating of books decreases the opportunities for making those little intellectual leaps that make reading both fun and valuable. If "straw boaters" had been replaced by "hats" or excised entirely in Dorita Fairlie Bruce's Dimsie adventures, I probably still wouldn't know what they were. I remember the rush of triumph when I worked out what "colours" were in Antonia Forest's Autumn Term (a kind of sporting award), although it took me most of the book and the end-of-term prize-giving scene to be sure.

Second, such changes collapse time and remove all sense of history. Hodder say the changes will make the books "timeless" rather than modern. But placement in time is important. As a child you naturally believe that the world around you is immutable. Thus it was, is now and shall be ever more. A gradual realisation that people once spoke, dressed and even thought differently from the way we do is a profound pleasure. "Queer" once primarily meant "odd". How weird. A tunic and a boater comprised a uniform. One day, of course, our children will be asking, "What's a uniform?" and we will have to revise again. "The honour of the school" was once a real and motivating force. I remember asking a teacher about the last one. She gazed at me with such sadness that I wished I had one of those handkerchief things I'd also read about. It struck me they would have been as good for mopping tears as they were for binding gorse-wrenched ankles during cliff-top rescues.

Without a sense of time, the integrity of the book begins to break down. More changes will soon be needed to make sense of "mums and dads" who let their children roam free on Kirrin Island. Of girls who "get lonely" because they are forced to stay behind and make bracken beds and tea for the boys. Root out "jolly" and you have to root out all these oddities – and the gorse bushes, too. When did you last see one of them? And then you'll be left with an awfully queer set of books indeed.

Extract from 'I say, chaps, the queerest thing has happened' by Lucy Mangan, guardian.co.uk

---

'Obviously' assumes that the reader agrees with the writer.

There is a comic use of bureaucratic health and safety language.

Mangan argues that Enid Blyton has a specific role in the development of children's reading.

She agrees with the changes if they allow Blyton to fulfil children's 'narrative appetite'.

Mangan disagrees with the changes because they will stop readers making intuitive leaps and connections.

She backs up this point with personal experiences.

She also disagrees with the publisher's aim to take the books out of their social and historical contexts.

Mangan discusses the pleasures of making linguistic discoveries whilst reading.

She makes the final point that this sort of 'tinkering' will be endless, and she illustrates language change over time from her personal experience.

Mangan emphasises the importance of a sense of time, and the need to see that the lives of children – and their expectations – change.

To finish the article, Mangan uses lexis that is typical of Enid Blyton.

This article is written to persuade. One technique it uses is the establishment of a rapport with the reader. Lucy Mangan provides some confessional details about her own reading experiences and assumes that the reader will find her point of view 'obvious'. She also establishes herself as an expert on the topic, and backs up her points in ways that show that she has an extensive grasp of the subject matter.

The core value expressed is enthusiasm for reading, and the importance of making a child's reading experience as rich as possible. The validity of the publisher's aim to make the books accessible is admitted, but the rest of the argument is that accessibility and ease of use are not the only positives that can be derived from reading Enid Blyton.

The publisher is underestimating the abilities of children to make sense of fictional worlds. Enid Blyton satisfies children's desire for narrative, but in reading her works in their original language they will also make interesting discoveries about the behaviour and language of previous generations. Particularly at the beginning and end of the article, Mangan plays around with the lexis that will be lost in the new editions.

> **KEY POINT**
>
> Some writers are very conscious and deliberate in their approaches – others write by 'feel'. If you belong to the latter group, leave your work for a while after you have written it so that you can approach your commentary with a fresh perspective.

> **PROGRESS CHECK**
>
> 1. Name two ways of organising biographical writing.
> 2. How does Donald Rumsfeld 'position' his opponents (see extract on page 151)?
> 3. What, according to Lucy Mangan, is the great strength of Enid Blyton's writing (see extract on pages 152–153)?
>
> 1 Chronological; thematic.
> 2 He suggests they are arrogant and even blasphemous for claiming omniscience.
> 3 Its narrative drive.

5.3 Planning and developing your work

LEARNING SUMMARY	After studying this section, you should be able to: • organise the ideas you have gathered for your writing • identify ways of planning your writing • write a first draft of your coursework

Planning

AQA **A P2** OCR **P2**
AQA **B P2** WJEC **P2**
Edexcel **P2**

As an experienced writer, you will probably have your own preferred methods of planning and drafting.

You will need to become more self-conscious about this aspect of your work, as it might inform your commentary writing. Some specifications explicitly encourage planning and drafting, although none of them requires you to hand in early drafts.

A plan makes an excellent basis for a focused discussion with your teacher, as you can pin down specifics rather than chat about vague ideas. The more detailed your plan is the better.

Plans tend to be either linear or thematic.

Linear plan

If you are working on a **chronologically organised** piece – recounting a story, for instance – then a linear plan is best.

Thematic plan

A spider diagram or mind map is better for a **thematically arranged piece of writing**, such as an argument.

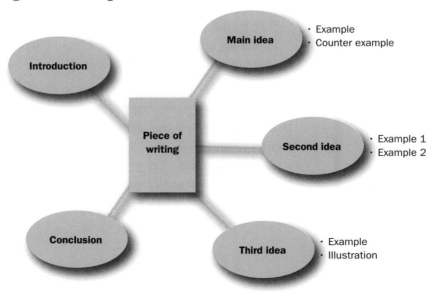

Starting writing

AQA **A P2** OCR **P2**
AQA **B P2** WJEC **P2**
Edexcel **P2**

Here are some useful pointers when beginning a piece of writing:
- Always consider the ending. In this way, you can avoid dead ends and false starts.
- Start with your **purpose**. For instance, do you want to make people laugh, or think, or feel angry?
- **How** will you achieve this purpose – for example, through argument, anecdote, subtle language use, exaggerated language?
- Who is the **audience** – friends, people your age, people you disagree with, etc?
- What **genre conventions** can you use to help you? Should you conform to expectations or break away from them in new and exciting ways?
- What **format** are you going to use? Examples might include letter, novel, etc.

How not to do it!

Every year, the Bulwer Lytton prize is awarded to the worst opening for a novel. Below are some examples from the 'Lyttony of Grand Prize Winners', with a commentary underneath each opening paragraph.

> Dolores breezed along the surface of her life like a flat stone forever skipping across smooth water, rippling reality sporadically but oblivious to it consistently, until she finally lost momentum, sank, due to an overdose of fluoride as a child which caused her to lie forever on the floor of her life as useless as an appendix and as lonely as a five-hundred-pound barbell in a steroid-free fitness center.
>
> *Linda Vernon, Newark, California (1990 winner)*

This opening is an example of how mixed metaphors can derail an author's intentions. The first part of the extract compares Dolores' life to a stone skipping across a pond. As a single image this would be effective, but it is undermined by an over-specific reference to childhood, and a second rather strained metaphor about loneliness.

> Sultry it was and humid, but no whisper of air caused the plump, laden spears of golden grain to nod their burdened heads as they unheedingly awaited the cyclic rape of their gleaming treasure, while overhead the burning orb of luminescence ascended its ever-upward path toward a sweltering celestial apex, for although it is not in Kansas that our story takes place, it looks godawful like it.
>
> *Judy Frazier, Lathrop, Missouri (1991 winner)*

This piece of writing dramatically fails to control its lexis. The initial vocabulary implies warmth and riches, but this is undermined by the intrusion of the harsh word 'rape' in place of, say, 'harvest'. The second part of the sentence also uses rather over-the-top vocabulary, which is then brought to a bathetic conclusion by the colloquial 'godawful'.

As the newest Lady Turnpot descended into the kitchen wrapped only in her celery-green dressing gown, her creamy bosom rising and falling like a temperamental soufflé, her tart mouth pursed in distaste, the sous-chef whispered to the scullery boy, "I don't know what to make of her."

Laurel Fortuner, Montendre, France (1992 winner)

The vocabulary, similes and metaphors in this opening are all related to food and cookery, but – as the ending admits – to no particular purpose.

She wasn't really my type, a hard-looking but untalented reporter from the local cat box liner, but the first second that the third-rate representative of the fourth estate cracked open a new fifth of old Scotch, my sixth sense said seventh heaven was as close as an eighth note from Beethoven's Ninth Symphony, so, nervous as a tenth grader drowning in eleventh-hour cramming for a physics exam, I swept her into my longing arms, and, humming "The Twelfth of Never," I got lucky on Friday the thirteenth.

Wm. W. "Buddy" Ocheltree, Port Townsend, Washington (1993 winner)

The words and phrases in this extract are all appropriate to 'hard-boiled' detective fiction, but are made absurd by the count from 1 to 13.

"Ace, watch your head!" hissed Wanda urgently, yet somehow provocatively, through red, full, sensuous lips, but he couldn't you know, since nobody can actually watch more than part of his nose or a little cheek or lips if he really tries, but he appreciated her warning.

Janice Estey, Aspen, Colorado (1996 winner)

This entry distracts attention away from a dramatic opening by speculating on the meaning of a common turn of phrase.

> **KEY POINT**
>
> Aim for consistency of language and style. Readers do not like to be jarred out of what they are imagining by sudden shifts from one way of writing to another.

Developing your work

AQA	**A P2**	OCR	**P2**
AQA	**B P2**	WJEC	**P2**
Edexcel **P2**			

For most of the writing you do, you check and edit as you write, crossing out on paper or deleting on screen. Earlier versions tend to disappear as you progress and polish.

When writing your coursework, it is worth saving different versions of your work under serial filenames (for instance, CW1, CW2, CW2.1, etc.) so that in your commentary you can easily discuss how your ideas developed. If you are working on paper, date and store successive versions of your coursework in a folder.

Once you have completed a draft, always re-read the whole thing to get a sense of how your text works. Reading aloud – to reveal repetitive or clumsy wording – is also useful at this stage. Remember that this is an English course, and so spelling and punctuation errors will be taken into account.

An example

Below is a first draft of a piece of coursework on representation.

> I'm sick and tired of people going on about science fiction and fantasy as if reading it was a sign of nerdiness. If science fiction and fantasy is so nerdy, why have films in the genre been so successful at the box office? *Avatar* is one of the most successful films of all time and it's hardly set in the Home Counties. Of the top ten best-selling movies of all time, seven out of ten are science fiction and fantasy.

Here is a second draft.

> Science fiction and fantasy films are amongst the most popular in the world. Of the top ten best-selling movies of all time, seven out of ten are science fiction and fantasy, and one of the most successful films of all time, *Avatar*, is hardly set in the Home Counties. People are clearly very keen to watch science fiction and fantasy, but they seem reluctant to read it; or possibly reluctant to admit that they read it for fear of being called nerds.

Here is the commentary for this section.

> I decided to persuade my readers with some facts and figures first. I used the name of a very popular science fiction film, *Avatar*, in the hope of reminding readers of their own positive experiences with this genre. I only introduced my main argument about reading in the second part of the paragraph. I deliberately used the word 'nerd' to evoke negative connotations, in contrast to the positive connotations of *Avatar*. In my original draft, I had been much more confrontational and had introduced the idea straight away as a strong personal opinion. In the second draft, I decided to build up my persona with the audience gradually so that they would trust me.

PROGRESS CHECK

1. What sort of plan is best for thematic writing?
2. Why should you keep your early drafts?
3. What is a mixed metaphor?

3 When two different metaphors derail each other.
2 They may be useful to reflect on in your commentary, to help explain the development of your work.
1 A mind map or spider diagram.

Coursework example

As detailed at the start of this chapter, the examining boards approach language production through coursework requirements, so we have not included a sample answer or exam question for this chapter.

Instead, we have provided an extract from a piece of genre writing, and an extract from the commentary, to try and illustrate what the examiner will be looking for in the coursework.

An extract from a piece of genre fiction coursework

This is atmospheric writing – the 'blood' moon foreshadows later events.

The description of street lamps places the story in the late nineteenth or early twentieth century.

'Mantle' is specialist vocabulary.

Transition to action.

The 'dog' is introduced.

The narrator's confusion over the dog is established.

'Darkness closed in' sets up the next paragraph.

This is a shocking, unexpected outcome – the student uses a short paragraph for emphasis.

Cognitive dissonance!

> The sun was setting and the light had gone from most of the street. The roofs of the houses on the left hand side glowed red and gold, and the moon looked as though it had bathed in blood. A mist was coming up from the river. A man carrying a long taper and a ladder moved from street lamp to street lamp. He lit most of them with the taper, but occasionally he used the ladder to climb up to the lamp itself and replace the delicate mantles of the gas lamps.
>
> As it grew darker there was a disturbance in the basement area of one of the houses. I thought it was a fox, but when the animal began to move along the street I began to think in terms of an Alsatian or some other large dog. Whatever it was, the animal was quite obviously stalking the lamp lighter. Perhaps it was his pet, or maybe he gave it scraps when he passed this way. The man seemed not to have noticed the dog, but quickened his pace, lighting the lamps as the darkness closed in.
>
> Just as he reached a small alley the animal leapt out, knocked him to the ground, and, very efficiently, tore out his throat.
>
> I took out my mobile and tried to ring an ambulance...

An extract from the commentary

Genre conventions are understood and discussed.

The student made a conscious decision to mislead the reader.

The student is aware of the role of lexis in creating atmosphere and authenticity.

The student shows awareness of the audience's needs and how to work with them.

The virtues of simple lexis and sentence structure are discussed confidently. The use of paragraphs is understood.

Technical vocabulary – 'reveal' and 'foreshadowing' – is used correctly. Clear and controlled lexical choices are discussed.

> This is the beginning of a science fiction novel involving being able to travel into other people's dreams. The main character is from the twenty-first century, but at this point I wanted the audience to think the novel was set in the early twentieth century. I signified the historical period by describing a lamp lighter at work. This involved a small amount of research and I was able to include the specialist term `mantle' in the description.
>
> I was aiming at a teenage audience, so I did not want to make the language or the sentences too difficult. In general the lexis is simple and straightforward so that the reader has a number of clear images - the rising fog, the blood-red moon, the mysterious dog and, finally, the man having his throat ripped out. I did not make this gory - I went for shock and surprise and made it stand out by placing it in its own paragraph.
>
> The `reveal' that all is not as it seems is carried out by introducing a mobile phone, but hopefully the reader would have been alerted to something odd by the dog killing the man in the previous paragraph. Also, I hoped they would have been given clues by the fore-shadowing of the blood-red moon, and the word `stalking' used with reference to the dog.

This extract and commentary would achieve marks at the highest level. The conventions of the genre are deployed subtly in the passage itself and discussed with confidence in the commentary.

6 Language variation and change

The following topics are covered in this chapter:

- **Social and regional language variation**
- **Dialects and sociolects**
- **Language change over time**
- **Attitudes to – and debates about – change and variation**

6.1 Social variation

LEARNING SUMMARY

After studying this section, you should be able to:

- understand the ways that English varies in different social contexts
- give examples of social variation
- comment on the implications of social variation

Regional and global English

AQA **A P3** OCR **P3**
AQA **B P3** WJEC **P4**
Edexcel **P3**

Depending on your perspective, the immense variability of language is one of its great beauties or one of its most regrettable faults. For historical and geographical reasons, English is spoken in many different ways around the world, and in a surprising variety of ways in the same city or even in the same household. The investigation of language variety is a major feature of most A-Level specifications.

If you are writing a text book or an instruction manual, then you are probably glad that **Standard English** can be understood by all educated speakers of English all over the world. If you speak with a strong **regional accent**, you may be annoyed by the assumptions that people make about you because of the way that you talk. In fact, all spoken Englishes vary, but some varieties – such as 'BBC' English or 'East Coast American' English – have more **prestige** than other forms.

The emergence of English as a global language for business and the Internet means that knowledge of Standard English is highly valued. In 2010, for instance, over 300 million Chinese people are said to have studied English at some level. Speakers of English as a foreign or second language, it is argued, should not have to keep up with constantly changing English, and there have even been proposals for an Academy of English to decide on 'correct' usage.

To favour one variety of English as 'correct' is viewed as suspicious by some, and as counterproductive by others. The way English is spoken and pronounced can be an important part of many people's **regional** or even **national identity**. People from Yorkshire or Texas or Australia employ different **dialects** of English, and it is not useful to state that these are in any sense 'wrong'. The way that you speak

English will be further influenced by your age, your gender, your social class, your ethnicity, and the groups you belong to.

> **KEY POINT**
>
> The media often influences language variation. For example, because of their popularity around the world, Hollywood films can often spread a particular usage very rapidly. Consider the way that young people use 'Whatever!'.

At the highest levels of English there are distinct differences between national varieties. American English has a different spelling system from British English, for instance, whilst Indian English makes extensive use of question tags as discourse markers. Each of the major English language speaking communities has an influence on World English, but many linguists argue that English has now escaped from the British Isles to become a truly global language of trade and ideas.

Types of variation

AQA	**A P3**	OCR	**P3**
AQA	**B P3**	WJEC	**P4**
Edexcel **P3**			

Speakers of English as a mother tongue tend to have a very good ear for differences in the lexis and accents of others. Dwellers in cities can often tell where in the city a person comes from, and country dwellers can instantly identify people from neighbouring villages. Socially isolated communities, such as boarding schools, develop their own way of speaking, and often develop slang that is deliberately impenetrable to newcomers.

Social class

In the preface to his play *Pygmalion*, George Bernard Shaw says that, 'It is impossible for an Englishman to open his mouth without making some other Englishman hate or despise him'. The central character of the play is a linguist called Henry Higgins who makes his money as an elocution teacher, helping people from lower down the social scale to conceal their origins. Notions of correctness in speech are subject to change, but in most communities there is a **prestige** accent. In *Pygmalion*, Higgins teaches a street flower seller to speak like a lady and 'correctly' pronounce the phrase 'The rain in Spain falls mainly on the plain'.

In the more democratic 1980s, this was parodied in a beer advertisement in which a 'posh' girl is taught to say 'The wartah in Majawkah don't taste like what it oughta' (as opposed to 'The water in Majorca doesn't taste quite how it should').

Whatever the historical period, wealth and level of education have a high impact on the way people speak, and how they are judged by others.

Age

Individuals are exposed to different language influences throughout life – starting with parental language and moving through peer group slang to specialised professional jargon.

Unfortunately, by the time anyone has compiled a dictionary of slang, the authentic users tend to have moved on.

Some individuals retain ways of speaking from earlier parts of their lives – saying things like 'fab' or 'ace'. Others attempt to use language that is not appropriate to their age group in an attempt to seem 'cool'. Teenagers often use new slang as a way of emphasising social identity.

Gender

The different ways that men and women create meaning have been the subject of extensive scrutiny in recent years (see Chapter 4). Discourse analysis has highlighted subtle and nuanced differences in communication styles between men and women. In addition, corpus linguistics has been able to demonstrate how gendered attitudes can construct language, for instance by looking at the number of times 'good' is collocated with 'girl' and with 'boy' in a large text sample.

Compare the following quotation from Shakespeare, which exemplifies historical social attitudes to women, with the contemporary phrase, 'screaming like a fishwife'.

> Her voice was ever soft,
> Gentle, and low, an excellent thing in woman
>
> *Extract from* King Lear *(Act V, Scene iii) by William Shakespeare*

Groups

Language is used to communicate between people, but it also plays a key part in separating them.

Different groups develop their own specialised languages to promote group coherence and to aid in the detection of outsiders. The most extreme or **deviant** forms of this tendency are thieves' slangs, cants such as Cockney rhyming slang, and the language of drug abusers. Professional groups need specialised language at work to avoid confusion, but using this specialised **jargon** outside of the workplace can promote solidarity and belonging. A similar tendency can be seen in the deliberate use of technical terms by hobbyists, for example 'L33t speak' on the Internet.

Ethnicity

The impact of ethnicity on English ranges from highly visible pidgins and Creoles (see pages 174–175), through to subtle 'mother tongue' influences, like the fact that a lack of a simple word for 'yes' or 'no' in Gaelic leads Irish people to prefer phrases like 'I do' and 'I won't'.

The development of English itself was profoundly influenced by contact with Old Norse and Old French, and the colonial period had a deep impact on both its lexical stock and on the number of people in the world who speak in English as either a mother tongue or a **lingua franca**.

PROGRESS CHECK

1 What would an Academy of English do?
2 What is the difference between slang and jargon?

2 Jargon usually starts out as being work based; slang is made up for fun or to exclude others.
1 Decide on correct usage of English.

6.2 Regional variation

LEARNING SUMMARY

After studying this section, you should be able to:

- understand the ways that English varies in different regions
- give examples of regional variation
- appreciate the implications of English being a world language

English regional accents and dialects

AQA	**A P3**	OCR	**P3**
AQA	**B P3**	WJEC	**P4**
Edexcel	**P3**		

Strong **regional variations** have always been present in English, because the English language developed from four distinct dialects of Anglo Saxon. When people did not travel much or only communicated with their neighbours, this was not a problem. However, when printers began manufacturing books for the whole of England, they had to standardise them in one form of English.

This can be seen in a story told by William Caxton (1415–1492), the first person to set up a printing press in England. A merchant, he tells us, was going down the Thames, but as there was no wind he landed on the Kentish shore to buy food.

> And specyally he axyed after eggys. And the good wyf answerde that she coude speke no frenshe. And the marchaunt was angry for he also coude speke no frenshe but wold haue hadde egges and she vnderstode hym not. And thenne at laste a nother sayd that he wolde haue eyren. Then the good wyf sayd that she vnderstood hym wel
>
> *Extract from the preface to* Eneydos *by William Caxton*

Clearly, the Kentish woman was using a dialect word 'eyren', whilst the merchant was using something closer to our modern word 'eggs'. Caxton stated that in choosing between such words he always attempted to use the language that would be recognised by 'a clerke and a noble gentylman', in other words by the educated and the wealthy.

> **KEY POINT**
>
> Prejudices about regional variants often go hand in hand with social snobbery.

English dialects

Dialect is a term used for a form of a language with distinct features of vocabulary, grammar, lexis and pronunciation. Any single language can usually be subdivided into a number of different dialects. They are called dialects rather than languages because they are mutually intelligible versions of the same language – in other words, the speakers of one dialect can, broadly speaking, understand the speakers of another dialect.

The term 'dialect' is most commonly used to refer to regional dialects – different varieties of a language spoken in different geographical regions – but it may also refer to social differences. In English, Glaswegian and Cockney are regional dialects, whilst Standard English is the main, high prestige social dialect.

As mentioned above, dialect usually describes variations in vocabulary and grammar, and is a much broader term than **accent**, which refers only to the pronunciation or words. In theory at least, it is possible to speak the same dialect in any number of accents. This is especially true of Standard English, which is spoken in hundreds of different accents around the world. The Speech Accent Archive currently has a collection of over 1300 English accents.

An often quoted remark about the difference between a dialect and a language is that a language is 'a dialect with an army and a navy'. In Italy, the Florentine dialect eventually became Standard Italian; in France, the northern **langue d'oeil** triumphed over the southern **langue d'oc**; and in England, modern Standard English developed out of the East Midland dialect.

In terms of its qualities as a language, Standard English is no better and no worse than any other variety of English – it merely has more prestige and is currently the best known variety. It is more generally accepted than other dialects and is explicitly taught in schools. It is the language of text books, newspapers, government, and most forms of written communication.

The concept of dialect has been extended by linguists to describe a number of types of variation. These include social dialects (or **sociolects**), occupational dialects, class dialects and even **idiolects** – the unique features of the language spoken by an individual.

PROGRESS CHECK

1. What is the highest prestige variety of English at present?
2. What is the difference between accent and dialect?
3. What is an idiolect?

3 The unique features of the language spoken by an individual.
2 Accent only concerns pronunciation of words; dialect covers grammar, lexis and vocabulary.
1 Standard English.

6.3 The features of regional dialects

LEARNING SUMMARY	After studying this section, you should be able to:
	• understand the lexical and grammatical nature of English dialects
	• understand the examples of semantic variation
	• discuss the way that dialects are represented in texts

Yorkshire English

AQA	**A P3**	OCR	**P3**
AQA	**B P3**	WJEC	**P4**
Edexcel	**P3**		

If you move around the British Isles, you will notice variations in dialect and accent from place to place, and you may spot that different areas have different words to describe the same thing. The very observant may also spot that different areas of the country employ different grammars. One large area that still preserves a distinctive dialect is **Yorkshire**.

The Yorkshire region was once part of the Danelaw, an area under the control of former Vikings who spoke Old Norse. This is reflected in the names of settlements ending in 'by' (meaning village) and 'borough' (meaning town), such as Whitby, Selby, Scarborough and Mexborough. Even today, the dialect spoken in the East Riding has some similarities with Danish; whilst in the West, elements of Icelandic still survive. The area to the south-west of the River Wharfe is descended from the Mercian dialect of Old English. The area to the north-east is more influenced by the Northumbrian dialect.

Area where the Yorkshire dialect is spoken

Grammar and lexis

Below are some features of Yorkshire grammar:
- The second person singular pronoun is used – i.e. 'thou' (often written 'tha') and 'thee' – for instance, 'What's up wi' thee?' This feature has been lost from Standard English.
- In the West Riding, the past tense of be is 'were' instead of 'was' – for example, 'I were going to fetch me coat'.
- The plural marker is omitted from nouns of quantity – for instance, 'ten pounds' becomes 'ten pound'; 'five miles' becomes 'five mile'.
- 'Of' is used more frequently in location descriptions – for example, 'Get off **of** the train' instead of 'Get off the train'.
- 'Us' is often used instead of 'me' – for example, 'Give us a go' – or instead of 'our' – for example, 'We'll need summat for us dinner'.
- 'I'm not' becomes' I aren't' in areas like York and Bradford.
- The definite article 'the' is often shortened to a 't' or omitted completely – for instance, 'Is tha' goin' t' market?' (Are you going to the market?), or even 'Down pub?'.

Here are a few examples of distinctive lexis:
- 'Aye' for ' yes' is common in many Yorkshire dialects.
- 'Owt' and 'nowt' from the Middle English 'aught' and 'naught' is used to mean 'anything' and 'nothing'. 'Summat' (something) comes from the Middle English 'some-aught'. In some areas, 'nobbit' or nobbut' (naught but) is used instead of 'only' – for instance, 'Nobbit a young lad'.

- 'With' is shortened – for example, 'Do you want bread wi' that?'
- 'While' means 'until' – for instance, 'He'll not be back while midnight' means that midnight is the earliest possible time of arrival.
- In cities such as Leeds and Sheffield, 'love' is a general term for another person. 'Duck' is also used in Sheffield and further south.
- 'Daft' means 'not very clever', rather than silly.
- 'Self' becomes 'sen' – for example, 'help tha sen' (help yourself). In the north-west, 'sel' is more common – for example, 'Sit thysel down'.
- The Viking verb 'laik' (sometimes spelt 'lake'), meaning 'to play', is still heard throughout Yorkshire.

Phonological features

Below are the main phonological features of Yorkshire English:
- A short [a] is used in words like 'bath', 'grass' and 'chance', as opposed to the long [ɑ:] of received pronunciation.
- There tends be no contrast between /ʊ/ /ʌ/, meaning that 'put' and 'putt' homophones both use the /ʊ/ sound.
- Broad Yorkshire accents use a long /u:/ in words like 'book', 'cook' and 'look' (rhyming with 'duke'). This is even more common in Lancashire.

Accent and dialect

Yorkshire accents are well regarded by most English people. In one recent study into dialect and perceived intelligence, reported by guardian.co.uk in 2008, Yorkshire residents were seen as 'wise, trustworthy, honest and straightforward', and were rated highly for their intelligence. In response to this, Yorkshire has become a preferred location for telephone call centres.

The Yorkshire dialect, or versions of it, is captured in films such as *Kes*, *Brassed Off* and *Little Voice*, and in television series such as *The Last of the Summer Wine* and *Emmerdale*.

The character of Joseph in *Wuthering Heights* speaks in what is now a very old-fashioned Haworth accent. In one of his comments, his use of 'thee' and 'you' reflects both dialect usage and much earlier conventions of politeness.

> Hareton, thah willn't sup thy porridge tuh neeght; they'll be nowt bud lumps as big as maw nave. Thear, agean! Aw'd fling in bowl un' all, if Aw wer yah! Thear, pale t'guilp off, un' then yah'll hae done wi't. Bang, bang. It's a marcy t'bothom isn't deaved aht!
>
> *Extract from Chapter 13 of* Wuthering Heights *by Emily Brontë*

When addressing the boy, Hareton, Joseph uses 'thah' and 'thy', but when speaking to the grown-up Isabella he uses the more polite 'you' (or 'yah' as it is spelled). Apart from pronunciation, indicated by the non-standard orthography, this passage also contains three dialect words – 'nave' for 'fist', 'guilp' for 'milk', and 'deaved' for 'knocked'.

In *Wuthering Heights*, Joseph speaks with an almost impenetrable Yorkshire accent, as an indication of his lower social status. There is a long tradition of this in English writing, going back at least to Shakespeare, whose 'low' characters often use non-standard forms.

Social and regional variation in *King Lear*

The aristocratic Edgar is in disguise when he meets Oswald.

OSWALD: Wherefore, bold peasant,
Darest thou support a published traitor? Hence;
Lest that the infection of his fortune take
Like hold on thee. Let go his arm.

EDGAR: Chill not let go, zir, without vurther 'casion.

OSWALD: Let go, slave, or thou diest!

EDGAR: Good gentleman, go your gait, and let poor volk pass. An chud ha' bin zwaggered out of my life, 'twould not ha' bin zo long as 'tis by a vortnight. Nay, come not near th' old man; keep out, che vor ye, or ise try whether your costard or my ballow be the harder: chill be plain with you.

OSWALD: Out, dunghill!

EDGAR: Chill pick your teeth, zir: come; no matter vor your foins.
[They fight, and Edgar knocks him down]

Extract from King Lear *(Act IV, Scene vi) by William Shakespeare*

Edgar's speech shows many features of the Kentish dialect that would have been familiar to his London audience. These include phonological features, such as substituting 'v' for 'f' and 'z' for 's', and non-standard lexis, like 'che' for 'I' and 'vor' for 'warrant'. Notice also that Oswald addresses his social inferior as 'thee'.

> **KEY POINT**
>
> Accents and dialects are subject to change over time, just as much as any other aspect of language.

Estuary English

AQA **A P3** OCR **P3**
AQA **B P3** WJEC **P4**
Edexcel **P3**

Yorkshire English is a well-established dialect of English, with roots that go back to the very earliest varieties of English.

Estuary English first came to public attention in 1984 through an article in the *Times Educational Supplement* by David Rosewarne, entitled 'Estuary English'. In his article, Rosewarne argued that the spread of Estuary English was part of a longer process, going back to the Middle Ages, in which the political and economic power of the capital has made itself felt in the way people communicate. Estuary English in its present form is midway between London (or Cockney) English and received pronunciation, but Rosewarne thinks that Estuary English has a good chance of affecting Standard English pronunciation in future.

Peter Trudgill[1] is more sceptical about its influence, but identifies it as one of a series of new modern dialects centred on cities like Belfast, Dublin, Cardiff, Glasgow, Newcastle, Nottingham, Leeds, Liverpool, Manchester, Birmingham and Bristol.

1 Trudgill, P. 2001. *Sociolinguistic variation and change*. Edinburgh University Press.

Phonological features

Here are the main phonological features of Estuary English:

- Glottal stops are used instead of 't' – for example, 'Sco'land', 'ga'eway', 'Ga'wick', 'sta'ement', 'sea'-belt', 'trea'ment' and 'ne'work'.
- The /j/ sound is lost after the first consonant in words like 'news' or 'tune'. However, this process is also found in received pronunciation, as it now sounds old-fashioned to pronounce a /j/ after the 'l' of 'absolute', 'revolution' or 'salute'.
- The /l/ sound in words like 'milk' and 'silk' has shifted to a semi-vowel, so these words sound like '/miwk/' and '/siwk/'.

Grammatical features

Grammatical features of Estuary English include:

- greater use of question tags – such as 'isn't it?' and 'don't I?' – than in Standard English
- using 'ain't' as a main verb in sentences
- replacing 'did not' with 'never' in sentences – for example, 'I never did', 'he never came'
- omitting 'ly' in some adverbs – for example, 'I sat quiet, the night was going slow'
- the extension of third person singular form, especially in narrative – for example, 'I picks him up at six and we gets there by eight'.

Most people will be familiar with Estuary English through the soap opera, *EastEnders*, and from the pronunciation of people like Janet Street Porter and David Beckham.

However, in spite of its use by many celebrities, the dialect is still criticised. For example, the *Daily Telegraph's* cricket correspondent said that, as someone who went to a good university, the cricketer Nasser Hussain has no excuse for speaking in 'ghastly estuary sludge'.

American English

AQA	**A P3**	OCR	**P3**
AQA	**B P3**	WJEC	**P4**
Edexcel **P3**			

George Bernard Shaw said that Britain and America were 'two nations divided by a common language'. At the time he was expressing an opinion, but recent research has shown that statistically, at least, he was right.

American and British English look similar, but thousands of small differences can make the task of communicating perilous. David Grote's *British English for American Readers*, for instance, runs to over 700 pages.

Even at a diplomatic level, there are potential pitfalls – below are a few examples.

> - On both sides of the Atlantic, 'to **scheme**' suggests plotting. However, Britons would have no moral objections to going along with 'a scheme', while Americans might be horrified by the word's connotations.
> - To '**table**' a motion in a British boardroom means that it is likely to be discussed. In America, 'tabling' something means that it is put firmly on the back burner.
> - '**Slating**' someone in America refers to him or her being favourably nominated for office. To receive a 'slating' in the UK means that a person is being criticised severely.

It is inaccurate to speak about American English as if it were one dialect. There is considerable variation along the East Coast, where there are long-established English speaking communities. Shakespeare would probably feel at home with the English of the Appalachian mountains, and there are many fascinating hybrids resulting from, for instance, the mixture with French in Louisiana and with Spanish in the South and South-west.

Phonology

There are many American accents – ranging from the Brooklyn accent made famous by Bugs Bunny, to the deep Southern drawl of the same cartoon's Foghorn Leghorn.

The equivalent of British received pronunciation is known as the General American accent, and it is spoken in many American films, TV series and nationwide advertising. The accent is most closely related to a generalised Midwestern form of spoken English.

Some common phonological features include:
- the merging of /ɑ/ and /ɒ/ to make 'father' and 'bother' rhyme
- the merging of /ɒ/ and /ɔ/ to make 'cot' and 'caught' homophones
- dropping the /j/ sound, so that 'new', 'duke', 'Tuesday', 'resume' are pronounced '/nu/', '/duk/', '/tuzdeɪ/', '/ɹɪzum/'
- the pin-pen merger, making pairs like pen/pin homophones.

Vocabulary

The earliest contributions of America to the English lexicon were the names of unfamiliar animals and plants found on the continent. These were often borrowed from native American languages and included words like 'opossum', 'raccoon', 'squash' and 'moose' from Algonquian. As non-English speaking colonists arrived, they added new words to American English, such as 'cookie' from Dutch, 'levee' from French, and 'barbecue' from Spanish.

As time passed, American English users re-purposed words to fit their new conditions, so that landscape words like 'creek', 'slough' and 'watershed' gained new meanings that were unknown in England. The reverse process is also true, and some American words preserve meanings that have disappeared in British English, such as 'gotten' and 'fall' (meaning autumn). As the British Empire waned and America became more influential, it became common to label anything that the speaker did not like as an 'Americanism', but this was often not true. For example, 'monkey wrench' and 'wastebasket' originated in nineteenth-century Britain.

A common source of confusion between British and American English is the use of different words/terminology to describe the same thing. The table below shows some examples.

American English	British English
Chips	Crisps
Hood	Bonnet
Trunk	Boot
Bathroom	Toilet
Eggplant	Aubergine

Morphology

There are no morphological features unique to American English, but the Americans have tended to be less resistant to new usages and coinages than the British. **Back-formation** – turning nouns into verbs or vice versa – seems particularly prevalent, and has been the subject of complaints by British writers.

Examples of verbs formed from nouns are:
- interview
- vacuum
- lobby
- pressure
- transition
- feature
- profile
- skyrocket
- showcase
- service
- corner
- torch
- exit
- gift.

Examples of nouns formed from phrasal verbs include:
- shoot-out
- hold-up
- hideout
- comeback
- kickback
- makeover
- takeover
- rip-off
- stand-in.

American English compounds that have gained a wider currency include:
- badlands
- landslide
- backdrop
- teenager
- brainstorm
- deadbeat
- foolproof
- nit-pick.

Grammar

The differences in grammar between American and British English are relatively minor and often pass unnoticed.

Here are some examples:
- Some verbal auxiliaries are used differently – for example, 'appeal a decision' in American English and 'appeal against a decision' in British English.

- In American English there is a formal agreement with collective nouns, so that 'the team is…' is normal. In British English the choice of 'is' or 'are' will depend on context.
- American English prefers 'learned' and 'burned' to 'learnt' and 'burnt', 'snuck' to 'sneaked' and 'dove' to 'dived'.
- Americans prefer 'different than' to 'different to'.

Orthography

The differences between British and American spellings are noticeable, but not extensive:

- Some differences are attributable to the spelling reforms of Noah Webster, the compiler of *An American Dictionary of the English Language*, which was published in 1828 (examples include 'color' for 'colour', 'center' for 'centre', 'traveler' for 'traveller', 'defense' for 'defence').
- The so-called American '-ize' ending was always a matter of printer's choice and is used, for instance, in the Oxford English Dictionary.
- A few of the different spellings reflect Francophile tastes in nineteenth-century England, which did not cross the Atlantic ('programme' for 'program', 'manoeuvre' for 'maneuver', 'skilful' for 'skillful', 'cheque' for 'check').

> **KEY POINT**
>
> American English is often seen by British users as newfangled, but in many cases American usage is more conservative.

Prosody

Perhaps one of the most distinctive features of American English is its **prosody**, or typical sound patterns.

For instance, most two-syllable verbs ending '-ate' stress the first syllable in American English and the second in British English, as the table below illustrates.

American English	British English
dictate	dic**tate**
donate	do**nate**
placate	pla**cate**
translate	trans**late**

The same pattern is found in many nouns.

American English	British English
mama	ma**ma**
princess	prin**cess**
controversy	con**trov**ersy
ice cream	ice **cream**

The opposite pattern is also found.

American English	British English
caf**feine**	**caf**feine
can**not**	**can**not
Kath**leen**	**Kath**leen
kilo**metre**	**kilo**metre

Some American English stress patterns alter if the same word is being used as a noun or a verb. For instance, for the word 'research', '**re**search' would be the noun form and 're**search**' the verb form.

A recent development in stress patterns has been the use of a rising tone for statements, so that they sound like questions. This has been particularly prevalent on the West Coast.

Again, it must be noted that there is a great deal of variation in American English, just as there is in all other forms of English. Language investigations that give in-depth data tend to cover small areas, and investigations that cover entire continents run the risk of being superficial.

British or American English?

AQA   **A P3**   OCR   **P3**
AQA   **B P3**   WJEC **P4**
Edexcel **P3**

One of the most fascinating things about British and American English at this point in history is that both varieties still have a high prestige. People who wish to learn to speak English have to decide which variety to study, and multi-million pound businesses on both sides of the Atlantic promote their particular versions. British English is obviously a major influence in British Commonwealth areas. However, the success and popularity of Hollywood films and American-dominated technological innovation via the Internet make American English the de facto world standard.

Figure 6.1 In major blockbusters, the hero (in this case, Kevin Costner playing Robin Hood) tends to have an American accent and the villain (in this example, Alan Rickman as the Sheriff of Nottingham) an English accent – is Hollywood trying to tell us something?!

A simple way to examine the extent of the differences between British and American English is to look up well-known points of divergence using an Internet search engine. Here are the results for some well-known differences in spelling.

Word	British English hits	American English hits
centre / center	536 000 000	1 040 000 000
colour /color	161 000 000	685 000 000
realise / realize	21 300 000	77 900 000
offence / offense	15 800 000	24 700 000
manoeuvre / maneuver	5 440 000	6 000 000

The most interesting of these results is the fact that 'color' is around four times more popular than 'colour'. The American spelling is used in computer programs and web pages.

English as a world language

AQA **A P3** OCR **P3**
AQA **B P3** WJEC **P4**
Edexcel **P3**

Perhaps both American and British English have passed their peak.

The table below shows the top ten largest English speaking communities. Although the figures are not precise, they do provide general evidence that England and America together do not dominate numerically. However, America still houses the largest single group of English speakers.

Rank	Country	% English speakers	Eligible population	Total English speakers	As first language	As an additional language
1	United States	96	262 375 150	251 388 300	215 423 560	3 964 740
2	India	23	1 100 000 000	232 000 000	226 450	223 000 000 *E2L* 8 773 000 *E3L*
3	Nigeria	53	148 093 000	79 000 000	4 000 000	>75 000 000
4	United Kingdom	98	60 975 000	59 600 000	58 100 000	1 500 000
5	Philippines	55	97 000 000	49 800 000	3 427 000	46 373 000
6	Germany	56	82 191 000	46 000 000	272 504	46 000 000
7	Canada	85	33 355 400	25 246 220	17 694 830	7 551 390
8	France	36	64 473 140	23 000 000		23 000 000
9	Australia	97	21 394 310	17 357 830	15 013 970	2 343 870
10=	Pakistan	10	164 157 000	17 000 000		17 000 000
10=	Italy	29	59 619 290	17 000 000		17 000 000

E2L = English as a second language
E3L = English as a third language

In addition to these figures, we must also add the enormous numbers of people who are learning English around the world.

There are a range of different versions of English, such as:
- African English – including South, West and Eastern varieties
- American English
- Australian, New Zealand and South Pacific English
- British English
- Canadian English
- Caribbean English
- East Asian English – including Hong Kong and Singapore
- South Asian English – including India, Pakistan and Sri Lanka.

Each variety of English has its own distinctive features, but at present they are all mutually intelligible. This would also have been true of Latin at the end of the Roman Empire when the languages that eventually became Italian, Spanish, French and Romanian were still Latin dialects.

Globish

Globish is a version of **glob**al Engl**ish** – codified by Jean-Paul Nerriere – that is designed to be used by people who have no language in common. It uses a subset of Standard English grammar and has a vocabulary of only 1500 words, so that it is easy to learn. Nerriere claims that globish is a naturally occurring language, unlike some other proposed lingua francas (or linguae francae) such as Esperanto.

It has been suggested by people such as Robert McCrum that access to globish gives access to economic advancement. However, some people disagree with this. Their view is that it is only the varieties of English acquired through extensive education – which are accessible to only a small and privileged minority – that pay economic dividends.

The problem is made worse by so much of the Internet being in English. So people who do not have access to English do not have access to a wide range of information available on the World Wide Web.

> **KEY POINT**
>
> The Internet and high-powered computers have given rise to machine translation. At present, few people use this, but the programs get better all the time. Might this one day affect how people speak and write?

Mixed English

Globish is by no means a new phenomenon – whenever English and economic activity go together, people develop **pidgins**, or trading languages. Like globish, they tend to have a small, specific vocabulary, a simplified grammar and a restricted range of uses.

Examples of Nigerian pidgin include:
- 'Wetin dey happen?' – 'What is happening?'
- 'Hin say make we dey go' – 'He said we should go'
- 'Hin don vex' – 'He is angry'
- 'I no no' – 'I don't know'.

Examples of pidgin used in the Solomon Islands are:

- 'Tanggio tumas fo helpem mi' – 'Thank you very much for helping me'
- 'No wariwari. Hem oraet nomoa' – 'No worries. It is all right now'
- 'Mi dae nau!' – literally 'I'm dying!', used to express surprise or shock
- 'Diswan hem bagarap' – 'This thing is broken'.

Typical features of pidgins are:

- a lack of variation in verb forms
- loss of determiners
- simple negations
- adverbs used to show modality
- a lack of word order variation for questions
- little or no plural marking.

If enough people speak pidgin for long enough, eventually it becomes a mother tongue – this is known as a **Creole**. When this happens the new mixed language becomes as subtle and rich as any other tongue, as it relates to all aspects of a speaker's life, not just trade.

Examples of Creoles are the Jamaican **patois**, Papua New Guinea's **Tok Pisin** and Singaporean **Singlish**:

- The Jamaican patois 'Im kiaan biit mi' means 'He can't beat me'.
- The Tok Pisin 'Mi laik baim sampela pis' means 'I want/would like to buy some fish'.
- The Singlish sentence, 'Yesterday, dey go there oreddy' means 'They already went there yesterday'.

Many Creoles were originally spoken by slaves or indentured labourers, and so had a very low social status. They were often regarded as 'degenerate' dialects of the local prestige language. Recent research and the emergence of Creole literature have changed this perspective, but the forces of globalisation mean that some Creole languages are now starting to disappear as their users are assimilated into mainstream English.

PROGRESS CHECK

1 What does the use of non-Standard English show in a Shakespearean text?
2 What is the main difference between a pidgin and a Creole?

1 Low social status.
2 A Creole is spoken as a mother tongue.

6.4 Attitudes to variation

LEARNING SUMMARY

After studying this section, you should be able to:

- understand the concept of linguistic prestige
- apply linguistic prestige to aspects of social and regional variation
- distinguish between prescriptivist and descriptivist approaches

The Queen's English

AQA	**A P3**	OCR	**P3**
AQA	**B P3**	WJEC	**P4**
Edexcel	**P3**		

There is no 'correct' way to speak any language. This is a simple linguistic fact, but it is one that many people find difficult to accept. Some people believe that there should be a standard by which to judge linguistic performance, and in the absence of a real standard many artificial ones get set up. As we mentioned earlier (see page 161), it used to be possible to make a living providing elocution lessons for people whose English wasn't 'good enough', and it was common practice until quite recently for people who wished to make their way in public life to drop their regional and social accents.

In terms of writing, Standard English is taught by law in every school to ensure that all students have access to the benefits of successful communication. Standard English is an arbitrary choice and, as we have said, there is nothing about it that marks it out as 'better' than, say, American Standard English or Standard Glaswegian. What it has got going for it is the prestige of approval by the government, schools and employers.

No one tends to speak Standard English as a mother tongue, as it is mostly deployed in its written form, but the language spoken in English middle-class homes tends to be closer to it, generally speaking, than that spoken in working-class homes. There is an argument that by 'favouring' Standard English, the people who already have power and influence are given more of it, and people speaking regional or social varieties are further deprived.

Elocution lessons are not as common as they used to be, but this does not stop people judging each other when they speak. It can be argued that the old Standard (known as received pronunciation, or, because it was used by BBC announcers, sometimes called BBC English) again favoured the educated and the wealthy. In a letter to *The Times Educational Supplement* in 1994, Paul Coggle made the following comments.

> While attacking people on ground of race, sex or age is considered politically incorrect, it is still surprisingly common to encounter attacks based on accent, especially if those accents originate in the lower classes. In theory, it ought to be possible to convince fair-minded people that all accents are equally valid, as long as they are mutually intelligible. However, since I and many other linguists have over the past two or three decades failed miserably in our efforts to convince, I have come to the conclusion that we should introduce into our schools 'language awareness programmes' which cover not only the features of Received Pronunciation and local accents, but also the common reactions which the more stigmatised varieties evoke.
>
> *Extract from a letter by Paul Coggle,* The Times Educational Supplement, *November 4, 1994*

Since 1994, the government has re-doubled its effort to give everyone access to Standard English. However, at the time of writing, it has refused to publish the materials exploring language processes developed by the Language in the National Curriculum (LINC) project, because it is too descriptive, rather than prescriptive, on language matters.

Dialect levelling

In his book about Estuary English, Coggle explains its appeal as a way of avoiding the pitfalls of upper- and lower-class accents, in what is known as **dialect levelling**.

> No accent is intrinsically good or bad, but it has to be recognized that the way we perceive accents does play a role in our attitude to others. Different people have differing perceptions. So there are significant numbers of young people who see Estuary English as modern, up-front, high on 'street cred' and ideal for image-conscious trendsetters. Others regard it as projecting an approachable, informal and flexible image. Whereas RP [received pronunciation], Queen's English, Oxford English and Sloane Ranger English are all increasingly perceived as exclusive and formal.
>
> *Extract from* Do you speak Estuary? The new Standard English – How to spot it and speak it
> *by Paul Coggle*

In 2006, an article in *The Telegraph* suggested that even the Queen was practising a subtle form of dialect levelling. A scientific study of the Queen's Christmas broadcasts to the Commonwealth since 1952 suggested that the Queen's vowel sounds had very slightly altered, and that, generally speaking, her speeches had moved from Upper received pronunciation towards Standard received pronunciation and Standard English.

Another example of dialect levelling is the use of mid-Atlantic English, which blends American and British without being particularly one or the other.

Figure 6.2 According to the film *The King's Speech*, King George VI had trouble speaking the King's English

KEY POINT

Dialect levelling is an example of language used to facilitate inclusion in a larger language community – no one wants to stand out. People who soften or modify their accents may, however, be criticised by members of their home community.

Prescriptivist and descriptivist approaches

AQA   A P3   OCR   P3
AQA   B P3   WJEC   P4
Edexcel P3

Some attempts at English are clearly wrong; for instance 'Cow the brown moo-ed', but generally speaking any sentence uttered by a native speaker is an example of 'correct' English, whether it be 'How now brown cow?' or 'Wassup you silly brown moo?' The differences between these two examples are in relation to levels of formality and appropriateness, rather than with breaking the rules for forming sentences in English, or of being intelligible.

Prescriptivist approach

Many users of English do not like to be in a state of linguistic uncertainty, and there is a multi-million pound industry based on telling people how to speak and write. A classic of its kind is Fowler's *A Dictionary of Modern English Usage*, which was first published in 1926 and is still in print. A newspaper advertisement for an 'Improve your English' course – with the headline 'Why Does Your English Let You Down?' – is one of the longest running of all time. Recently, Lynne Truss wrote a British and American best-seller entitled *Eats, Shoots & Leaves: The Zero Tolerance Approach to Punctuation*.

From a linguistic point of view, notions of correctness are not very informative. 'Gerrout the way!' is rather a rude and aggressive way of speaking, but it would be the correct form to use if, for instance, you saw a car coming towards someone at speed. Equally, a dissertation entitled *The Role of Affection in Human Pair Bonding* is unlikely to endear you to your boyfriend or girlfriend, even if it is well argued and statistically valid. Generally speaking, a better criterion for judging 'correct' language is appropriateness in context.

Many of the **prescriptive** statements about English have led to people feeling anxious about elements of speaking and writing. For instance, some people are aware that you are supposed to avoid split infinitives, but are not quite sure what one is (a split infinitive is when you place a word between 'to' and the infinitive form of a verb).

Fowler makes the following comments about split infinitives.

> The English-speaking world may be divided into
> (1) those who neither know nor care what a split infinitive is;
> (2) those who do not know, but care very much;
> (3) those who know and condemn;
> (4) those who know and approve; and
> (5) those who know and distinguish.
>
> *Extract from* A Dictionary of Modern English Usage *by H. Fowler*

The most famous split infinitive is Star Trek's 'To **boldly** go where no man has gone before'. The number of people who 'know and condemn' is quite small nowadays compared to when Fowler's book was first published.

Another difficulty with prescriptive, rule-bound approaches is that often the best use of language breaks accepted rules. This was highlighted recently when exam boards tried to mark work by computer.

Pieces of writing by famous authors, including Ernest Hemingway and William Golding, were perceived as below par by the proposed computerised marking system, which was being tested in the American equivalent to an A-Level English exam. The famous speech by Winston Churchill, which included the well-known phrase 'we shall fight on the beaches', was also dismissed by the computer as having a style that was too repetitive, and it rated Churchill as below average (you may remember seeing an extract from this speech in Chapter 1).

Descriptivist approach

Descriptivist linguists, who try to substitute appropriateness for correctness, are accused of avoiding the issue or of 'getting rid of rules'. This is not the case. Rules always apply, or communication would be impossible. Descriptivists are interested in how meaning is made, and it would be naïve of any linguist not to be aware of the social and psychological context of an utterance.

> **KEY POINT**
>
> Most linguists are descriptivist, but non-specialists often seek – and indeed give – advice about 'correct' English.

Multilingual environments

AQA	**A P3**	OCR	**P3**
AQA	**B P3**	WJEC	**P4**
Edexcel	**P3**		

In the debate about language, the dilemma for schools is how to give children who speak a non-standard form of English access to the prestige form without subliminally transmitting the message that there is something wrong with the child's home language.

Wheeler and Swords[2] outlined the importance of using a **contrastivist** rather than a **correctivist** approach to the issue of home language amongst black American primary school children. The contrastivist approach showed that 'language comes in diverse varieties', and this 'linguistically-informed model' recognised that a student's home language was just as valid as the school language. Teachers helped 'children become explicitly aware of the grammatical differences' between formal 'Standard English' and informal home language. 'Knowing this, children learn to code-switch between the language of the home and the language of the school as appropriate to the time, place, audience, and communicative purpose.'

In the most complex situations, children and adults who live in multilingual environments quickly learn to **code-switch**. For instance, a child might speak only Hindi with her grandparents, a mixture of English and Hindi with her parents, a blend of English and Hindi amongst friends, and only Standard English at school.

2 Wheeler, R. and R. Swords. 2001. 'My goldfish name is Scaley' is what we say at home: code-switching – a potent tool for reducing the achievement gap in linguistically diverse classrooms', *ERIC Document* (ED461877), p.7.

At an everyday level, we are all code-switchers, because we live in a range of linguistic environments that call for different linguistic strategies. Children quickly learn what can and cannot be said at home, and adults address their work colleagues in a different way from how they chat with their friends.

PROGRESS CHECK

1. What is dialect levelling?
2. Why should you 'care' a little about split infinitives?
3. Why is it important to use a contrastivist approach rather than a correctivist one?

1 The tendency of speakers to decrease dialect differences.
2 A very small number of people are still offended by them.
3 The contrastivist approach does not make children think there is something 'wrong' with their home language.

6.5 Language variation over time

LEARNING SUMMARY

After studying this section, you should be able to:

- outline the history of English up to the modern period
- understand some of the processes that caused language variation
- understand the historical context of debates over prestige varieties, standardised forms, and prescriptivist attitudes to English

English and invasions

AQA	A P4
AQA	B P4
Edexcel	P4
OCR	P3 P4
WJEC	P3 P4

The language that we call English was first spoken by Angles, Saxons and Jutes, who invaded and then settled in the British Isles in a period spanning the fifth and sixth centuries. The Britons they displaced spoke a Celtic language, but little of this is preserved in England except in place names. The newcomers came from Northern Germany and spoke a variety of the Frisian language.

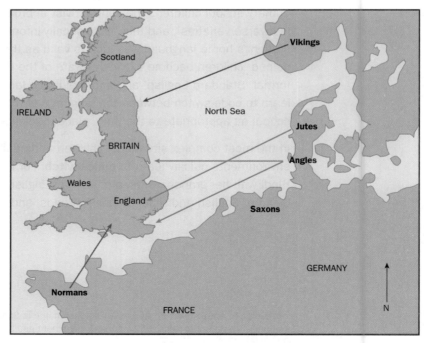

Figure 6.3 Invasions from the fifth to the eleventh centuries

In the next 400 years, four major dialects of Anglo-Saxon developed, based largely on the geographical origins of the invaders. These dialects were West Saxon, Northumbrian, Mercian and Kentish. We know most about the West Saxon variety because more written texts have survived in it – partly as a result of the political success of King Alfred the Great, and partly because the first flowerings of English literature were written in it.

The people doing the writing at this time were almost always monks or other religious people. They wrote histories, pious lives of saints, official documents, and at least one of them decided to commit the epic poem *Beowulf* to parchment. Anglo-Saxon scribes had similar training and it seems that they made a good job of writing the sounds of Anglo-Saxon down. In addition to the letters of today's alphabet they used two additional runic symbols – þ (thorn) for 'th' and p (wynn), which had a 'w' sound. So the earliest English spelling system was consistent with the sound system. If nothing further had happened, English would probably have developed as a dialect of Old German.

Figure 6.4 Manuscript showing ancient script

Unfortunately for the Anglo-Saxons, a new wave of invasions and eventual settlement began in the eighth century, with attacks by Old Norse-speaking Vikings. Old English and Old Norse speakers lived together in an area called the Danelaw, and in order to understand each other both groups simplified their way of speaking – English even borrowed the pronouns 'they', 'their' and 'them' from Old Norse. This is highly unusual, as borrowing normally involves content rather than grammatical words. In another far-reaching development, Anglo-Saxon dropped a complex system of inflectional endings, and adopted a system where meaning was dependent on word order.

Inflections are when words change according to their grammatical function. The most common one in English is adding an 's' for a plural. In Anglo-Saxon, the grammatical form of the word would tell the listener who was looking and who was being looked at, not the order of the words.

Seo cwen geseah þone guman.	The woman saw the man
Þone guman geseah seo cwen.	
The man saw the woman would be	Se guma geseah þa cwen

Notice how 'guman' changes to 'guma' when it becomes the subject of the sentence. Every noun and every verb used to change in this way.

The changes brought about by the contact with Old Norse are difficult to study, as written Anglo-Saxon practically disappeared as a result of a third invasion. The Normans who invaded in 1066 spoke Old French, which is from a completely different branch of the language family tree, as it had Latin rather than Germanic roots. The new language was spoken on all official occasions, and a great number of the words now used for government, the military and the law date from this period, for instance parliament, lieutenant and attorney.

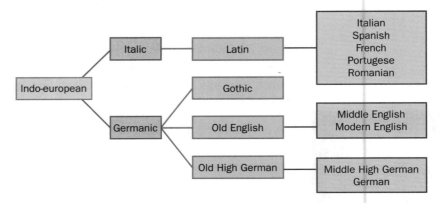

Figure 6.5 The simplified Northern Indo-european language family tree

One of the great misfortunes of this period is that French scribes had different spelling conventions from English ones. So when English re-emerged as a written language, the connections between sounds and spellings had been lost, for instance in the use of 'qu' in place of 'cw', the replacement of Anglo-Saxon 'c' with 'ch', and the 's'/'c' sound confusions in words like 'cercle' and 'cell'. In addition to confusion caused by scribal conventions, the vowel sounds of English underwent a major long-term change in this period.

> **KEY POINT**
>
> It is rather depressing for language reformers that problems that arose over a thousand years ago have still not been sorted out.

The revival of English

AQA   **A P4**
AQA   **B P4**
Edexcel **P4**
OCR   **P3 P4**
WJEC   **P3 P4**

The first Norman English king who could actually speak to his subjects in English was probably Edward I, who reigned from 1239–1307. English was used for the first time in the opening of Parliament in 1362, and in the same year the use of English was officially allowed in law courts. The revival of English writing can be seen in William of Nassyngton's decision to write in English in 1325. This is what he wrote (Þ is pronounced as th).

> No Latin wil I speke no waste,
> But English, þat men vse mast
> Þat can eche man understande,
> Þat is born in Ingelande.

Five Middle English dialects developed from the Anglo-Saxon ones, but it was the **East Midlands dialect** – which contained within its area the nation's two universities, its political and economic capital, and the thriving woollen industries of Norfolk and Suffolk – that eventually became the prestige form and gave rise to modern English.

Figure 6.6 Dialects of Middle English

French

There were two other prestige forms of language throughout most of the Middle English period, one of which was French.

Enormous numbers of French words (probably over 10 000) entered English at this time via their use in official life. The courtier, diplomat and writer Geoffrey Chaucer was deeply familiar with French, and his earliest literary works were translations from it. Chaucer preferred French-style rhyming poetry to the old-fashioned Anglo-Saxon alliterative tradition. One of his characters makes fun of alliteration by claiming to be a sophisticated southerner.

> I am a southern man,
> I cannot gest, rom, ram, ruf, by my letter;
>
> (I am southern man I can't tell stories, rom, ram, ruf, by letters)

Latin

Latin – the language of the Church and of scholarship – had even more prestige than French, and several thousand words came into use, usually in religious, legal, medical and literary contexts. Some authors attempted to achieve a 'high' style by excessive borrowing of Latin terms, but few people were impressed and the style did not catch on.

Increasing the English word stock

By the end of the medieval period, it was possible to construct triplets containing the same idea, using words of Anglo-Saxon, French and Latin origins. The table on the next page shows some examples.

Anglo-Saxon	French	Latin
Rise	Mount	Ascend
Ask	Question	Interrogate
Fast	Firm	Secure
Kingly	Royal	Regal
Holy	Sacred	Consecrated
Fire	Flame	Conflagration

Borrowing was not the only way in which the English word stock increased during this period. The Anglo-Saxon and Germanic tendency to run words together continued into Middle English and produced new compounds like 'blackberry', 'grandfather', 'highway' and 'schoolmaster'. The '-er' suffix produced 'bricklayers', 'housekeepers' and 'moneymakers', and a number of new phrasal verbs like 'go out' and 'fall by' emerged.

> **KEY POINT**
>
> Along with borrowing, compounding and back-formation **coining**, the invention of new words is one of the chief sources of new English words.

Modern English

AQA   **A P4**
AQA   **B P4**
Edexcel **P4**
OCR   **P3 P4**
WJEC   **P3 P4**

By the beginning of the sixteenth century, Middle English had given way to Early Modern English. Most inflections had disappeared, the sound system had stabilised, and the nation's vocabulary was rich and flexible. At the same time, people began to be a little more reflective about their language use and make explicit comments on such things as grammar and morphology. Although literacy levels were not high in England during this period, two major changes occurred that encouraged reading and writing at all levels of society – the invention of the printing press and access to the Bible. We will discuss each of these in turn.

Invention of the printing press

The invention of the moveable type **printing press** meant that for the first time books and writing could be made accessible to a large audience.

Figure 6.7 A printing press

A whole book might be beyond the dreams of an ordinary person, but there were plenty of cheap ballads and broadsheets – written in English rather than Latin or French – for sale. As the quotation from Caxton on page 163 shows, a large audience required a 'standard' English. This did not exist in the 1470s, but the existence of printing presses in places like London and Oxford helped to spread the East Midlands dialect throughout the country.

Access to the Bible

Access to the Bible was strictly controlled in the medieval period. It was mostly available in Latin, and only educated priests could read and distribute portions of it to the population. When people began to question the wisdom of the Catholic Church, they looked to the Bible for answers. One of the first things that Protestant reformers like Martin Luther did was to translate the Bible into their mother tongues.

The first major English translation of the New Testament of the Bible was made by William Wycliffe in the 1390s. It was roundly condemned for making 'the jewel of the clergy' into 'the toy of the laity'. It was suppressed, and the translation of Bibles into English was technically illegal until 1611 when the King James Version was published. William Tyndale's Bible was published abroad in 1525 and Tyndale was eventually executed as a result.

As illustrated in the table below, the difference between Tyndale's and Wycliffe's language (using modern spelling) shows clearly how modern the English language had become by 1525. The translators of the King James Bible had access to Tyndale's banned version and re-used much of his language. His words still seem familiar today.

Wycliffe	Tyndale
Blessed ben poor 'men' in spirit, for the kingdom of heaven is herne.	Blessed are the poor in spirit, for theirs is the kingdom of heaven.
Blessed ben mild 'men', for they schulen welde the earth.	Blessed are the meek, for they shall inherit the earth.
Blessed ben they that mournen, for they schulen be comforted.	Blessed are they that mourn, for they shall be comforted.

Protestantism and free access to the Bible went hand in hand, and provided a major incentive for people to learn to read. They wanted to be able to interpret the Bible for themselves rather than rely on the words of priests. Great family Bibles became fixtures in many homes from the seventeenth century onwards.

Another contribution of radical Protestantism to the English language was brought about by the great propaganda battles of the English Civil War (1642–1648). Printers had been in the habit of adding extra letters to words simply to help them to right justify their text. In the hurried circumstances of leaflet printing, printers tended to pick a single spelling and keep to it. The idea of a standard spelling of English caught on over the next hundred years, with the publication of various 'hard word' lists and eventually dictionaries.

Expansion and the Inkhorn debate

AQA   **A P4**
AQA   **B P4**
Edexcel **P4**
OCR   **P3 P4**
WJEC **P3 P4**

Books such as Mulcaster's Elementarie did much to encourage the standardisation of English.

The period of political stability provided by the long reign of Elizabeth I enabled the English language to flower in terms of vocabulary, and confidence in itself as a literary medium. Sir Thomas More (under Henry VIII) wrote *Utopia* in Latin. Edmund Spenser (under Elizabeth) wrote *The Faerie Queen* in English. Spenser consciously used old-fashioned English words, but other writers – including the dramatists Marlowe, Shakespeare and Jonson – felt free to borrow words from abroad or make up new ones. Both tendencies were criticised in what is known as the **Inkhorn debate**. (An inkhorn was an inkwell typically used by a scholar.)

Shakespeare is credited with the first use in print of several thousand words (this does not mean he made the words up himself), and it is generally thought that his influence added about 1500 words to the English Lexicon.

Some of his additions included:

- abstemious
- accommodation
- bloodstained
- cake (as a verb)
- countless
- juiced (as an adjective)
- rant (from Dutch)
- sanctimonious
- zany (from Italian).

This list shows that Shakespeare (and his contemporaries) was happy to borrow from foreign languages, re-arrange Latin roots, or make new compounds from English originals.

Shakespeare also used words that did not make it into mainstream English, for example 'conspectuities', 'germins', 'incarnadine', 'oppugnancy' and 'relume'. Critics would regard these words as 'inkhorn' terms, borrowed unnecessarily from Latin or Greek when words with identical meanings already existed in English.

Writers like Thomas Elyot and George Pettie borrowed enthusiastically from classical languages. However, John Cheke had this to say.

> I am of this opinion that our own tung should be written cleane and pure, unmixt and unmangeled with borowing of other tunges; wherein if we take not heed by tijm, ever borowing and never paying, she shall be fain to keep her house as bankrupt.

'Dismiss', 'celebrate', 'encyclopaedia', 'commit', 'capacity' and 'ingenious' all started out as inkhorn terms, but seem to have filled a lexical gap. Some writers insisted on using older English words like 'gleeman' for 'musician' and 'inwit' for 'conscience'. Alternatively, like William Barnes, they invented words like 'starlore' for astronomy and 'speechcraft' for grammar, which used only Germanic roots.

The borrowers and adapters clearly won the argument in the sixteenth and seventeenth centuries. However, even in the twentieth century, authors like George Orwell were critical of this approach.

In the seventeenth century, some people felt that the language had somehow become 'corrupt', and that efforts were needed to return it to its (mythical) pure state. The idea of an Academy of English that would decide on the correct use of English was proposed early in the century, but nothing came of it.

The poet and grammarian John Dryden tried again in 1664, and a committee for 'improving the English language' was actually set up as part of the Royal Society, but again nothing materialised. Daniel Defoe proposed an Academy in 1697, as did Jonathan Swift in 1712.

> **KEY POINT**
>
> The idea that the English language is in terminal decline is a popular one, even today.

Samuel Johnson

The anxieties over the 'decline' of English led to the demand for a great dictionary to 'fix' the language. The task of producing the first major English dictionary fell to Dr Samuel Johnson, who quickly realised that **prescriptivism** in matters of language was a waste of effort. In his preface to the dictionary, he says that the hope of preserving a language from change and decay is foolish.

With this hope, however, academies have been instituted, to guard the avenues of their languages, to retain fugitives, and repulse intruders; but their vigilance and activity have hitherto been vain; sounds are too volatile and subtle for legal restraints; to enchain syllables, and to lash the wind, are equally the undertakings of pride, unwilling to measure its desires by its strength.

Extract from Preface to a Dictionary of the English Language *by Samuel Johnson*

> **PROGRESS CHECK**
>
> 1 Which three languages have made significant contributions to the development of English?
> 2 Which Middle English dialect eventually gave rise to modern English?
> 3 What is the word 'relume' (meaning 'to light again') an example of?
>
> 1 Anglo-Saxon; Old Norse; Old French.
> 2 East Midlands.
> 3 Inkhorn English.

6.6 Texts in historical context

LEARNING SUMMARY	**After studying this section, you should be able to:** • recognise the lexical, graphological and grammatical features of English in different historical periods • discuss how these features of English are used and applied within a text

Texts in time

AQA   **A P4**
AQA   **B P4**
Edexcel **P4**
OCR   **P3 P4**
WJEC   **P3 P4**

Several specifications ask you to look at texts from different historical periods, and to identify and discuss their distinctive features. In this section, we look at a selection of these texts.

Early Modern English

AQA   **A P4**
AQA   **B P4**
Edexcel **P4**
OCR   **P3 P4**
WJEC   **P3 P4**

Lack of standardisation is one of the characteristics of language use in the Early Modern English period. Shakespeare couldn't even decide on the spelling of his own name – it is spelt in six different ways in the six known examples of his signature.

Individuals may have developed and followed consistent systems, but there were many complaints at the time about the use of superfluous letters, in particular the **silent final 'e'**. In the Ascham text shown on the next page (see Figure 6.8), 'tong' and 'tonge' appear within three lines of each other – presumably the 'e' in the second occurrence was to help with the justification of the text.

To modern readers, the use of the **long 's'($\int$)** is particularly noticeable. This had disappeared by the beginning of the nineteenth century, but in texts before this time it is highly visible. It was used in initial and medial positions, but not at the end of words. The appearance of the word '$\int$ufficient' in the Ascham text gives some idea of why this grapheme died out.

The letters 'u' and 'v' are used interchangeably in some texts, but typically 'v' was used at the beginning of words and 'u' was used in the middle. For example, in the original title page of Shakespeare's *King Lear*, 'vnfortunate' and 'v$\int$ually' follow this pattern. For the modern reader, words like 'seruants' and 'v$\int$ually' present a visual challenge. Another feature of the time which is unfamiliar to today's readers is that '$\int$t' is printed as a ligature (i.e. as a single piece of type – two letters written as one), and 'i' is used instead of 'j' in 'maiestie'.

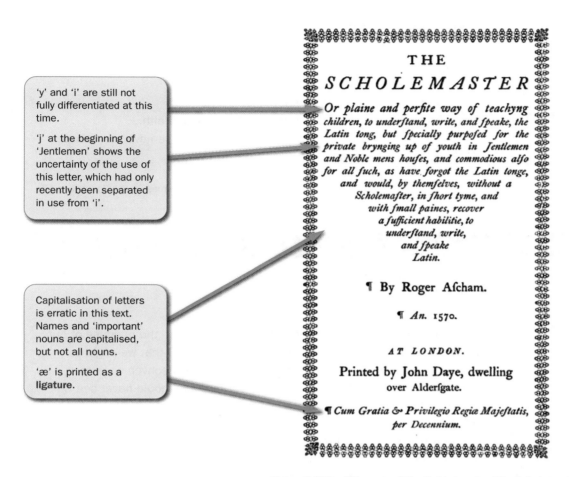

'y' and 'i' are still not fully differentiated at this time.

'j' at the beginning of 'Jentlemen' shows the uncertainty of the use of this letter, which had only recently been separated in use from 'i'.

Capitalisation of letters is erratic in this text. Names and 'important' nouns are capitalised, but not all nouns.

'æ' is printed as a **ligature**.

THE SCHOLEMASTER

Or plaine and perfite way of teachyng children, to underſtand, write, and ſpeake, the Latin tong, but ſpecially purpoſed for the private brynging up of youth in Jentlemen and Noble mens houſes, and commodious alſo for all ſuch, as have forgot the Latin tonge, and would, by themſelves, without a Scholemaſter, in ſhort tyme, and with ſmall paines, recover a ſufficient habilitie, to underſtand, write, and ſpeake Latin.

¶ By Roger Aſcham.

¶ An. 1570.

AT LONDON.

Printed by John Daye, dwelling over Alderſgate.

¶ Cum Gratia & Privilegio Regiæ Majeſtatis, per Decennium.

Figure 6.8 The title page of *The Schoolmaster (The Scholemaster)*

Grammar

The grammar of this period was recognisably modern. The **double negative** constructions had not yet been condemned, and sentences like 'I cannot go no further' were perfectly acceptable. 'Do' was much more commonly used as an auxiliary in phrases like 'our best men with thee do go' and in emphatic statements like 'we that do hearken to thee'. By the nineteenth century, this use was found only in poetry, as it was a way of securing rhymes. In Standard English, verb inflections like 'sleepeth', 'know'st' and 'spake' fell out of use.

By the middle of the seventeenth century, 'thee' and 'thou' had virtually disappeared from standard speech. Only the Religious Society of Friends, or Quakers, kept the forms alive as a statement of social equality. The rules for 'thee' and 'thou' depended heavily on social status. 'Thee' was used with equals and friends, but also to address social inferiors. 'You' was used to social superiors, such as servants to masters or children to parents. A husband might address his wife as 'thou' and the wife call him 'you'. In *King Lear*, the King addresses his daughter, Cordelia, as 'you' when he is happy with her (for example, 'What can you say…'), but as 'thy' when she upsets him (for instance, 'But goes thy heart with this?').

Sentence structures were often consciously and artfully constructed in imitation of Classical models. For instance, suspended sentences deliberately piled on detail until a final verb was reached, in order to create a sense of suspense and anticipation.

Here is a famous example.

> And though I have the gift of prophecy,
>   and understand all mysteries,
>   and all knowledge;
>   and though I have all faith,
>   so that I could remove mountains,
>   and have not charity,
>   I **am** nothing.
>
> *Extract from* The King James Bible, I Corinthians 13

Eighteenth-century English

AQA   **A P4**
AQA   **B P4**
Edexcel **P4**
OCR   **P3 P4**
WJEC   **P3 P4**

The text below, written by Jonathan Swift, has many typical features of eighteenth-century writing.

> The whole of the first word of a paragraph is capitalised.

> Not all nouns are capitalised, e.g. 'thing', 'way' and 'matter'.

> 'Hath' as the past tense of 'hath' still survives, but most other verb endings are modern.

> This form of 'possessed' (possed) is now archaic, as is the spelling of 'extreme' (Extream).

> Italicised font is used here for quoted phrases. Earlier in the text, it was used for emphasis.

> A long suspended sentence.

> 'Over-run' is still hyphenated, suggesting that it is a recent compound.

> This alternative spelling of 'shew' has only recently disappeared.

ANOTHER Cause... which hath contributed not a little to the maiming of our Language, is a foolish Opinion, advanced of late Years, that we ought to spell exactly as we speak; which beside the obvious Inconvenience of utterly destroying our Etymology, would be a thing we should never see an End of. Not only the several Towns and Countries of *England*, have a different way of Pronouncing, but even here in *London*, they clip their Words after one Manner about the Court, another in the City, and a third in the Suburbs; and in a few Years, it is probable, will all differ from themselves, as Fancy or Fashion shall direct: All which reduced to Writing would entirely confound Orthography. Yet many People are so fond of this Conceit, that is sometimes a difficult matter to read modern Books and Pamphlets, where the Words are so curtailed, and varied from their original Spelling, that whoever hath been used to plain *English*, will hardly know them by sight.

SEVERAL young Men at the Universities, terribly possed with the fear of Pedantry, run into a worse Extream, and think all Politeness to consist in reading the daily Trash sent down to them from hence: This they call *knowing the World*, and *reading Men and Manners*. Thus furnished they come up to Town, reckon all their Errors for Accomplishments, borrow the newest Sett of Phrases, and if they take a Pen into their Hands, all the odd Words they have picked up in a Coffee-House, or a Gaming Ordinary, are produced as Flowers of Style; and the Orthography refined to the utmost. To this we owe those monstrous Productions, which under the Names of *Trips*, *Spies*, *Amusements*, and other conceited Appellations, have over-run us for some Years past. To this we owe that strange Race of Wits, who tell us, they Write to the *Humour of the Age*: And I wish I could say, these quaint Fopperies were wholly absent from graver Subjects. In short, I would undertake to shew Your Lordship several Pieces, where the Beauties of this kind are so prominent, that with all your Skill in Languages, you could never be able either to read or understand them.

Extract from A proposal for correcting, improving, and ascertaining the English tongue (addressed to the Earl of Oxford) *by Jonathan Swift*

The principal graphological difference between Swift's text and a modern text is the use of **capitalisation** and **italics**. The long 's' of previous generations has been abandoned, and there are no ligatures in evidence. The use of capital letters stands out because almost all nouns are capitalised (as in modern German), and, for the most part, italics are used in the place of modern quotation marks. Spelling is very close to modern conventions, except in words like 'extream', 'sett' and 'shew'. 'Extream' seems to be modelled on 'stream', whilst 'sett' has been exclusively associated with the home of a badger in modern usage. 'Shew' was used on railway station signs in living memory.

As Swift's subject is language use, the use of language seems careful and highly structured. The sentence beginning 'Thus furnished...' is a satiric attack on young men fresh from universities in the form of a **complex suspended sentence**. Dryden condemned ending sentences with prepositions, but Swift writes 'a thing we should never see an End of', with more concern for emphasis than for a polished style. Grammatically, the only outstanding features are the use of the old-fashioned 'hath' for 'has' and 'possed' for 'possessed'.

The other difference is chiefly in Swift's **lexis**. Several terms that he used in his writing – such as 'fancy' for 'imagination', 'conceit' for 'a fanciful notion' and 'ordinary' for 'inn' – have acquired different meanings since then. He uses 'countries' in the sense of country areas rather than nations, whilst 'fopperies for foolishnesses' has almost completely disappeared. At least two of the slang terms Swift criticises in this extract – 'trips' and 'spies' – clearly never caught on. Swift also uses the word 'wit' in a specialised eighteenth-century sense, in that it indicates the sort of person who uses words with facility, rather than the ability to do so as in the modern sense. The word 'humour' is not used in the context of being amusing, but in relation to the medieval meaning of typical character.

Swift's ideas on reforming spelling are conservative rather than radical. He speaks of words 'varied from their original Spelling' as if there was a standard from which they have decayed and, in the second paragraph, he seems to blame fashionable wits for this corruption of the language. He points out that a phonetic spelling system would prevent people from seeing the etymological connections between words. For instance, if the unpronounced 'a' in real was dropped, its relation to the word 'reality' would no longer be apparent. This point is frequently raised by objectors to phonetic spelling reform.

Swift's proposal is addressed to the Earl of Oxford, and towards the end of the final paragraph the Earl is politely referred to as 'Your Lordship'. Swift and the Earl both seem to live in London, because the young men from the universities are described as reading trashy newspapers from 'hence', before they eventually come up to 'Town' as London was frequently called.

> **KEY POINT**
>
> Much of the literary writing of the eighteenth century is London centric, as this was a centre of wealth, literacy and publishing.

Nineteenth-century English

AQA   **A P4**
AQA   **B P4**
Edexcel **P4**
OCR   **P3 P4**
WJEC   **P3 P4**

The following passage is taken from the novel *Pickwick Papers* by Charles Dickens. Mr Tony Weller – a coachman – and his son Sam – a manservant – are in conversation.

> Long, lightly punctuated sentences.
>
> The authorial voice uses educated Standard English.
>
> The 'g' has been dropped.

We have said that Mr. Weller was engaged in preparing for his journey to London—he was taking sustenance, in fact. On the table before him, stood a pot of ale, a cold round of beef, and a very respectable-looking loaf, to each of which he distributed his favours in turn, with the most rigid impartiality. He had just cut a mighty slice from the latter, when the footsteps of somebody entering the room, caused him to raise his head; and he beheld his son.

'Mornin', Sammy!' said the father.

The son walked up to the pot of ale, and nodding significantly to his parent, took a long draught by way of reply.

> The letter 'w' is used for 'v'.
>
> Many words are clipped.
>
> 'I des-say' means 'I dare say'.
>
> 'Gammoned' means 'cheated'. 'Mulberry' refers to the colour of the cheat's clothing.

'Wery good power o' suction, Sammy,' said Mr. Weller the elder, looking into the pot, when his first-born had set it down half empty. 'You'd ha' made an uncommon fine oyster, Sammy, if you'd been born in that station o' life.'

'Yes, I des-say, I should ha' managed to pick up a respectable livin',' replied Sam applying himself to the cold beef, with considerable vigour.

'I'm wery sorry, Sammy,' said the elder Mr. Weller, shaking up the ale, by describing small circles with the pot, preparatory to drinking. 'I'm wery sorry, Sammy, to hear from your lips, as you let yourself be gammoned by that 'ere mulberry man. I always thought, up to three days ago, that the names of Veller and gammon could never come into contract, Sammy, never.'

'Always exceptin' the case of a widder, of course,' said Sam.

'Widders, Sammy,' replied Mr. Weller, slightly changing colour. 'Widders are 'ceptions to ev'ry rule. I have heerd how many ordinary women one widder's equal to in pint o' comin' over you. I think it's five-and-twenty, but I don't rightly know vether it ain't more.'

'Well; that's pretty well,' said Sam.

> The letter 'v' is used for 'w'.
>
> There is internal clipping.
>
> No use of 'an'.
>
> 'Know'd' is used instead of 'known'.

'Besides,' continued Mr. Weller, not noticing the interruption, 'that's a wery different thing. You know what the counsel said, Sammy, as defended the gen'l'm'n as beat his wife with the poker, venever he got jolly. "And arter all, my Lord," says he, "it's a amiable weakness." So I says respectin' widders, Sammy, and so you'll say, ven you gets as old as me.'

'I ought to ha' know'd better, I know,' said Sam.

Extract from Pickwick Papers *by Charles Dickens*

This extract from a novel is completely modern in its graphology and layout, and in its grammar and syntax in the narrative sections. It is interesting linguistically, because in the dialogue Dickens tries to capture how two working-class Londoners of the period spoke. Tony Weller is a coachman and his son Sam is a manservant, which would make them both respectable, but not formally educated.

The main feature of Dickens' lower-class speech is the switching of 'w' and 'v'. This is a characteristic of the Kentish dialect that goes all the way back to the Anglo-Saxon period, but which has now almost entirely disappeared. Dickens also makes his characters clip their words, either at the beginning with ''ere' or at the end by frequently dropping the letter 'g'. The word 'gentlemen' ('gen'l'm'n') apparently has only one vowel. Other aspects of pronunciation are the use of 'ar' for 'af' in 'arter all' and the lack of an intervening consonant in 'a amiable'. The spelling of 'widders' probably indicates an unstressed final 'ə' sound. Modern London sounds and speech habits can perhaps be detected in 'pint' for 'point' and in the emphatic use of 'never'. The Wellers seem to use Standard English grammar except for Sam's use of an '-ed' past tense marker in 'know'd' rather than 'known'. This is sometimes heard in modern London speech.

Social attitudes can be seen in the sections relating to women and wife beating. Old Mr Weller seems to find independent women – widows – at least 25 times more threatening than women who are controlled by either their fathers or their husbands. The story about wife beating when drunk makes light of the crime by describing it as 'a amiable weakness'; in other words, one that is more excusable within a relationship than, say, beating strangers 'with the poker'. The use of the euphemism 'jolly' for 'drunk' shows a tolerant attitude towards alcohol abuse.

It is difficult to tell how good Dickens' ear for ordinary people's speech was, but people like the Wellers would have been known to his contemporary audience, and if he had been too inaccurate his books might have been less popular. The tradition of ordinary people speaking non-Standard English is a long one, and there is a sense that the Wellers are part of the 'comic relief' of this story.

> **KEY POINT**
>
> Dickens was one of a number of writers (see also, for instance, the extract from *Wuthering Heights* on page 166) who observed and chronicled the very different language styles of rich and poor English people.

Twentieth-century English

AQA **A P4**
AQA **B P4**
Edexcel **P4**
OCR **P3 P4**
WJEC **P3 P4**

The extract on the next page is from a poem called *The Chaos*. It was written by the Dutch writer, traveller and teacher Dr Gerard Nolst Trenité. He studied classics, law and political science, and taught in California and Holland. The poem was written for a linguistics column in an Amsterdam newspaper, which he wrote using the pseudonym Charivarius.

The poem is addressed to a child, possibly the poet's daughter.

Homographs.

Inconsistent spelling of 's' and 'z' sounds.

Homographs.

Irregular spelling of vowel sounds.

Irregular endings.

Homographs.

Irregular spelling of vowel sounds.

Dearest creature in creation,
Study English pronunciation.
I will teach you in my verse
Sounds like corpse, corps, horse, and worse.
I will keep you, Suzy, busy,
Make your head with heat grow dizzy.
Tear in eye, your dress will tear.
So shall I! Oh hear my prayer.

Just compare heart, beard, and heard,
Dies and diet, lord and word,
Sword and sward, retain and Britain.
(Mind the latter, how it's written.)
Now I surely will not plague you
With such words as plaque and ague.
But be careful how you speak:
Say break and steak, but bleak and streak;
Cloven, oven, how and low,
Script, receipt, show, poem, and toe.

Retention of foreign pronunciation.

Stresses – or lack of them – on word endings.

The use of a hard and soft 'g'.

Retention of foreign pronunciation.

Hear me say, devoid of trickery,
Daughter, laughter, and Terpsichore,
Typhoid, measles, topsails, aisles,
Exiles, similes, and reviles;
Scholar, vicar, and cigar,
Solar, mica, war and far;
One, anemone, Balmoral,
Kitchen, lichen, laundry, laurel;
Gertrude, German, wind and mind,
Scene, Melpomene, mankind.

...

Hard and soft 'g' is used.

Vowel sound modified by preceding letter.

Irregular spelling of vowel sounds.

Face, but preface, not efface.
Phlegm, phlegmatic, ass, glass, bass.
Large, but target, gin, give, verging,
Ought, out, joust and scour, scourging.
Ear, but earn and wear and tear
Do not rhyme with here but ere.
Seven is right, but so is even,
Hyphen, roughen, nephew Stephen,
Monkey, donkey, Turk and jerk,
Ask, grasp, wasp, and cork and work.

Retention of foreign pronunciation.

Spelling and sound divergence.

The letter 's' has been added for etymological reasons.

Pronunciation — think of Psyche!
Is a paling stout and spikey?
Won't it make you lose your wits,
Writing groats and saying grits?
It's a dark abyss or tunnel:
Strewn with stones, stowed, solace, gunwale,
Islington and Isle of Wight,
Housewife, verdict and indict.

Spelling and sound divergence.

Finally, which rhymes with enough —
Though, through, plough, or dough, or cough?
Hiccough has the sound of cup.
My advice is to give up!!!

Extract from The Chaos *by Dr Gerard Nolst Trenité (1870–1946)*

This poem is a light-hearted attack on the English spelling system by someone with a very thorough knowledge of its irregularities. The most common problem that the poem points out is the use of homographs, which are words – or collections of letters within a word – that are written the same way, but which have different pronunciations. The most extreme example of this is 'corpse' and 'corps', where the lack of a final 'e' makes the 'p' sound disappear. The reason for this is the English habit of borrowing foreign words – in the case of 'corps' from French – without regularising the spelling. Other examples of this are 'Terpischore', 'anemone', 'Melpomene' and 'Psyche', all of which are from Greek.

Another large set of irregularities are found in the spelling of vowel sounds. This is a major problem for all learners of English, as there are only 5 vowels in the English alphabet and approximately 20 vowel sounds. Historically, vowel sounds 'drift' more than consonants, and the 'ough' group mentioned in the last verse provide an extreme example. The treatment of the hard and soft 'g' is also shown to be highly irregular.

Historical change can be seen in the pronunciation of words like 'groats' as 'grits' and 'gunwale' as 'gunnel'. There is also an extra – and never pronounced – 's' in 'Isle', the result of etymological interference from lexicographers.

The tone of this poem is humorous, but it did raise a number of issues that needed to be addressed by spelling reformers. 'Groat' and 'gunwale' remind us that the pronunciation of words changes over time. Would a phonetic system of spelling keep up with this? Words like 'Psyche' are borrowed from Greek and follow a foreign system of spelling – if spelling was regularised, the etymological routes for these kinds of words would be lost. (These points were also raised by Swift on page 190.)

A more serious point for spelling reformers was the issue of the alphabet. Was it possible to have a regular system of pronunciation using 26 letters to represent 44 sounds?

Twentieth-century social dialects

Finally in this section, we will look at three texts from the late 1950s and early 1960s that reflect attitudes to language and to language change.

In 1954, Alan S. C. Ross wrote an account of upper class (U) and non-upper class English (Non-U). His ideas were popularised by Nancy Mitford, John Betjeman and others in a 1956 book entitled *Noblesse oblige: an inquiry into the identifiable characteristics of the English aristocracy*. The poem on the next page appears at the end of the book and satirises fussy middle-class behaviour by using exclusively Non-U language. The U equivalents are given in the margin.

U – 'Ring'.

U – 'napkins'.

U – 'lavatory'.

> Phone for the fish knives, Norman
> As cook is a little unnerved;
> You kiddies have crumpled the serviettes
> And I must have things daintily served.
>
> Are the requisites all in the toilet?
> The frills round the cutlets can wait
> Till the girl has replenished the cruets
> And switched on the logs in the grate.

U – 'cruets' not used and the log fire would be real.

U – 'drawing room'.

U – just 'riding' – horse would be understood.

> It's ever so close in the lounge dear,
> But the vestibule's comfy for tea
> And Howard is riding on horseback
> So do come and take some with me
>
> Now here is a fork for your pastries
> And do use the couch for your feet;
> I know what I wanted to ask you–
> Is trifle sufficient for sweet?

U – 'sofa'.

U – 'pudding'.

U – 'jam'.

U – a different pronunciation of 'scones' (that rhymes with 'John's').

> Milk and then just as it comes dear?
> I'm afraid the preserve's full of stones;
> Milk and then just as it comes dear
> With afternoon tea-cakes and scones.

How to Get On in Society by John Betjeman

Absolute Beginners is set in and around Notting Hill, and is credited as one of the first texts to spot the emergence of teenagers as a group. It was published in 1959.

Long, loosely organised sentences.

> He didn't wig this, so giving me a kindly smile, he stepped away to make himself respectable again. I put a disc on to his hi-fi, my choice being Billie H., who sends me even more than Ella does, but only when, as now, I'm tired, and also, what with seeing Suze again, and working hard with my Rolleiflex and then this moronic conversation, graveyard gloomy. But Lady Day has suffered so much in her life she carries it all for you, and soon I was quite a cheerful cat again.
> 'I wish I had this one' I said, when Mr P. appeared.
> 'Take it, please,' he told me, beaming.

Extract from Absolute Beginners *by Colin MacInnes*

In this extract:
- 'wig' means understand
- 'hi-fi' (meaning hi-fidelity) is a record player
- 'Billie H.' is Billie Holiday
- 'sends' means affects or moves
- 'Ella' is Ella Fitzgerald
- 'Rolleiflex' is an expensive camera
- 'Lady Day' means Billie Holiday
- 'cat' means person.

A *Clockwork Orange* was published in 1962. It is narrated by Alex – he writes in a slang called Nadsat, which is based mainly on Russian. English equivalents are given in the margin. In this scene he has been made to watch violent films, to cure him of his violent tendencies, using aversion therapy.

'Govoreet' means say. 'Slovo' means 'word' and 'malenky' little.

The no-nonsense scientist uses 'Now, then' as a discourse marker.

Non-standard use of 'pervert'.

'Grahzny' means dirty and 'veshches' means things. 'Gulliver' is another word for head and 'plott' means body.

Informal use of 'like'.

Clipped informative speech, valuing facts over empathy.

'You seem a sufficiently intelligent young man. You seem, too, to be not without taste. You've just got this violence thing, haven't you? Violence and theft, theft being an aspect of violence.' I didn't govoreet a single slovo, brothers, I was still feeling sick, though getting a malenky bit better now. But it had been a terrible day. 'Now, then,' said Dr Brodsky, 'how do you think this is done? Tell me, what do you think we're doing to you?

'You're making me feel ill, I'm ill when I look at those filthy pervert films of yours. But it's not really the films that's doing it. But I feel that if you'll stop these films I'll stop feeling ill.'

'Right,' said Dr Brodsky. 'It's association, the oldest educational method in the world. And what really causes you to feel ill?'

'These grahzny sodding veshches that come out of my gulliver and my plott,' I said, 'that's what it is.'

'Quaint,' said Dr Brodsky, like smiling, 'the dialect of the tribe. Do you know anything of its provenance, Branom?'

'Odd bits of old rhyming slang,' said Dr Branom, who did not look quite so much like a friend any more. 'A bit of gipsy talk, too. But most of the roots are Slav. Propaganda. Subliminal penetration.'

Extract from A Clockwork Orange *by Anthony Burgess*

These three texts all show language being used to define particular groups and to exclude others.

The concept of upper-class, high-prestige language is redolent of snobbery and social exclusion, and Betjeman's poem uses it to look down on a woman who fails to use U terminology. The general idea behind U speech seems to be elegant simplicity. 'Fish knives' and 'frills round the cutlets' are not signifiers of wealth, but of pretension. U people have been rich for generations and do not need to show off. Horseback riding is understood to be the norm, and words like 'jam' and 'pudding' reflect simple tastes.

In the Bible the Gileadites had defeated the Ephraimites in battle. The Gileadites asked refugees to say 'shibboleth', as Ephraimites could not pronounce 'sh'. If they could not say it, they were killed.

The speaker in the poem is using what she thinks is high-prestige language (in a Lakoffian manner), but in Betjeman's satire virtually everything she says is wrong. She is clearly financially well off as she has a cook and a maid, but she confuses elegance with euphemism. 'Requisites' sounds smart, but actually means 'things that are needed' such as, presumably, toilet paper, soap and towels. She also exhibits another trait identified by Lakoff in her use of hedges, such as 'I know what I wanted to ask you– is...?' A U speaker would begin such a question with the word 'Is'. According to Ross and Mitford, U speech acts as a kind of shibboleth that allows U people to identify each other. The main focus of this kind of behaviour is vocabulary, but in the final word of the poem the speaker fails a pronunciation test as well.

If the Betjeman poem reflects the language of a long-established elite, the extract from *Absolute Beginners* shows the emergence of a new force in Western European life – the teenager with time and money on his or her hands. Like U speech, the teenage speech in the novel is meant to be understood by a small and exclusive group, but its focus is narrower – in this extract it is on music and gadgets. 'Hi-fi', meaning hi-fidelity, was a new and expensive technology in the 1950s, and only people for whom music was very important were using it then. The familiar way in which the narrator refers to female jazz singers – and expects his readers to understand – is typical of language used for group bonding. He not only expects the readers to be familiar with the singer's repertoire, but also with her nicknames ('Billie H.' and 'Lady Day') and the details of her life – 'But Lady Day has suffered so much in her life she carries it all for you'.

Similarly, the narrator refers to his Rolleiflex camera in the same way that a modern writer might refer to an iPhone or a pair of Nike trainers. The important point is not what the camera does, but its brand. Other members of the group are meant to recognise this and be impressed. Elsewhere, the narrator uses standard vocabulary in new ways. 'Wig' (meaning understand) is clearly something head related and 'cat' (meaning person) reflects American slang of the period. The slang use of the word 'send' in the sense of moving is another Americanism, which was almost exclusively used in terms of music. (Interestingly, MacInnes is quoted in the Oxford English Dictionary for his use of the words 'hi-fi', 'cat' and 'send'.)

By the time Anthony Burgess wrote *A Clockwork Orange*, the idea of rebellious teenagers was well established. In writing about them he clearly wished to show how they used language, but using contemporary teen slang would mean that his book would date very quickly. He therefore uses a typical science fiction trope by turning a contemporary trend on its head. If 1960s teens were influenced by America, perhaps future teens would be influenced by Russia – Russia was the other great superpower in the 1960s.

The fact that the novel is narrated in Nadsat means that the reader has to work out what each word means from context. This immediately puts the reader in the same 'group' as Alex the narrator – the reader is addressed as brother – and increases sympathy for him in spite of his violent and criminal ways. In the above extract, Alex's loose and inventive slang is contrasted with the didactic and hectoring tone of the chief scientist. He treats Alex like a school boy, asking him questions that he already knows the answers to and then talking across him to his fellow scientist. Both scientists use an abrupt telegraphic style to convey information rather than emotion.

The language used in *A Clockwork Orange* and *Absolute Beginners* conforms to Trudgill's[3] theories about overt and covert prestige. The scientists use a style of language that has **overt prestige** based on Standard English, which implies education and intelligence. Alex and the narrator of *Absolute Beginners* achieve **covert prestige** through not using a 'standard' language, valuing group loyalty and solidarity. It is significant from this point of view that the speaker in the Betjeman poem is female.

3 Trudgill, P. October 1972. 'Sex, covert prestige and linguistic change in the urban British English of Norwich', *Language in Society*, 1 (2), 175–195.

All three texts position the reader in a particular way. Betjeman's poem makes no sense unless you are aware of the difference between U and Non-U speech, and it invites the reader to become part of an 'in' crowd looking down on someone. It is an example of how not to get on in society, which activates the reader's own snobbery. It is partly redeemed by its humorous intent – television sitcoms, such as *Keeping up Appearances*, have been built around laughing at this sort of behaviour.

MacInnes' narrator is much less self-conscious about his use of language, but sharing it with the readers creates a bond of mutual understanding. Burgess uses the same technique, but sets himself – and the readers – a much tougher challenge by using an unfamiliar source for his slang.

> **KEY POINT**
>
> One way of looking at language development in the last 300 years is as a story of widening access to print, as literacy has expanded. The exclusive club of Londoners in the eighteenth century was replaced by the populist Charles Dickens, who wrote with sympathy about most social classes. In the twentieth century, excluded groups such as the young and the poor gained access to print, and in the twenty first century, almost anyone can be published on the Internet.

> **PROGRESS CHECK**
>
> 1 What is a ligature?
> 2 What, briefly, is the etymological argument against spelling reform?
> 3 What does U stand for in U and Non-U?

3 Upper class.
2 The connection between words with similar origins would not be visible in a phonetic spelling system.
1 Two letters written as one.

6.7 Technology and text

LEARNING SUMMARY	After studying this section, you should be able to:
	• identify some of the key features of electronic-based texts
	• discuss how these features are used and applied

Key features of electronic-based texts

AQA	A P4
AQA	B P4
Edexcel	P4
OCR	P3 P4
WJEC	P3 P4

In *Star Trek* and other science fiction futures, almost nobody writes. Computers can be addressed by voice, and 'logs' are audio recordings rather than written documents. These features have obvious advantages for the makers of television series, but it is unlikely that anyone in 1966, when *Star Trek* was first broadcast, could have guessed how much typing everyone would be doing in the twenty first century. Mobile phones, e-mail, instant messaging, tweeting and blogging all require interactions with a keyboard or keypad. In 2009, about 247 billion e-mails a day were sent, whilst the average American teenager originated around 80 texts every day.

Many of the key characteristics of texts are the result of trying to enter alphabetical text using a numerical keypad. For instance, on most keypads the letters PQRS share the same key, and it therefore takes four key presses to reach one of the most common letters in English, 'S'. On most phones it takes four presses to reach an apostrophe, and so on. Therefore, users are unlikely to use traditional English orthography to text.

In his book on texting, entitled *Txtng: The Gr8 Db8*, David Crystal identifies five main strategies used by texters to shorten the keying process, and one example of language play. These are illustrated in the table below.

Feature	Examples	
Pictograms and logograms	b	be
	2	to
	@	at
	x	'kiss'
	b4	before
	:-)	'smile'
Initialisms	GF	girlfriend
	DL	download
	JK	Just kidding
	LOL	Laugh out loud
Omitted letters	plsed	pleased
	msg	message
	xlnt	excellent
	txtin	texting
Non-standard spellings	cos, cuz	because
	fone	phone
	luv	love
	da	the
Shortenings	arr(ive)	
	uni(versity)	
	bro(ther)	
	hol(iday)s	
Language play	IMHO	in my humble opinion
	IMCO	in my considered opinion
	IMHBCO	in my humble but correct opinion
	IMNSHO	in my not so humble opinion

Crystal points out that none of these features is unique to texting, and expresses surprise at the apparent hostility of many people to texting. When analysing the language of texts, it is probably best to go beyond the surface features of messages and look at things like communication strategies and audience positioning.

The need for speed

The following extract is from a spoof chatroom, but it exhibits many of the features of texting and instant messaging. As you will see, the key constraints are typing as quickly as possible in order to keep up with a conversation, and making such things as jokes and asides clear.

Should you be able to say what you like in a chatroom?

Welcome to the current affairs forum – CyberRoom – at doyouhavesomethingtosay.com, the No. 1 chatroom site.

Connecting to server...

Host_CyberBob: Hi, everyone.

Current topic: A local councillor, Peter Thomson, has successfully won a libel case against one of his employees, Jason Coldsmith, who posted abusive messages about him on an Internet message board. Mr Coldsmith accused Mr Thomson of being a 'racist', a 'pompous windbag' and of having the general hygiene of a 'dung beetle'. Mr Coldsmith was ordered to pay £5000 in damages.

Do you think this is a reasonable application of existing law, or should you be able to say what you like in a chatroom? Thoughts please.

Knucklehead: im in shock, that is like sooo big bro

Femanist_1: shut up sexist! y not big sis rite? Equality 4 all, yeh?

Knucklehead: like whatevr.

Femanist_1: You are such an IDIOT!

Knucklehead: Hey, I was JK! Of course we all have the right to our own view.

Femanist_1: THANKS KNUCKLEHEAD

Pompous: GETTING BACK TO THE SITUATION UNDER DISCUSSION, I THINK THAT THIS ISSUE SHOWS HOW IMPORTANT IT IS TO USE RESPONSIBLE POSTING IN CHATROOMS.

Host_CyberBob: most cases like these are settled out of court, but I think that this ruling has huge ramifications for ISPs.

Lardypants: ooohh, 'ramifications' – get u smarty!

Knucklehead: LOL

Sarita has entered the room.

Sarita: Hi everyone

Femanist_1: wotcher Sar

Host_CyberBob: Sarita, we are discussing the latest ruling of a libel trial in favour of Cllr Peter Thomson. What implications do you think this victory holds?

Sarita: i know him like! he does have the hygiene of a dung beatle!

Host_CyberBob: the moderators of somethingtosay aren't liable for remarks made in its chatrooms, btw

This section is in normal English as the moderator has had time to think it through and type it out.

No capital letters are used, there is no apostrophe for 'I'm' and brother is abbreviated to 'bro'.

The username is misspelt, initialism is used, it is abusive language and 'right' is misspelt as 'rite', something which would not be noticed by a spellchecker. '4' is used as a logogram.

Femanist uses abusive language and capitals – the equivalent of shouting.

Knucklehead uses an initialism ('JK') – is this used to defuse the situation? It could also be seen as ironic, and deliberately provocative.

Is this a joke, or an ironic response?

Again, this is all in capitals – equating to shouting.

Standard English is used by the host, although without an initial capital, and he uses an acronym.

Mocking language.

Initialism is used here – is 'LOL' an attempt to soften the sarcasm?

Femanist_1 uses an informal name and greeting.

The 'host' greets Sarita more formally.

Sarita uses libellous language, no capitals and misspelling.

Again, Standard English is being used, but without capitals. Another example of initialism is 'btw'.

One of the issues raised in the exchange is **anonymity**. In face-to-face conversations with friends, you can judge people's reactions and moderate your own contributions to avoid offence. In at-a-distance conversations with strangers, it is difficult to tell how they might react to your statements (hence the need for emoticons and abbreviations like LOL), and it is very easy for 'flame wars' – angry exchanges of messages – to break out.

Social networking sites, like Facebook, in theory only allow 'friends' to make comments on status updates, but some people's ideas of friendship and plain speaking do not match. Sometimes when you post a status update on a social networking site, you can make yourself vulnerable to insult, as shown in the fictional example below.

The difference between wall postings and a live exchange is that on a wall posting each person involved has time to think about what to write. When writing is between friends it tends to be informal in style, but more of the conventions of spelling and punctuation are followed than in a live exchange of messages.

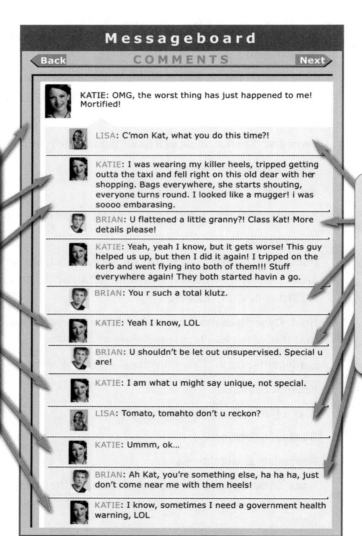

The original status update teases by not going into details.

'Embarrassing' is misspelt and 'i' is a typo used for 'it'.

Non-standard spelling of 'so' for emphasis.

Katie makes light of the insult. She shows amusement by typing 'LOL'.

Katie refuses to take offence – she supplies an alternative term.

Katie shows her uncertainty by writing 'Ummm'.

Katie agrees.

A request for clarification.

A second friend joins in asking for details.

Insult.

The insult is reiterated as a statement of fact.

Lisa counters that this is just playing with words.

Brian intervenes by agreeing that the incident is funny.

Messageboard

COMMENTS
Back   Next

KATIE: OMG, the worst thing has just happened to me! Mortified!

LISA: C'mon Kat, what you do this time?!

KATIE: I was wearing my killer heels, tripped getting outta the taxi and fell right on this old dear with her shopping. Bags everywhere, she starts shouting, everyone turns round. I looked like a mugger! i was soooo embarasing.

BRIAN: U flattened a little granny?! Class Kat! More details please!

KATIE: Yeah, yeah I know, but it gets worse! This guy helped us up, but then I did it again! I tripped on the kerb and went flying into both of them!!! Stuff everywhere again! They both started havin a go.

BRIAN: You r such a total klutz.

KATIE: Yeah I know, LOL

BRIAN: U shouldn't be let out unsupervised. Special u are!

KATIE: I am what u might say unique, not special.

LISA: Tomato, tomahto don't u reckon?

KATIE: Ummm, ok...

BRIAN: Ah Kat, you're something else, ha ha ha, just don't come near me with them heels!

KATIE: I know, sometimes I need a government health warning, LOL

Twentieth-century language growth

AQA   **A P4**
AQA   **B P4**
Edexcel **P4**
OCR   **P3 P4**
WJEC   **P3 P4**

The word 'blog' is an excellent example of how words change and adapt to the needs of new technologies. Its origin lies in the practice of throwing a log off a ship, attached to a rope, and then counting the evenly spaced knots on the rope to get some idea of the boat's speed in the water. On ships a careful record of speeds and distances travelled is important, and so the noun 'log' was applied to the records themselves. 'Log' then took on its secondary sense of 'to record', and eventually became associated with computer use. The term 'weblog' was coined in 1997 as a **blend** of 'web' and 'log', and was **clipped** shortly thereafter. **Back-formation** resulted in 'blogger', and then further blending turned 'blog-' into a root or suffix.

Noun	Verb	Adjective	Notes
Log			A log was thrown off a boat to gauge a ship's speed in knots
		Log book	Where the speed readings were recorded, i.e. a record book
Ship's log			Where all activities were recorded
Log	To log		The 'ship's log' was clipped, and became 'log' A 'record' became the verb 'to record'
	To log on/off		To begin or end a computer session
Web-log			A log or diary on the World Wide Web
Blog	Blogging		A blend of we**b** and **log**
Blogger			One who blogs
		Blog spot	A place for blogging
Blogware			Software for blogging – 'blog' has now become a root word
Blogosphere			By analogy with Ionosphere

Technology, in particular, has added to the English lexicon in the twentieth century, through this kind of adaptation, and a number of other processes.

These processes include:
- **acronyms**, e.g. GPS (Global Positioning Satellite); LED (Light Emitting Diode)
- **borrowing**, e.g. 'wiki' from the Hawaiian word for 'fast'
- metaphors, e.g. World Wide Web; (computer) mouse.

The preference is generally for familiar sounding terms, but initial encounters with a technology are also important. In Britain, 'mobile' phone describes the fact that you can make phone calls whilst on the move, but in America 'cell' phone is the preferred term because the first mobile phones were connected by cellular networks.

Contemporary language debates

AQA	A P4
AQA	B P4
Edexcel	P4
OCR	P3 P4
WJEC	P3 P4

The article below quotes a report on the damage that text messaging is doing to English, but then begins to play with the form.

Text messages destroying our language

I have speculated on this for many years, but it seems to have finally come true: Cell phones are evil. Well, grammatically speaking.

In a report released from the State Examination Commission in Ireland, our ability to write in English is slowly deteriorating. The main culprit behind this deterioration? Text messaging.

That's right. According to this report, all those messages you send your friends and family at work, on the bus or during class are leading to a weaker understanding of correct grammar and spelling. We are forming shorter sentences, using simpler tenses of verbs and, worst of all, little punctuation.

I knew this was coming. From the first time one of my friends sent me the message "I've got 2 go, talk to U later," I knew the end was near. The English language as we once knew it is out the window, and replacing it is this hip and cool slang-induced language, obsessed with taking the vowels out of words and spelling fonetikally.

I'm glad they finally found something to blame 4 this mess. For a long time, I thought ppl had just become lazy and didn't want to spend the time or effort to type complete and coherent sentences. But apparently, it's the technology itself causing the downfall of writing.

Extract from 'Text messages destroying our language' by Eric Uthus,
The Daily of the University of Washington

You can imagine similar articles in the fifteenth century, making statements such as 'Printing destroying our language'. Innovations are almost always resisted, but somehow language manages to survive and prosper.

We saw earlier in this chapter how Jonathan Swift thought that the language of his time was in decay. Today, Swift and his contemporaries are held up as models of wit and elegant language use.

We also saw how the great lexicographer Dr Johnson ridiculed **prescriptivist** attitudes to language. Even today – rather than taking a **descriptivist** stance – there are those who appeal to the publishers of the Oxford English Dictionary to prevent people using derogatory terms like 'couch potato' and 'McJobs', as if the dictionary was in charge of the English language.

The other major debate over language is **political correctness**, which has usually 'gone mad' by the time it reaches the media. See Chapter 4 (section 4.3) for more information on this.

PROGRESS CHECK

1. Why do texters miss out letters?
2. Why do people in live discussions miss out letters?
3. Is texting ruining English?

3 No. Languages cannot be either improved or damaged.
2 To enable them to type faster and keep up with the conversation.
1 To reduce the number of key presses needed to send a message.

6.8 Theories of language change

LEARNING SUMMARY	**After studying this section, you should be able to:**
	• identify key theories of language change
	• compare the strengths and weaknesses of the key theories
	• relate the theories to texts

Why change?

AQA	**A P4**
AQA	**B P4**
Edexcel	**P4**
OCR	**P3 P4**
WJEC	**P3 P4**

Depending on the theory of language acquisition, the reasons for language change over time or space can be difficult to explain. If, as Sapir-Whorf theorised, language precedes thought and controls it, then our language would define our existence and change would be impossible. This idea was exploited by George Orwell in *1984* when he imagined a synthetic language called Newspeak, which would reduce rather than expand the mind.

> The purpose of Newspeak was not only to provide a medium of expression for the world-view and mental habits proper to the devotees of IngSoc [English Socialism], but to make all other modes of thought impossible. It was intended that when Newspeak had been adopted once and for all and Oldspeak forgotten, a heretical thought — that is, a thought diverging from the principles of IngSoc — should be literally unthinkable, at least so far as thought is dependent on words.
>
> *Extract from 1984 by George Orwell*

The fact that language change does occur rather undermines the strong determinist case, but a weaker version argues that language only influences thought rather than controlling it. The problem with this view is that it still leaves us at the mercy of our thoughts – political correctness is a waste of time because language use **reflects** mental processes. These views are sometimes known as **mould theories**, as they claim that language moulds thoughts. In contrast are **cloak theories**, which assume that language is but the 'dress of thought'.

This is what Alexander Pope says.

> True Wit is Nature to advantage dress'd,
> What oft was thought, but ne'er so well express'd
>
> *Extract from* An Essay on Criticism *by Alexander Pope*

The idea that thoughts somehow exist independently of language is also difficult to sustain.

Most linguists accept that language influences thought, but tend to see language in a set of wider contexts than simple object–word correspondences. Trudgill,[4] for instance, argues that language change is determined by such factors as frequencies of interactions within communities.

Language progress and decay

It should be clear from this chapter alone that language is always thought to be in a state of decay. Aitchison[5] points out that language is also continually undergoing 'therapy', so that irregularities are ironed out or ambiguities are cleared up over time. Change is an inevitable consequence of a combination of sociological and psychological factors, and there is simply no way to tell if any given language is getting 'better' or 'worse' at any point in its history. Pinker[6] argues that perceived irregularities in language were all at some time regular, the problem being that a different model has been used to put the irregularities back into order than the one that created them. This process can be seen in children who try to regularise verb forms like 'went' and 'got' into 'wented' and 'gotted'.

Some **functional models of language change** emphasise external processes like technological progress, but they only tend to explain differences in vocabulary. For example, the fact that we no longer wear armour explains why most people do not know the meaning of the word 'greave' (a shin protector), but it does not explain why we no longer use 'thou' as the second person singular pronoun.

4 Trudgill, P. 2004. *New-dialect formation: the inevitability of colonial Englishes*. Edinburgh: Edinburgh University Press.

5 Aitchison, J. 1981. *Language change: progress or decay?* Cambridge University Press.

6 Pinker, S. 1999. *Words and rules*. Orion.

The S-curve model of language change, outlined by Chen,[7] describes how change propagates through a population. At first, a small group changes language slowly, then the change reaches a tipping point and becomes very rapid, and finally small resistant groups gradually change language again.

S-curve as Model of Language Change

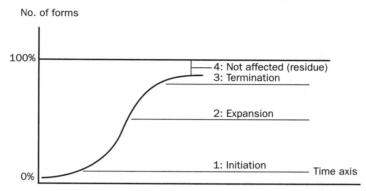

Figure 6.9 Chen's S-curve

PROGRESS CHECK

1. What is the main problem with the determinist model of language?
2. What does a cloak model suggest?
3. Do languages ever make 'progress'?

1 It does not permit change.
2 That thought precedes language.
3 It is impossible to tell.

7 Chen, M. and W. Wang. 1975. 'Sound change: actuation and implementation', *Language*, 51 (2), 255–281.

Sample question and model answer

Analysis of written language through time

The three texts that follow are all extracts from diaries.

Text A is from the diary of Samuel Pepys (1661).

Text B is from the diary of Mary Boykin Chesnut (1863).

Text C is from the diary of David Sedaris (1997).

Analyse and compare the use of language in these three texts as examples of diary writing from three different periods. In your answer you should consider the different concerns of the writers, the way they use the diary form, and the influence of the contexts in which they were written on their use of language.

(40 marks)

Text A from the diary of Samuel Pepys (1633–1703)

Background information
In the year of these entries, Pepys was 'clerk of the king's ships' and was living in London.

'Sexton' means church official.
'Leads' refers to the roof top of the house.

Wednesday 25 December 1661
In the morning to church, where at the door of our pew I was fain to stay, because that the sexton had not opened the door. A good sermon of Mr. Mills. Dined at home all alone, and taking occasion from some fault in the meat to complain of my maid's sluttery, my wife and I fell out, and I up to my chamber in a discontent. After dinner my wife comes up to me and all friends again, and she and I to walk upon the leads, and there Sir W. Pen called us, and we went to his house and supped with him, but before supper Captain Cock came to us half drunk, and began to talk, but Sir W. Pen knowing his humour and that there was no end of his talking, drinks four great glasses of wine to him, one after another, healths to the king, and by that means made him drunk, and so he went away, and so we sat down to supper, and were merry, and so after supper home and to bed.

Sample question and model answer
(continued)

Text B from the diary of Mary Boykin Chesnut (1823–1886)

Background information

Mary Chesnut was the wife of a senator in the Confederate States of America during the American Civil War.

'Hood' refers to John Bell Hood, who was a Confederate general with a reputation for bravery and aggressiveness.

'Sam' was Hood's nickname.

Christmas Day, 1863. Yesterday dined with the Prestons. Wore one of my handsomest Paris dresses (from Paris before the war). Three magnificent Kentucky generals were present, with Senator Orr from South Carolina, and Mr. Miles. General Buckner repeated a speech of Hood's to him to show how friendly they were. "I prefer a ride with you to the company of any woman in the world," Buckner had answered. "I prefer your company to that of any man, certainly," was Hood's reply. This became the standing joke of the dinner; it flashed up in every form. Poor Sam got out of it so badly, if he got out of it at all. General Buckner said patronizingly, "Lame excuses, all. Hood never gets out of any scrape – that is, unless he can fight out." Others dropped in after dinner; some without arms, some without legs; von Borcke, who can not speak because of a wound in his throat. Isabella said: "We have all kinds now, but a blind one." Poor fellows, they laugh at wounds. "And they yet can show many a scar."

We had for dinner oyster soup, besides roast mutton, ham, boned turkey, wild duck, partridge, plum pudding, sauterne, burgundy, sherry, and Madeira. There is life in the old land yet!

Text C from the diary of David Sedaris (1956–)

Background information
At the time of this diary entry David Sedaris was working as an elf in Macy's department store in New York.

I spent a few hours in the Maze with Puff, a young elf from Brooklyn. We were standing near the Lollipop Forest when we realized that Santa is an anagram of Satan. Father Christmas or the Devil — so close but yet so far. We imagined a Satan Land where visitors would wade through steaming pools of human blood and feces before arriving at the Gates of Hell, where a hideous imp in a singed velvet costume would take them by the hand and lead them toward Satan. Once we thought of it we couldn't get it out of our minds. Overhearing the customers we would substitute the word Satan for the word Santa.

"What do you think, Michael? Do you think Macy's has the real Satan?"

"Don't forget to thank Satan for the Baby Alive he gave you last year."

"I love Satan."

"Who doesn't? Everyone loves Satan."

Sample question and model answer
(continued)

This is a confident response, which looks at individual texts in detail, but also makes valid comparisons. It is well expressed and structured.

The contents have been summarised.

Comments are made about sentence structure.

Semantic features are identified and commented on.

Language features are used to assess purpose and impact.

Knowledge is shown of language change over time.

Technical terms are used correctly.

Knowledge is shown of regional variation.

Author positioning is understood and commented on.

Model answer

All three texts concern Christmas, and are characteristic of their age and times. Text A is written in Early Modern English and shows a much greater concern for the religious aspects of Christmas than the other two. Text B focuses on the social aspect of Christmas day, whilst Text C mocks Christmas traditions.

Text A is mostly factual in content and its simple language is loosely structured by the events described. So one sentence is given to going to church, another is given to Pepys' argument with his wife, and one very long sentence is given to the account of dinner with Sir W. Pen. Pepys' opinion of the sermon is given a sentence to itself.

Text B is mostly an account of a dinner party. Like Pepys, Chesnut uses ellipsis to shorten her account (`yesterday dined' compared to `dined at home…'), but unlike Pepys she quotes some of the words she heard in conversation. Sedaris does not use ellipsis, but he does quote other people's words. Chesnut's quotation gives some idea of the kind of conversation that might be heard at an elegant dinner party and features well-turned ideas and phrases. Chesnut comments on the performance of others by using critical vocabulary such as `patronizingly' and `poor Sam'. On occasion, Chesnut boasts about her dress or the quality of the food. Sedaris' account seems less immediate than the other two and has possibly been altered for publication. Evidence of this is when he consciously introduces a character: `Puff, a young elf from Brooklyn'. At other times, however, he mentions aspects of the environment from the point of view of someone who is familiar with it, for instance when he mentions the Maze and the Lollipop forest.

Each text reflects its historical period. Pepys' vocabulary is recognisably modern, with the exception of the phrase `I was fain to stay', which would nowadays be expressed as `I was forced to wait'. The word `sluttery' has undergone pejoration and would now have a sexual connotation rather than a domestic one. `Humour' is used in its old-fashioned sense of `character'. Pepys' use of pronouns is now non-standard in `a good sermon of…' and he uses `discontent' as a noun. The midday meal at this time is called dinner, whereas later this would be an evening meal, as we find in Text B. Chesnut makes greater use of adjectives than Pepys and in general is more concerned to give a sense of how special the occasion is (for instance, `handsomest' and `magnificent'). She uses `Paris' as a pre-modifier about her dress and then inserts the fact in parentheses that the dress actually came from Paris - in case the reader thought she just meant a Paris-style dress. Chesnut's language is high prestige Standard English throughout, with the possible exception of the colloquial expression `it flashed up in every form', which seems to be an unconsidered aside. With the exception of the `z' spelling in `patronizing', the orthography seems to be Standard English. An American spelling of `feces' is used in Text C.

Sedaris intends to be humorous and casually sets up an absurd-sounding conversation with an elf in a maze near some lollipop trees. He then takes the absurdity further by re-imagining the scene as if it were from hell. A string of adjectives (`hideous', `singed' and `velvet') is used to make this final vision vivid. This situation is based on a simple and well-known anagram of Santa. The fact that the writer is amused by it constructs him as being slightly immature, or possibly made desperate by the job.

Exam practice question

Language focus

The following text is from a contemporary web page.

Task

Analyse and discuss the use of language in this text to convey attitudes.

In your answer you should consider:

● how the language choices convey attitudes to boys and girls and their respective roles in society
● what you can deduce and infer from the use of language about attitudes to relationships
● your views on this as a text for girls. **(20)**

_____

_____

_____

_____

_____

_____

_____

_____

_____

[Please continue your answer on separate paper.]

7 Language and context

The following topics are covered in this chapter:

- **How the context of a text influences its reception**
- **Instrumental language – the law**
- **The types of influence texts can have**
- **Techniques used to influence people**

7.1 Language and power

LEARNING SUMMARY

After studying this section, you should be able to:

- understand critical discourse analysis
- understand rhetoric
- interpret – and comment on – examples of critical discourse analysis and rhetoric

Language in context

AQA	A P4
AQA	B P4
Edexcel	P4
OCR	P3
WJEC	P4

Language production always takes place in a particular context, and how we understand or share a particular context will influence how we understand and respond to it. For example, I may tell you a story simply to entertain you, but I am more likely to tell you a story to make a point about language. Some people might tell you a story as a way of persuading you to do or to buy something.

Sometimes (for instance, in advertising or political speeches) our relationship to the language being used is clear – we know that we are being persuaded. At other times, the effect of language is more subtle.

Critical discourse analysis

AQA	A P4
AQA	B P4
Edexcel	P4
OCR	P3
WJEC	P4

Fairclough[1] identified three levels of textual analysis:

1. The language of the text itself.
2. Discourse practice – how texts are produced, distributed and consumed.
3. How texts relate to wider societal contexts.

The study of the language of power goes all the way back to the Ancient Greeks, who realised that success in society was dependent on success at persuading other people to do what you want.

Aristotle's Rhetoric recognised three components to persuasion:

1. Logos – the words used.
2. Ethos – how people felt about the speaker.
3. Pathos – the emotions that were aroused.

1 Fairclough, N. 2001. *Language and power*. Longman.

We can see that for both Fairclough and Aristotle words come first. As part of discourse practice, Fairclough also uses the concept of **synthetic personalisation**, which he describes as follows.

> ... a compensatory tendency to give the impression of treating each of the people 'handled' en masse as an individual. Examples would be air travel (*have a nice day*), restaurants (*welcome to Wimpy!*) and the simulated conversation (e.g. chat shows) and bonhomie that litter the media.
>
> *Extract taken from* Language and power *by N Fairclough*

This is similar to Aristotle's ethos, in that we are more likely to accept the message of speakers or writers if we recognise some similarities with them. Talbot,[2] for instance, showed how teenage girls' magazines used pronouns, pre-suppositions and positive politeness to construct a **synthetic sisterhood** – or false friendships – between reader and producer.

Rhetorical techniques

AQA	A P4
AQA	B P4
Edexcel	P4
OCR	P3
WJEC	P4

Rhetoric – or the art of persuasion – applies particularly to politics and advertising, but you will find its techniques deployed in all aspects of language, from newspaper editorials to instruction manuals.

Making comparisons

Explicitly comparing one thing to another using 'as' or 'like' is a **simile**. Saying one thing is another is a **metaphor**. Some metaphors are so frequently used that we are scarcely aware of them, for example when someone 'running' for office 'fishes' for compliments – these are known as **dead metaphors** (a phrase which in itself is a dead metaphor).

When analysing similes and metaphors at a linguistic level, it is useful to focus on the connotations that are being deployed. For instance, campaigning politicians seem fond of things like 'mud-slinging' and 'muck raking', as if they were determined to fire the imagination of farmers, who are usually referred to as 'grass roots' supporters.

Recent British political rhetoric seems to favour moving forward in a straight line. This means that the phrase 'U-turn' – which is used to describe any slight change of policy, and to 'spin' a story (put a positive or negative slant on it) – is perceived as a positive evil.

Mixed metaphors are a succession of different ideas in one statement that do not relate to one another. They are often a feature of political debates as participants string ideas together. Figure 7.1 shows an example of a mixed metaphor.

Another form of metaphorical thinking in politics is the persistent use of a **false analogy**, as in the idea of a 'war' on poverty or cancer or global warming. Borrowing terminology from the semantic field of war is dramatic and exciting, but

> Even the word 'campaign' means an operation conducted in the countryside.

> Our backs are to the wall, so we need to put our shoulders to the wheel and our noses to the grindstone.

Figure 7.1 An example of a mixed metaphor

2 Talbot, M. 1995. 'A synthetic sisterhood: false friends in a teenage magazine', in K. Hall and M. Bucholtz (eds) *Gender articulated: language and the socially constructed self*, pp.143–65. New York: Routledge.

the idea of, for example, 'bombing' cancer into submission is not a constructive way of deciding on policy.

Occasionally in speeches, politicians will make use of an **extended metaphor** as a cohesive device. A famous example of this is Abraham Lincoln's Gettysburg Address, which is structured around ideas of birth, death and re-birth.

> Four score and seven years ago our **fathers brought forth** on this continent a **new** nation, **conceived** in liberty, and dedicated to the proposition that all men are **created** equal.
>
> *Extract from the* Gettysburg Address *by Abraham Lincoln (emphasis added)*

The address (dedicating a cemetery for the war dead) places the lives of the fallen within the larger and grander context of the life and survival of their nation.

> ... this nation, under God, shall have a **new birth** of freedom – and that government of the people, by the people, for the people, **shall not perish** from the earth.
>
> *Extract from the* Gettysburg Address *by Abraham Lincoln (emphasis added)*

> **KEY POINT**
>
> Politicians often invoke images of family – the home country is the 'fatherland' or the 'motherland' and our fellow citizens are often 'brothers' and 'sisters'. British politicians used to speak of their 'American cousins', but nowadays there is some doubt if even a 'special relationship' exists between the two countries.

Going beyond the text – quotations

It is not always necessary to make a new impression, and there are many rhetorical devices that rely on the audience's prior knowledge, preconceptions or memories. The simplest method is to quote someone else – either because the other person expressed an idea powerfully, or because the audience respects the person who said the original words. The important thing to observe is what the **choice of quotation** and the person quoted say about the speaker and audience – for instance, fundamentalist Christians are unlikely to choose quotations from Charles Darwin to back up their arguments, and quoting something from a current pop song will probably not impress an older audience.

Going beyond the text – allusions

A slightly more involving – but also riskier – technique is allusion. In a quotation it is normal to reference the source of the words you use, but an allusion usually reminds the audience of other words or actions. If the allusion is recognised, the audience feels that it is on the same wavelength as the speaker. If not, the audience might be confused, or even alienated.

An example of a classical allusion is 'flying too close to the sun', which assumes that the audience is familiar with the story of Icarus. Referring to someone as 'a Mr Micawber' is a literary allusion that assumes that the audience knows the story of *David Copperfield*. Saying 'Here's lookin' at you kid' is an allusion to the film *Casablanca*, and so on.

Unless you yourself are 'in the know', it is impossible to spot allusions in the texts you are commenting on. If you do see an allusion, it reveals a great deal about the author's assumptions about his or her audience.

Going beyond the text – facts and figures

Facts and figures that have a real existence beyond the text can be very persuasive. In theory, facts and figures are checkable, but in reality we tend to take them on trust if we trust the source we are reading or listening to. The presentation of facts and figures can be made visually stimulating with graphs and charts, but if the ethos is wrong then they will not be accepted.

Structuring devices

When enumerating the qualities of something, finding three things to say seems to sound better than two – 'tall, dark and handsome' sounds more considered than 'tall and dark'. **Lists of three** qualities are very common in writing and in prepared speech. In a speech delivered to a receptive audience, the 'and' that precedes the final word tells them that the list is over and that it is time to applaud the speaker, in what is known as a 'clap-trap'. Lists of three are also more memorable – for example, Julius Caesar famously said 'Veni, Vidi, Vici' ('I came, I saw, I conquered'), and St Paul identified the three cardinal virtues as 'faith, hope and charity'.

Repetition of sounds, words or clause structures can be a very powerful device. Repeating initial sounds is called **alliteration**, and repeating medial vowel sounds is **assonance**. Rhyme is seldom used in politics, but it is in advertising. The repetition of words can be extremely emphatic, and the repetition of similar clause structures makes comparisons and contrasts stand out. One US vice president famously criticised his less optimistic opponents for being 'nattering nabobs of negativism'.

In his 'Big Society' speech, delivered in March 2010, David Cameron also attacked pessimists.

> A series of statements using 'They see... but...'.

> There is a slight change to 'They experience... but...'.

> Cameron says that he shares the people's pain (he uses a personal pronoun), but that action is possible if everyone ('we') acts together.

> They see drug and alcohol abuse,
>   but feel there's not much we can do about it.
> They see the deep poverty in some of our communities,
>   but feel it's here to stay.
> They experience the crime, the abuse, the incivility on our streets,
>   but feel it's just the way [we] are going.
> They see families falling apart,
>   but expect that it's an irreversible fact of modern life.
> I despair at all these things too.
>   But I don't accept them.
> We should not accept them.
>
> *Extract from the 'Our "Big Society" plan' (speech delivered by David Cameron)*

In this extract, the four examples of problems that people feel powerless to deal with are built up as a comprehensive picture of society's ills, and Cameron's rejection of inaction is emphasised by the repeated idea of not accepting despair. The change of personal pronoun from 'I' to 'we' emphasises the need for consensus if progress is to be made. The technical term for Cameron's technique is **antithetical parallelism**, but other forms of **parallelism** are common, especially in older speeches and in books like the Bible.

In his essay, *Of Studies*, Francis Bacon uses a list of three to produce a punchy opening statement, and then uses parallelism to expand his ideas more fully.

> Studies serve **for delight**, **for ornament**, and **for ability**.
> Their chief use **for delight**, is in privateness and retiring;
> **for ornament**, is in discourse; and **for ability**, is in the judgment, and disposition of business.
>
> *Extract taken from 'Of studies' by Francis Bacon (emphasis added)*

The carefully balanced statements give the impression of someone who has considered his words seriously, and add gravity to Bacon's ideas.

Wordplay

Aristotle pointed out that successful persuaders need to have a sense of decorum – by this he meant appropriateness to audience. We do not normally expect our politicians to be funny, for instance, but they can engage in wordplay.

Margaret Thatcher made use of allusion and even a pun (on U-turn) when she expressed her determination to press on.

> You turn if you want to. The lady's not for turning.
>
> *Extract from Speech to Conservative Party Conference ('The lady's not for turning'), 1980*

The allusion was to a play by Christopher Fry called *The Lady's Not For Burning*.

Benjamin Disraeli said the following about his great rival William Gladstone.

> The difference between a misfortune and a calamity is this: If Gladstone fell into the Thames, it would be a misfortune. But if someone dragged him out again, that would be a calamity.

At least one modern politician has attempted a career in stand-up comedy when he was not returned to Parliament.

Constructing politicians

AQA	**A P4**
AQA	**B P4**
Edexcel	**P4**
OCR	**P3**
WJEC	**P4**

This section looks at the way that politicians are 'constructed' across the world and through history.

Great Britain

In Great Britain there is a great deal of common ground between different political parties, and it is sometimes difficult to tell one party's policies from another.

Traditionally, the Labour Party was the party of the workers and the Conservative Party the party of the bosses, but these simple paradigms are increasingly difficult to apply as both parties have attempted to take control of the middle ground of politics.

In general, British politicians want to be the voter's friend or champion, and they boast of their high levels of commitment to represent all their constituents. Another common construction is the politician as family person – openly gay and lesbian politicians have only recently become part of British political life. At election times, politicians frequently appear in staged photo opportunities to show how 'normal' they are. A good example of this is the way in which David Cameron showed his concern for the environment by cycling to work. Unfortunately, his official papers had to travel behind him in a car.

Another technique that many politicians use is to personalise their political experiences. During the 2010 election campaign, David Cameron met so many people who apparently agreed with his views that it became something of a joke.

America

Figure 7.2 'Hope' and Barack Obama

In America, politicians are much freer to build up images. This is because the amount that they can spend on a campaign is limited only by the donations they receive, whereas in Britain there are strict limits on campaign spending. As a result, in America literally millions of dollars are spent on communicating a candidate's personality to the wider public.

Barack Obama's campaign for the presidency was noticeable for its use of social networking and e-mail technology, but it also made excellent use of an old-fashioned poster (Figure 7.2). The red, white and blue stylised image of Obama above the word 'Hope' became instantly recognisable. It combined patriotic colours with the ideas of optimism and change.

The rest of the world

Elsewhere in the world, political leaders are given varying degrees of respect – and even veneration.

The president of Turkmenistan, for instance, briefly re-named the months of the year after himself and members of his family – no doubt inspired by the fact that the English months of July and August are named after Roman emperors. In authoritarian states, the head of state is typically positioned as the 'father' of the country or, if there has been a revolution in the recent past, its saviour. Regime change in these states will often involve the removal of large numbers of statues dedicated to the 'great' leader. In the Second World War, the communist dictator Josef Stalin was humanised by his allies as 'Uncle Joe', Kim Jong-il of North Korea is known as the 'Dear Leader', and the fictional leader of George Orwell's totalitarian state in *1984* was 'Big Brother'.

Political satire

Politicians do not always control how they are represented, and in the course of political debate insults and smears are frequently exchanged. Satirical political cartoons go back at least to the eighteenth century, when artists like Gilray lampooned the politicians of the day.

Political cartoons often use national stereotypes to represent nations – the United Kingdom is often portrayed as John Bull and the United States as Uncle Sam.

Political satire is also found in magazines like *Private Eye* and on television programmes like *Have I Got News for You*. *Private Eye* always features some form of communication from the political leader of the day. When Tony Blair was prime minister, this was a church newsletter from the vicar. Under Gordon Brown, however, it changed to a series of Stalinist communiqués from the 'Great Leader'.

PROGRESS CHECK

1. What is a clap-trap?
2. Why are allusions risky?
3. How do authoritarian countries tend to characterise their leaders?

3 As a father or older relative.
2 The audience might not 'get' them, and might be alienated.
1 The use of a list of three to prompt applause.

7.2 Instrumental language – the law

LEARNING SUMMARY

After studying this section, you should be able to:

- identify the characteristics of legal language
- explain how the adversarial process works
- understand how the legal process signals its own importance

The language of law

AQA   A P4
AQA   B P4
Edexcel P4
OCR   P3
WJEC   P4

The language of the law is interesting on three levels:

1. Some speech acts in law courts (such as 'I sentence you') are actions in the real world.
2. The law courts are sites of highly constrained argument and debate.
3. Part of a lawyer's job is to restrict the meaning of words.

The laws of the land are drawn up by Parliament, but they have to be contained in words. Frequently, the exact meaning of a particular wording is in dispute and has to be tested in a court of law.

A number of recent court cases have concerned not just the meaning of laws, but the meaning of everyday words.

Here are a couple of examples:

- Does a Melton Mowbray pork pie have to be made in Melton Mowbray? (The answer was 'no'.)
- Does Parma ham have to come from Parma? (The answer was 'yes'.)

Constructing the legal process

AQA   A P4
AQA   B P4
Edexcel P4
OCR   P3
WJEC   P4

Almost everything about the legal process is designed to impress people with how important it is. Trials take place in specific buildings, and people wear very out-moded clothes in the courtroom. In fact, the law is a kind of theatrical performance, and it is not surprising that 'courtroom dramas' are a recognisable film and television sub-genre.

The most important person in a courtroom is the judge, and special rules apply to how he or she is treated. The judge has the privilege of entering the room last, and everyone is expected to stand to show respect. The judge also wears robes and a wig that are generally much more impressive than the other robes and wigs in the room. Current courtroom fashions are identical to those of the mid-eighteenth century. The fact that they have not changed in all that time implies that they must be 'right' in some sense.

The building and costumes are accompanied by a specialist vocabulary that in some cases goes back to the Norman Conquest, when French became the language of the courts – examples include 'lien', 'plaintiff', 'tort' and 'bailiff'. French was replaced by Latin in the Middle Ages and continued until the seventeenth century. Examples of legal Latin include 'mens rea', 'ab initio' and 'habeus corpus'.

Unlike some legal systems, English law is not codified – in other words, based on a set of general rules. It is instead based on precedent – rules that have been established in the past. Distinctions that have great significance in law can be contained in particular legal usages, so modernising legal language is far from easy. Even simple modal verbs like 'may', 'must' and 'shall' have precise and long-established legal meanings.

Courtroom praxis

AQA   A P4
AQA   B P4
Edexcel P4
OCR   P3
WJEC   P4

The procedures and behaviour of members of the legal profession in criminal courts are highly formalised and rule bound.

These rules include:
- relevance of subject matter
- kinds of evidence
- kinds of argument
- turn taking
- deference to the authority of the judge.

A typical criminal case has the following sequence.

Opening statements by:
- counsel for the prosecution
- counsel for the defence

Testimony of witnesses and presentation of evidence by:
- counsel for the prosecution
  - direct examination of prosecution witnesses by counsel for the prosecution
  - cross-examination of prosecution witnesses by counsel for the defence
  - re-direct examination of prosecution witnesses by counsel for the prosecution

- counsel for the defence
    - direct examination of defendant's witnesses by counsel for the defence
    - cross-examination of defendant's witnesses by counsel for the prosecution
    - re-direct examination of defendant's witnesses by counsel for the defence

Selection and preparation of jury instructions by the judge

Jury instructions presented

Closing arguments by:
- counsel for the prosecution
- counsel for the defence
- counsel for the prosecution to close the case

Jury deliberations

Verdict

Courtroom etiquette

In English law, the defence does not have to prove innocence – merely expose flaws in the prosecution's argument, or show that the case has not been proved **beyond reasonable doubt**. 'Leading questions' (that imply their own answers) are not allowed, and the judge may intervene to clarify points as he or she sees fit. Under disclosure rules, each side must reveal to the other before the beginning of the trial all evidence to be used.

Below is a short extract from the inquest on Princess Diana.

2   LORD JUSTICE SCOTT BAKER: Mr Mansfield?
3   MR MANSFIELD: Sir, may I be permitted just this once to
4   indicate, as you did to the jury at the beginning, that
5   we have, where there are areas of common interest,
6   divided up the task of putting questions. So in
7   relation to the crash, my learned friends are dealing
8   with that.
9   LORD JUSTICE SCOTT BAKER: Thank you very much. Mr Keen, it
10 is you, is it?
11 Questions from MR KEEN
12 MR KEEN: I wonder, sir, if I might be permitted to ask
13 a number of questions of the witness.
14 LORD JUSTICE SCOTT BAKER: Yes, certainly.
15 MR KEEN: I am obliged.
16 Good afternoon, Mr Lopes Borges. My name is
17 Richard Keen and I am the counsel instructed on behalf
18 of the parents of the late Henri Paul. I would like to
19 ask you a number of questions with regard to the night
20 of the crash.
21 Now you have already mentioned that on
22 24th September 1997 you gave a statement to a police
23 Lieutenant in the criminal investigation department. Is
24 that right?
25 A. Yes.

This part of the proceedings is almost entirely to do with who is speaking, but what is most obvious is the very high levels of politeness exercised by all concerned. Everyone is addressed as 'Mr', with the exception of the judge, who is addressed as 'Sir'. The barrister presenting the main case is Mr Michael Mansfield QC and he is extremely polite when he asks the judge's permission to hand over questioning to a colleague. This very high level of deference is a way of making the judge seem important, as is the legal fiction that the judge never forgets anything. Mr Keen is even more polite in wondering if he might be permitted to do the job he has been retained for. Conversational turn-taking is strictly controlled, and interruptions are very rare.

In essence, a jury trial is a verbal duel between two people who are experts at presenting cases. The jury has to pay close attention in order to arrive at a just decision.

Restricting meaning

AQA	**A P4**
AQA	**B P4**
Edexcel	**P4**
OCR	**P3**
WJEC	**P4**

In the following extract from *A Night at the Opera*, two men are discussing a contract.

> **Driftwood:** Now pay particular attention to this first clause because it's most important. It says the, uh, "The party of the first part shall be known in this contract as the party of the first part." How do you like that? That's pretty neat, eh?
>
> **Fiorello:** No, it's no good.
>
> **Driftwood:** What's the matter with it?
>
> **Fiorello:** I don't know. Let's hear it again.
>
> **Driftwood:** It says the, uh, "The party of the first part shall be known in this contract as the party of the first part."
>
> **Fiorello:** (*pausing*) That sounds a little better this time.
>
> **Driftwood:** Well, it grows on ya. Would you like to hear it once more?
>
> **Fiorello:** Uh, just the first part.
>
> **Driftwood:** What do you mean? The party of the first part?
>
> **Fiorello:** No, the first part of the party of the first part.
>
> **Driftwood:** All right. It says the, uh, "The first part of the party of the first part shall be known in this contract as the first part of the party of the first part shall be known in this contract" – look, why should we quarrel about a thing like this? We'll take it right out, eh?
>
> **Fiorello:** Yeah, it's a too long, anyhow. (*They both tear off the tops of their contracts.*) Now, what do we got left?
>
> **Driftwood:** Well, I got about a foot and a half.

The point of this satire on legal language is its apparent redundancy, but the extract also demonstrates how easy it is to be confused if you use language loosely. Statements like 'the party of the first part shall be known ...' are designed to restrict meaning, to avoid confusion and possible legal action in future.

This famous scene gives its name to The Party of the First Part website, which specialises in pointing out the follies of legal language. One example is where an insurance company states that it will not pay for any damages caused by war. The contract states that 'war' means the following.

> any undeclared war, civil war, insurrection, rebellion, revolution, warlike act by a military force or military personnel, destruction or seizure or use for a military purpose, and including any consequence of any of these. Discharge of a nuclear weapon shall be deemed a warlike act even if accidental.
>
> *Extract from State Farm Condominium Unit Owners' Insurance Policy,*
> *taken from The Party of the First Part website*

As The Party of the First Part website comments, this contract assumes that the word 'war' might be ambiguous, but then goes on to define war as including any 'warlike act'. If you did not understand 'war', how does 'warlike' clear things up? The long sentences and exhaustive lists of possible meanings are typical of legal language.

If you would like to experience legal language for yourself, try reading the End-User Licence Agreement next time you install a piece of software. You will almost certainly find exhaustive lists, frequent use of parentheses, and subordinate clauses added to clarify preceding clauses. Many lawyers are trying to move away from this style, but there is also a suspicion amongst some that ambiguity and misapprehension leads to lawyers getting more work in the future.

Just as a court case is a battle between experts at arguing, much legal activity is centred on contested definitions of words. For instance, were the 9/11 impacts of aeroplanes on the World Trade Center one event, with a single plan behind them, or were they two separate events? If two events took place, billions of dollars more will be paid out in insurance.

KEY POINT

Generally speaking, legal language seeks to avoid ambiguity, but in doing so it sometimes becomes over-complicated and thus, ironically, ambiguous.

PROGRESS CHECK

1. Generally speaking, what do lawyers try to remove from language?
2. Why do courtroom lawyers wear out-moded clothes?
3. What standard of proof is required to secure a conviction in a jury trial?

3 Beyond reasonable doubt.
formality of proceedings within this context.
2 As a 'theatrical costume' to emphasise their importance, and signify status and the
1 Ambiguity.

7.3 Media and cultural production

<table>
<tr><td rowspan="3">LEARNING SUMMARY</td><td>After studying this section, you should be able to:</td></tr>
<tr><td>● understand how cultural ideas are transmitted in the media
● discuss cultural contexts</td></tr>
<tr><td>● analyse some of the techniques used in media and cultural production</td></tr>
</table>

Embodying cultural values

AQA	A P4
AQA	B P4
Edexcel	P4
OCR	P3
WJEC	P4

All texts are the product of their social environments, and express cultural values. We need to take this into account when we look at them, particularly if they come from the past or from a culture different from our own. For instance, if we look at something as simple as the front covers of novels, we can gain some insight into the society that produced them.

  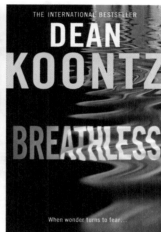

Figure 7.3 The covers of novels reveal our expectations

Without knowing anything about these texts, we can tell whether they are aimed at men or women, and even whether they are likely to be funny. Each of the covers uses the title and author's name in ways that signal to the reader which of the two they should be paying most attention to. A well-known author's name speaks for itself – less well-known writers are often given praise from others. These covers encode cultural stereotypes, such as blue for boys, pink for girls, and black for serious people. When looking at media texts, you need to think about how they embody values – not necessarily in terms of bias, but in terms of social and cultural perspectives and underlying attitudes.

The language of the media is difficult to pin down, since it can involve anything from a live phone-in radio show to an editorial in *The Times*. However, it tends to be public rather than private, and involves distribution on something more than sound waves. Examples include newsprint, radio waves or digital signals. 'Old' media – such as newspapers, book publishing and broadcast television – tend to be controlled by a few powerful individuals or the state. New media – largely enabled by recent developments in electronics – are more widely distributed and permit access to the worldwide stage by amateurs and enthusiasts. Both levels of the media are constrained by the laws of the land and by underlying cultural perspectives and attitudes.

Profanity

The issue of profanity is an interesting one in regards to the media. In real life people often swear, but in most of the media swearing is restricted, as it might offend the sensibilities of some of the general public.

Films in Great Britain are age restricted if they contain swear words – comedians like Lenny Bruce and George Carlin have been arrested for using and commenting on them. In British broadcasting, certain swear words are only permitted after 9pm, and there was controversy in America over the broadcasting of the swearing used by some of the 9/11 response teams. What all of this tells us is that media language is an artificial construct that embodies cultural values.

Current bad language rules seem to be aimed at protecting children from being exposed to the harsh realities of life too early. However, in 1960, a barrister at the *Lady Chatterley's Lover* obscenity trial famously had this to say.

> What does this suggest about the relationship between power and profanity?

You may think that one of the ways in which you can test this book, and test it from the most liberal outlook, is to ask yourselves the question, when you have read it through, would you approve of your young sons, young daughters – because girls can read as well as boys – reading this book? Is it a book you would have lying around in your own house? Is it a book you would even wish your wife or your servants to read?

Quotation from Your Archives website, The Chatterley Trial 1960 web page (DPP 2/3077)

Pragmatics in the media

AQA **A P4**
AQA **B P4**
Edexcel **P4**
OCR **P3**
WJEC **P4**

It is useful to remember that most of the things you see in the media have been constructed, either literally or figuratively. Television studios are artificial environments and increasingly, thanks to computer generated imagery (CGI), we can spend hours being entertained by things that have no real-world existence at all.

Even when the media is forced to deal with reality, it constructs it in particular ways. In news reports, for instance, there is usually someone standing between the raw news and the viewer. Newspapers will publish photographs of bombed buildings, but they do not show the full extent of the injuries to people out of respect for their suffering.

Presentation in the news and print media

The news media take a great deal of care over presenting themselves. Radio news bulletins use dramatic music to inject a sense of urgency – television adds impressive graphics to the music.

In the print media, broadsheet newspapers strive for dignity and elegance with their choice of fonts, logos and headlines, whilst the red tops (or tabloids) aim for immediacy and clarity. In their Internet versions, Mail Online accompanies every story with a photograph, whilst the guardian.co.uk typically offers multimedia content.

PROGRESS CHECK

 Have a look at the presentation of the news on Mail Online (www.dailymail.co.uk) compared to guardian.co.uk. What similarities and/or differences particularly strike you?

In addition to appearance, newspapers have recognisable sets of **news values**. Broadsheets like *The Times* and *The Guardian* have a wide agenda that includes foreign, financial and environmental issues. Red top papers like *The Sun* or *Daily Mirror* tend to favour human interest stories and focus more on domestic issues, celebrities and sport.

Presentation in television news and politics

The ethos of television news presentation is always fascinating.

As well as the music and graphics, there are many factors to consider about how the presenters will be constructed:
- What will they be called – a presenter or a newsreader?
- Are they seated or standing?
- Are they dressed formally or informally?
- Do they say who they are or 'Here is the news'?
- Do they refer to papers or scripts?
- Is there a co-presenter?
- How do they address other reporters?
- If they interview someone, are they polite or aggressive?
- At the end of the news programme, do they shuffle their papers or peer into a laptop?

Different news organisations have different approaches to all of these elements. Audience preferences are taken into account as organisations change. So, for example, formal authority figures seated behind desks are now less frequent.

A good example of the constructed nature of televised political debate can be seen in the preparation for the 2010 election debates between the leaders of the three main parties.

At a series of meetings, the politicians and the broadcasters hammered out a 76-point programme format agreement. As a result, questions were put by a carefully selected audience – who were not allowed to boo or cheer or even to clap – and during the debates the political parties each had a live hotline to the broadcasters to appeal against what they saw as unfair camera shots or lack of balance. Also, unlike on the BBC's *Question Time*, audience members could not ask specific personal questions to individual leaders.

Sue Inglish, the BBC's Head of Political Programmes, chaired the negotiations. When the journalist Michael Cockerell asked her about people's fear that the 76-point plan might strangle the life out of the debates, she said that the programmes were inevitably going to have a unique structure. She commented that from a broadcaster's perspective, one of the aims was to deliver programmes that people 'would recognise' as proper debates.

Another example of the constructed nature of political debate is 'doughnutting'. In televised Parliamentary debates, this is when supporters surround and applaud a speaker for the benefit of the cameras recording the session.

General knowledge quizzes

General knowledge quizzes provide a good insight into the way that television presents expertise and knowledge in our culture.

At the most extreme end is *Mastermind*, which features obscure knowledge and intense grilling of an individual. The presenter is a journalist and the set is a threatening black chair. Portentous music introduces the show. No prize money is given, just a glass trophy.

In *The Weakest Link*, the focus is on playing against others and using strategy to eliminate them. The music is serious and spot lighting is used to pick out players. Questions are not hard, but there is a great deal of pressure to answer quickly and correctly. The presenter is a former journalist who is famously insulting. The prize money is low. Contestants comment on their own performance.

In *University Challenge*, teams of university students answer difficult questions on a range of high prestige topics, such as science and classical music. Emphasis is on team work and co-operation, though individuals can shine. The presenter is a journalist, well known for being rude to his interviewees. As with *Mastermind*, there is no prize money – only a trophy.

In *Who Wants to be a Millionaire?*, questions get progressively more difficult, but a number of help options are available. There is an element of gambling, with the focus on whether to take risks on the winnings the contestant has already achieved. The host is a former DJ and comedian, who is friendly but sometimes teases contestants. The potential prize money is extremely high.

Are You Smarter than a Ten Year Old? features supposedly easy general knowledge questions, leading to a high cash prize. Contestants work with school children who have usually revised beforehand. The emphasis is on embarrassing and humiliating the adult contestants. The presenter is a former DJ and the show has a jokey format.

Each of these formats tells us something about how knowledge is regarded in our society.

Mastermind and *University Challenge* present knowledge as valuable for its own sake, and focus on questions that the average viewer finds difficult to answer. *The Weakest Link* focuses on winning the game rather than knowledge – the prize money is not high, but the prestige of getting through to the final stage is very important. *Who Wants to be a Millionaire?* again implies that knowledge is valuable, and, given the way that help is structured, that co-operation and trust are as well. *Are You Smarter than a Ten Year Old?* returns knowledge acquisition to a schoolroom level, and turns the usual adult/child expert/learner equation on its head.

Other quizzes have different messages. Some imply that ordinary people are too 'boring' (and so introduce celebrities) or too unskilled (and so employ experts). All quizzes, however, use the available resources of lighting, music and simple human interaction to construct tension-filled entertainment.

> **KEY POINT**
>
> Quizzes are reflections of social value. The majority of quizzes show that we value contextless general knowledge over skill and problem-solving abilities.

Lexis and semantics

AQA	**A P4**
AQA	**B P4**
Edexcel	**P4**
OCR	**P3**
WJEC	**P4**

The lexis of any given text reveals underlying assumptions and values.

Have a look at the following extract.

Family fun as Barack Obama splashes around on a beach weekend with his daughter Sasha

From shooting the breeze with his daughters in the Oval Office to cooking his family a meal once a week, President Barack Obama has made it clear that he has one role that's non-negotiable – his job as First Dad.

This weekend the world's most powerful man snatched a 24-hour break with his wife Michelle and their youngest, nine-year-old Sasha in a Florida coastal resort.

With her big sister Malia at summer camp, the youngest had her father all to herself and was revelling in the attention, smiling from ear to ear as the pair went swimming at Panama City's beach.

Then Barack, a keen golfer, took his girls off to Pirates' Island miniature course.

Much to the US leader's delight Sasha got a hole-in-one on her first attempt. He gave her a high-five, declaring her stroke "unbelievable".

The proud father then turned to the press and asked: "Did you see that?"

Their flying visit, which included a dolphin-spotting cruise, also served as a gesture of support for the Gulf region after the recent oil spill.

"As a result of the clean-up effort beaches all along the Gulf Coast are clean, they are safe and they are open for business," the president told reporters. "That's one of the reasons Michelle, Sasha and I are here."

'Family fun as Barack Obama splashes around on a beach weekend with his daughter Sasha',
hellomagazine.com

Annotations (left margin):

The most powerful man on earth is presented as an ordinary family man.

This is a reference to the fact that the wife of the President is known as the First Lady.

The apparent reason for the story – what and when.

Background information, plus an inference about Sasha's state of mind.

Michelle and her daughter are both 'his girls'.

Obama is portrayed as a proud father.

The real reason for the photo opportunity.

Interestingly, this story is in the Royalty section of the *Hello* magazine website.

This story has accompanying photographs of Barack Obama with his wife and daughter. It positions Obama as a modern family man who even cooks for his wife and children once a week, but it also shows him being in charge and involving his daughter in his own interest in golf. The strong patriarchal notions underlying this aspect of the story are revealed when the phrase 'his girls' is used to refer to both the President's daughter and his wife.

The early part of the story suggests that the reporter had some privileged access to the President and his family, but the final paragraphs reveal that the events are simply part of a set of photo opportunities staged by the President in support of Gulf Coast resorts. As newspaper articles usually put the least important information last, it is clear that the writer of this piece thinks that the magazine's audience is not interested in Obama as a politician, but simply as a father.

> **KEY POINT**
>
> Photo opportunities and other staged media events, such as press conferences, are often presented as news in spite of being artificial. They are easy for news makers and news organisations to deal with, unlike, say, a story about a hurricane or even war.

In any given text, ask yourself these questions:
- What is being approved of?
- What is being disapproved of?

This information will often be revealed in the lexical choices being made by the writer. In a newspaper article, for instance, are you encouraged to think about 'the plight of oppressed refugees' or 'a sorry tale of bogus asylum seekers'?

In the article from *Hello* magazine, President Obama is presented as a 'new man' and 'First Dad', rather than the infinitely stuffier 'First Father'. However, the **politically correct** stance slips slightly in the 'his girls' remark.

Standards of lexis vary according to context. Introductory and closing monologues by presenters on chat shows can be serious and structured, even when the rest of the programme is not. This is often parodied on *South Park* when one of the children pauses briefly to say what he has learnt.

Reality shows appear to present real-life language, but it is important to remember that these are always edited, and that even phone-in programmes tend to have a ten-seconds-to-air delay so that swear words can be beeped out. The comedians Jonathan Ross and Russell Brand caused serious damage to their careers when they went too far in a prank call. Much of the criticism afterwards focused on the fact that the producers allowed the call to be broadcast, even though they knew its content.

Grammar

AQA	**A P4**
AQA	**B P4**
Edexcel	**P4**
OCR	**P3**
WJEC	**P4**

There is a full spectrum of grammatical structures in the media, but some genre conventions have developed within media formats.

For instance, sports commentators have developed various strategies to convey information rapidly.

These include:
- verbless sentences – for example, 'To Smith. To Jones. And upfield to Davis. Goal!'
- short subject–verb sentences – for example, 'He shoots! He scores!'

This older type of spoken commentary has recently been joined by live blogs, which also adopt distinctive strategies to convey information quickly.

4.44pm: ENGLAND CORNER! Johnson takes it. Short corner from the right, Milner gains possession. The full-back closes down Milner, who plays a one-two with Johnson. Milner swings the ball into the box. The keeper punches clear but Rooney fires it back towards goal. Handball! Surely it's a penalty? Yes, the referee is pointing to the spot! The defender blocked Rooney's goal-bound shot with his arm!

4.45pm: RED CARD! The referee shows the red card to Sanchez. The centre-half clearly used his left arm to stop the ball going into the net.

4.46pm: PENALTY! Rooney carefully places the ball on the spot. What an opportunity he's got to put England into the semi-final. He steps back, takes one look at the keeper and runs up … Goal! Right into the top corner! Surely that's England into the last four.

Excitement is conveyed by using capitals, exclamation marks and bold font. Verbs are still missed out (e.g. 'short corner from the right'). Short sentences predominate, but longer ones are also strung together using commas rather than conjunctions.

In the news, a subject + verb + object + adverbial structure is very common. As the table below illustrates, this is a very efficient formula, as it foregrounds the questions that listeners want answered.

Who	The sentence subject	Police
Did what	The verb	raided
To whom or what	The object	a cannabis farm
Where and when	Adverbials	in Sussex early this morning

In the closing lines of the *Life of Mammals*, David Attenborough uses techniques that would not have disgraced an elegant seventeenth-century essayist.

Contrastive parallel between footprints in the sand and on the moon.

A short, emphatic, verbless sentence.

Long rhythmic sentences using subordinate clauses.

Planet earth is set in a larger context. There is a reminder of the moon reference.

There is a contrastive parallel between man and the environment, and reversal of the usual ideas.

Three and a half million years separate the individual who left these footprints in the sands of Africa from the one who left them on the moon. A mere blink in the eye of evolution. Using his burgeoning intelligence, this most successful of all mammals has exploited the environment to produce food for an ever-increasing population. In spite of disasters when civilisations have over-reached themselves, that process has continued, indeed accelerated, even today. Now mankind is looking for food, not just on this planet but on others. Perhaps the time has now come to put that process into reverse. Instead of controlling the environment for the benefit of the population, perhaps it's time we control the population to allow the survival of the environment.

Extract from wikiquote website, David Attenborough web page

Transmitting cultural values

AQA	A P4
AQA	B P4
Edexcel	P4
OCR	P3
WJEC	P4

Figure 7.4 The Mona Lisa painting by Leonardo da Vinci is an example of high art

How do you know that the painting of the Mona Lisa (shown in Figure 7.4) is of cultural significance? One indicator is that you will have to queue up to see it behind its bullet-proof glass protection in the Louvre Gallery in Paris. In cultural matters we tend to pay attention to what other people think is important first, and then, possibly, argue about it afterwards.

Feminists, for instance, have argued that high culture has been wrongly obsessed by Dead White European Males (DWEM). Marxists tend to prefer 'folk art' over 'high art', and so on.

In literature and many other forms of high art, there is a **canon** – a list of important works that everyone is supposed to agree on. Of course, not everyone does agree, and people debate about issues such as who should be in the canon, or whether there should be a canon at all.

In popular culture, canons are often represented as lists of top 10s or top 100s, or 'all-time greatest'. People seem to enjoy this kind of ranking and selecting exercise as an activity in its own sake. For example, one film blog uses ranking in a poll as a way of provoking discussion on what makes a good or bad film.

Open discussion and debate is one thing, but often culture is transmitted more subtly. As our earlier discussion of quiz shows demonstrates, the aspects that are given attention send powerful messages about cultural attitudes. So reality TV and the cult of celebrity inform some people's thinking about what is valuable and worthwhile.

In many cases, representation in the media allows people to think about previously unconsidered areas. An example of this is how a sufferer of Tourette's syndrome winning *Big Brother* increased understanding of the condition. Britain's longest running serial, *The Archers*, was created partly to help convey information to farmers, and soap operas frequently mention help lines at the end of episodes that deal with difficult issues.

Old-style high culture is promoted through adaptations of high prestige 'classic' texts, or through generous air time, which, it could be argued, emphasises its importance. One view is that, generally speaking, high culture is housed in museums and opera houses, whereas popular music increasingly seems to take place in open spaces, like fields.

> **KEY POINT**
>
> High culture tends to have government support in the form of grants and subsidies, whereas popular culture does not. Is support of high culture (like opera and ballet) by the tax payer justified?

7.4 Advertising

LEARNING SUMMARY

After studying this section, you should be able to:

- understand some of the techniques used in advertising
- discuss how advertising positions its audience
- analyse the appeal of advertising

How advertising works

AQA	**A P4**
AQA	**B P4**
Edexcel	**P4**
OCR	**P3**
WJEC	**P4**

It is often difficult to decide where product labelling ends and advertising begins. As products do not appear in the same, standard packaging, the choices that manufacturers make inevitably affect our response to the goods they offer. A tea called 'rich blend' is obviously going to be better received than one called 'barrel scrapings'! Even the font choice and package colour can have some effect on whether we buy a product.

Some supermarkets exploit our suspicions about the deceptive nature of packaging – and advertising in general – by producing 'value' ranges in plain packaging.

Naming and packaging are certainly the first stages in advertising, but the term is generally applied to more deliberate attempts to affect people's decision making.

How advertising works precisely is still something of a mystery – very few people see an advertisement and then go out and buy the product – but numerous studies have shown that advertising a product usually increases its sales in a measurable way. The problem for manufacturers was defined by Lord Leverhulme, when he said the following.

> Half the money I spend on advertising is wasted; the trouble is I don't know which half.

The language of advertising

AQA	A P4
AQA	B P4
Edexcel	P4
OCR	P3
WJEC	P4

Commercial advertising employs a recognisable lexis, conveying ideas of:

- vibrancy – for instance, 'new', 'whiter'
- pleasant sensations – such as 'soft', 'washable'
- positive feelings – for example, 'safe', 'strong'.

Superlatives – such as 'best' and 'perfect' – are also often used.

Typical **qualifiers** include:

- better
- crisp
- good
- fine
- fresh
- free
- improved
- natural
- new
- proven.

Popular **verbs** – often in the imperative – are:

- buy
- give
- go
- feel
- look
- taste
- use.

Frequently used **adverbs** include:

- now
- quickly
- soon
- today.

Grammatically, the language of advertising tends to be conversational, elliptical, and often quite vague. Phrases such as 'up to 50% off' or 'now 20% better' sound positive, but are not very informative.

Here are a few examples of ellipsis:

- 'Does what it says on the tin.'
- 'Starts Thursday.'
- 'Connecting people.'
- 'Apply now.'

Such statements are grammatically incomplete, but the reader or viewer is expected to fill in the meaning from the context.

In the creation of memorable **slogans** particularly, advertising deploys the same resources as literature, including:

- figurative expressions – for example, 'Sleeping on a Seely is like sleeping on a cloud'
- deviant graphology – for instance, *Phones4U*
- sound effects – such as rhythm, alliteration and rhyme – for example, 'This is comparethemeerkat.com, **not** comparethemarket.com' reflects rhyme and rhythm.

Some types of advertising employ special registers, such as engineering, computing and even pseudo-scientific language:

- Car advertisements feature words and phrases such as '*ABS* braking', 'particulates', 'Duratorq TDCi engines'.
- Computer advertisements refer to terms such as 'RAM', 'Wi-Fi', 'quad core processor'.
- Baffling concepts are sometimes mentioned in advertising, for instance 'quantum water', 'energised crystals', '*nanotechnology*-infused plates'. They sound scientific, but are not, so they cannot be explained.

Types of advertising

AQA   **A P4**
AQA   **B P4**
Edexcel **P4**
OCR   **P3**
WJEC   **P4**

Advertising comes in many different forms – from subtle product placement in films to giant billboards alongside major roads.

Print advertising subsidises the cost of newspapers and magazines, and television, radio and films also recoup costs by advertising. In 2009, Google made 23 billion dollars of advertising revenue so that its search engine and products like Google Maps could remain 'free' to the end user. As well as professionally produced advertising, we are also exposed to other forms of advertising, such as personal advertisements in newspapers and product descriptions on eBay.

Remarkably, there seems to be little stylistic variance across all types of advertising. The new and unique always seems to sell – from houses to life partners.

Given the limited time that advertisers generally have to get their point across, advertising language and imagery has to work remarkably hard. Television advertisements have around 30 seconds to engage an audience, and print adverts have to make an impression – with eye-catching slogans and visuals – before the reader turns the page.

> **KEY POINT**
>
> Like legal language, advertising has a measurable effect. Successful advertising campaigns can transform a company's profits and profile. Advertising therefore always uses the most powerful language and imagery available – no one advertises a 'quite good' product.

Advertising techniques

Advertising often adopts textual structures from elsewhere to maximise impact.

For instance, the 'Cleaner Close' advertising campaign for Daz washing powder parodies and relies on the conventions of soap operas to deliver a simple narrative, with a positive message about washing powder, in a very short space of time. The slogan – 'Daz – the soap you can believe in!' – both positions Daz as a reliable product, but also makes fun of some of the more extreme situations depicted in soap operas.

In another example, Guinness used the techniques of computer-enhanced nature documentaries to run backwards through millions of years of evolution in 52 seconds. This was done to illustrate the slogan, 'Good things come to those who wait'.

As we have already mentioned in this section, advertising uses language techniques to engage audiences.

These techniques include making use of:

- rhyme – for example, 'Don't be vague, Ask for Haig' and 'We all adore a Kia-Ora'
- rhythm – for example, 'If you want to get ahead, get a hat' and 'Let the train take the strain'
- assonance – for example, 'Milk's gotta lotta bottle'
- wordplay – for example, 'Won't make a pom tiddly' (in relation to Swan Light Beer – allusion to 'tiddly pom'), 'Taste not Waist' (a pun), 'A newspaper, not a snoozepaper...' (new compound)
- alliteration – for example, 'You can break a brolly but you can't k-nacker a Knirps' (referring to an umbrella).

Advertisements for the Sega Megadrive (which is now defunct) used a graphological pun, which depended on you reading the brand name (SEGA) backwards. The slogan was 'To be this good takes "AGES"'.

The prevalence of rhyme in many well-known advertisements is another factor in their memorability.

Brand values and semantics

AQA   **A P4**
AQA   **B P4**
Edexcel **P4**
OCR   **P3**
WJEC   **P4**

It is not worth a company spending millions of pounds on advertising its brand of fishcakes and then finding out that all fishcake sales have gone up. It is important that buyers can identify your product easily and associate it with certain positive ideas. The overall image of a product in the marketplace is known as its **brand**. Companies go to a great deal of trouble to establish a brand and then maintain its presence.

A key purpose of advertising is to make consumers feel good about their purchases. Some brands do this by appealing to our baser instincts, such as our desire to have a faster car than anyone else, but other brands work hard to create an image that makes them seem like forces for good – so that buying their products feels like a virtuous act.

The 'innocent' brand started off being innocent in terms of its content – only 'natural' ingredients were used – but this has been extended into a general concern for the environment.

The 'innocent' message is conveyed by:
- the 'saintly' logo
- the use of a lower case sans serif font on the product packs
- the hand-written, simply drawn style of its advertising.

Figure 7.5 Innocent – a 'saintly' brand

Concern for the environment is also shown by brands such as Starbucks and Ben and Jerry's, whilst concern about workers receiving a fair deal has boosted the success of numerous **fairtrade** brands.

Another method of making people feel good about their purchases is to associate a product with a celebrity. This is particularly prevalent in sport and haute couture. Perfume, make-up and hair products are often advertised by television and film celebrities – recent examples are Charlize Theron and Nicole Kidman.

Well-known people can earn millions by associating their names and images with products. An interesting example is Elvis Presley. He has been dead since 1977, but the continued popularity of his 'name' had earned over 55 million dollars by 2009.

KEY POINT

Celebrities are their own brands and have to be careful what they associate themselves with. Many Hollywood stars avoid advertising work in America, but earn large amounts of money in places like Japan.

Pragmatics and advertising

AQA	**A P4**
AQA	**B P4**
Edexcel	**P4**
OCR	**P3**
WJEC	**P4**

As well as closely observing advertisers' language, it is also useful to think about the methods they use to engage audiences.

We have already discussed how the words in print advertisements do a great deal of work, and some of the visual imagery used in advertising posters is genuinely striking and original. Television advertisements use methods like sound, music, familiar voice-over personalities, the latest in computer graphics, multiple cuts and actors to 'grab' and maintain an audience. Advertisements are – technically speaking – dense texts, which often reward careful unpicking and analysis.

It is also useful to think about how you are being positioned as a viewer, listener or reader. Ask yourself these kinds of questions:
- Are you obsessed with getting the best value product, or are you a sophisticated and discerning consumer who doesn't mind paying a little bit more for the right thing?
- Are you worried about how white your shirts could be, or do you just want to wash and go?
- Does the advertisement address you directly (for instance, about how easy it is to clean up the mess in your kitchen), or is there someone for you to identify with in the advert itself?

PROGRESS CHECK

1 What is the basic problem with advertising identified by Lord Leverhulme?
2 What is a brand?
3 Why are advertisements such dense texts?

3 They have to work hard to grab the interest of people who may not be very interested in them.
2 The overall identity of a product, built up over time.
1 It increases sales, but not in a way that is easy to explain.

Sample question and model answer

Section D – Language, power and identity

1. The following texts are **both** about journeys to places that don't exist. By close reference to both texts, make a detailed critical analysis of the linguistic approaches used by the authors. You should also analyse and evaluate the influence of contextual factors, like time and mode of production, and, where appropriate, refer to your wider knowledge and study of this topic.

(30 marks)

Text A – *Gulliver's Travels* by Jonathan Swift (1735)

Gulliver, on his third voyage, visits Laputa, an island that floats in the air.

At my alighting, I was surrounded with a crowd of people, but those who stood nearest seemed to be of better quality. They beheld me with all the marks and circumstances of wonder; neither indeed was I much in their debt, having never till then seen a race of mortals so singular in their shapes, habits, and countenances. Their heads were all reclined, either to the right, or the left; one of their eyes turned inward, and the other directly up to the zenith. Their outward garments were adorned with the figures of suns, moons, and stars; interwoven with those of fiddles, flutes, harps, trumpets, guitars, harpsichords, and many other instruments of music, unknown to us in Europe. I observed, here and there, many in the habit of servants, with a blown bladder, fastened like a flail to the end of a stick, which they carried in their hands. In each bladder was a small quantity of dried peas, or little pebbles, as I was afterwards informed. With these bladders, they now and then flapped the mouths and ears of those who stood near them, of which practice I could not then conceive the meaning. It seems the minds of these people are so taken up with intense speculations, that they neither can speak, nor attend to the discourses of others, without being roused by some external action upon the organs of speech and hearing; for which reason, those persons who are able to afford it always keep a flapper (the original is CLIMENOLE) in their family, as one of their domestics; nor ever walk abroad, or make visits, without him. And the business of this officer is, when two, three, or more persons are in company, gently to strike with his bladder the mouth of him who is to speak, and the right ear of him or them to whom the speaker addresses himself. This flapper is likewise employed diligently to attend his master in his walks, and upon occasion to give him a soft flap on his eyes; because he is always so wrapped up in cogitation, that he is in manifest danger of falling down every precipice, and bouncing his head against every post; and in the streets, of justling others, or being justled himself into the kennel.

Gulliver is introduced to the King and given a chance to learn Laputan.

Those to whom the king had entrusted me, observing how ill I was clad, ordered a tailor to come next morning, and take measure for a suit of clothes. This operator did his office after a different manner from those of his trade in Europe. He first took my altitude by a quadrant, and then, with a rule and

Sample question and model answer
(continued)

compasses, described the dimensions and outlines of my whole body, all which he entered upon paper; and in six days brought my clothes very ill made, and quite out of shape, by happening to mistake a figure in the calculation. But my comfort was, that I observed such accidents very frequent, and little regarded.

During my confinement for want of clothes, and by an indisposition that held me some days longer, I much enlarged my dictionary; and when I went next to court, was able to understand many things the king spoke, and to return him some kind of answers.... On the second morning, about eleven o'clock, the king himself in person, attended by his nobility, courtiers, and officers, having prepared all their musical instruments, played on them for three hours without intermission, so that I was quite stunned with the noise; neither could I possibly guess the meaning, till my tutor informed me. He said that, the people of their island had their ears adapted to hear "the music of the spheres, which always played at certain periods, and the court was now prepared to bear their part, in whatever instrument they most excelled."

...

The knowledge I had in mathematics, gave me great assistance in acquiring their phraseology, which depended much upon that science, and music; and in the latter I was not unskilled. Their ideas are perpetually conversant in lines and figures. If they would, for example, praise the beauty of a woman, or any other animal, they describe it by rhombs, circles, parallelograms, ellipses, and other geometrical terms, or by words of art drawn from music, needless here to repeat. I observed in the king's kitchen all sorts of mathematical and musical instruments, after the figures of which they cut up the joints that were served to his majesty's table. Their houses are very ill built, the walls bevil, without one right angle in any apartment; and this defect arises from the contempt they bear to practical geometry, which they despise as vulgar and mechanic; those instructions they give being too refined for the intellects of their workmen, which occasions perpetual mistakes. And although they are dexterous enough upon a piece of paper, in the management of the rule, the pencil, and the divider, yet in the common actions and behaviour of life, I have not seen a more clumsy, awkward, and unhandy people, nor so slow and perplexed in their conceptions upon all other subjects, except those of mathematics and music. They are very bad reasoners, and vehemently given to opposition, unless when they happen to be of the right opinion, which is seldom their case. Imagination, fancy, and invention, they are wholly strangers to, nor have any words in their language, by which those ideas can be expressed; the whole compass of their thoughts and mind being shut up within the two forementioned sciences.

Sample question and model answer

(continued)

Text B – *Erewhon* by Samuel Butler (1872)

In *Erewhon*, a traveller enters a land where ill-health is treated as a crime and where criminals are treated for sickness. The inhabitants have also abandoned machines. Arowhena is a native girl.

Thus they hold it strictly forbidden for a man to go without common air in his lungs for more than a very few minutes; and if by any chance he gets into the water, the air-god is very angry, and will not suffer it; no matter whether the man got into the water by accident or on purpose, whether through the attempt to save a child or through presumptuous contempt of the air-god, the air-god will kill him, unless he keeps his head high enough out of the water, and thus gives the air-god his due.

This with regard to the deities who manage physical affairs. Over and above these they personify hope, fear, love, and so forth, giving them temples and priests, and carving likenesses of them in stone, which they verily believe to be faithful representations of living beings who are only not human in being more than human. If any one denies the objective existence of these divinities, and says that there is really no such being as a beautiful woman called Justice, with her eyes blinded and a pair of scales, positively living and moving in a remote and ethereal region, but that justice is only the personified expression of certain modes of human thought and action—they say that he denies the existence of justice in denying her personality, and that he is a wanton disturber of men's religious convictions. They detest nothing so much as any attempt to lead them to higher spiritual conceptions of the deities whom they profess to worship. Arowhena and I had a pitched battle on this point, and should have had many more but for my prudence in allowing her to get the better of me.

I am sure that in her heart she was suspicious of her own position for she returned more than once to the subject. "Can you not see," I had exclaimed, "that the fact of justice being admirable will not be affected by the absence of a belief in her being also a living agent? Can you really think that men will be one whit less hopeful because they no longer believe that hope is an actual person?" She shook her head, and said that with men's belief in the personality all incentive to the reverence of the thing itself, as justice or hope, would cease; men from that hour would never be either just or hopeful again.

I could not move her, nor, indeed, did I seriously wish to do so. She deferred to me in most things, but she never shrank from maintaining her opinions if they were put in question; nor does she to this day abate one jot of her belief in the religion of her childhood, though in compliance with my repeated entreaties she has allowed herself to be baptized into the English Church. ...

I own that she very nearly conquered me once; for she asked me what I should think if she were to tell me that my God, whose nature and

Sample question and model answer
(continued)

attributes I had been explaining to her, was but the expression for man's highest conception of goodness, wisdom, and power; that in order to generate a more vivid conception of so great and glorious a thought, man had personified it and called it by a name; that it was an unworthy conception of the Deity to hold Him personal, inasmuch as escape from human contingencies became thus impossible; that the real thing men should worship was the Divine, whereinsoever they could mind it; that "God" was but man's way of expressing his sense of the Divine; that as justice, hope, wisdom, etc., were all parts of goodness, so God was the expression which embraced all goodness and all good power; that people would no more cease to love God on ceasing to believe in His objective personality, than they had ceased to love justice on discovering that she was not really personal; nay, that they would never truly love Him till they saw Him thus.

She said all this in her artless way, and with none of the coherence with which I have here written it; her face kindled, and she felt sure that she had convinced me that I was wrong, and that justice was a living person. Indeed, I did wince a little; but I recovered myself immediately, and pointed out to her that we had books whose genuineness was beyond all possibility of doubt, as they were certainly none of them less than 1,800 years old; that in these there were the most authentic accounts of men who had been spoken to by the Deity Himself, and of one prophet who had been allowed to see the back parts of God through the hand that was laid over his face.

This was conclusive; and I spoke with such solemnity that she was a little frightened, and only answered that they too had their books, in which their ancestors had seen the god; on which I saw that further argument was not at all likely to convince her; and fearing that she might tell her mother what I had been saying, and that I might lose the hold upon her affections which I was beginning to feel pretty sure that I was obtaining, I began to let her have her own way, and to convince me; neither till after we were safely married did I show the cloven hoof again.

Model answer

Both of these texts use travelogue as a means of satirising their own societies. Swift seems to be attacking the scientific speculators of the eighteenth century and Butler seems to be attacking Victorian religion. The advantage of using travelogue in this manner is that the narrator can appear to be an innocent commentator on what he or she sees, leaving the readers to draw their own conclusions.

Both Swift and Butler are concerned with the physical reality of abstract thought. Swift defines abstract thought in his satire as music and mathematics, and imagines a community where these two sets of ideas dominate everything else, from decorations on clothes to musical performances. The highest practitioners are so lost in thought that they need servants to assist them in the real world. These 'flappers' are forced to directly stimulate the organs of speech, hearing and sight with noisy little balloons.

(sidebar annotations)

This is a very cogent response to the question, which shows a good understanding of audience and purpose, and which features a good range of subject-specific knowledge and vocabulary. Perhaps more attention could have been paid to the specific features of eighteenth- and nineteenth-century English in the two texts, but this response would achieve a high grade.

The genre and purpose of the two texts is identified.

A reason for choosing this genre is given.

The linguistic similarities and techniques are identified.

The student refers closely to the text.

Sample question and model answer
(continued)

The student uses a quotation to make a point.

The student distinguishes the authorial voice from the narrator.

There is a discussion about the likely audience.

The student talks about the contemporary relevance of Swift's text.

Eighteenth- and nineteenth-century audiences are distinguished, and the impact of this difference is discussed.

Authorial techniques are discussed in detail.

The student introduces relevant linguistic theory.

Lexis is discussed.

The student looks at discourse techniques.

Connotations are identified.

The student uses explicit comparison.

Concluding paragraph.

Butler describes a group of people who worship gods who are simply personified virtues like hope and justice. He is easily able to show that this practice is absurd through his argument with Arowhena: `Can you really think that men will be one whit less hopeful because they no longer believe that hope is an actual person?´ However, when she turns this argument against him by suggesting that the God he worships is merely a more complex example of the same thing, he is forced to back track and base his argument for the existence of God on the existence of certain old books. Butler the writer is clearly not convinced by these arguments, and so he allows his narrator to look absurd in making them.

Both texts reflect the social attitudes of their times. Swift's traveller moves among the top layers of society, who are educated but distracted from everyday realities, just as the English aristocracy was in the eighteenth century. At the next level down are artisans who are less well-educated and prone to mistakes in both tailoring and architecture. This criticism of English education is still made today, in that it is easier to get onto a university course than it is to get practical training. Women are hardly mentioned in Swift's text, but this reflects his likely eighteenth-century audience of mostly educated men.

Butler's narrator is romantically involved with Arowhena, but treats her in a patronising manner, describing her `artless way´ of talking and lack of `coherence´. She is described as deferring to the narrator `in most things´, but not shrinking from maintaining her opinions. This would make her quite forthright in Victorian terms. By creating an artless but articulate non-Christian, Butler is able to cast doubt on Christian beliefs. By the Victorian era, many more women were readers and many more of them were keen to enter into intellectual debate, in spite of being patronised by people like the narrator.

Swift's main satirical technique is physical description, through which he builds up an increasingly ugly and unpleasant picture of Laputan society. The aristocracy have their heads to one side or another, with one eye looking upward and one eye looking inward. They can barely function as human beings without the aid of `flappers´ and, it emerges, they dress in ugly clothes and live in ugly houses. Because they are so focused on maths and science, they are strangers to `imagination, fancy, and invention´ and most interestingly of all, they have no words to express these concepts. This observation is similar to the claims made by various adherents of the Sapir-Wharf hypothesis – without words for these things the Laputans are `shut up´ within the sciences. Swift implies that this would be very bad for society as a whole.

Butler uses theological language to explain drowning at the beginning of the extract. This shows the attitudes and beliefs of the Erewhonians to be naïve at best, and certainly absurd. However, he is more concerned with making his narrator and the society he comes from seem absurd. This is largely done through `artless´ honesty on the narrator's part. The narrator is shown at first to be attracted to Arowhena and he therefore `allows´ her to win arguments. It is only when they are married that the narrator shows `the cloven hoof´ once more. Butler's choice of the phrase `cloven hoof´ suggests a devilish rather than godly approach, and readers are unlikely to be impressed by such hypocrisy.

Both authors are attacking something that they don't like, but by using a narrative rather than an obviously persuasive framework, they can convince their readers in a subtle manner. Swift builds a picture of a mental tunnel vision by gradually revealing more and more absurd aspects of the society his narrator is travelling through. Butler, on the other hand, gradually reveals how untrustworthy and hypocritical his narrator is. By the end of the passage, the reader is far more likely to reject his judgements than accept them.

Exam practice question

Section D – Language, power and identity

1 The following two texts relate to the role of girls in society.

By close reference to **BOTH** texts, make a detailed critical analysis of the linguistic approaches used by the authors. You should also analyse and evaluate the influence of contextual factors, like time and mode of production, and, where appropriate, refer to your wider knowledge and study of this topic.

(30)

Text A – Boys and girls (1964)

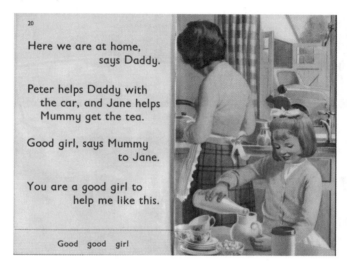

20

Here we are at home,
          says Daddy.

Peter helps Daddy with
     the car, and Jane helps
     Mummy get the tea.

Good girl, says Mummy
          to Jane.

You are a good girl to
     help me like this.

Good   good   girl

Text B – Something for the girls

For 100 years, the Girl Guide movement has presented girls with challenges – whether it be earning a badge, helping out in times of need or raising funds for special projects. Each generation faces new and exciting ways of proving themselves and the goals they achieve have inevitably altered over the years. But no matter how times change one thing remains constant – a Guide always rises to a challenge.

In the year England celebrated its World Cup win, a group of determined guiding members scored a victory of their own. The summer of 1966 saw six girls break the female record for a cross-Channel relay swim when they swam from Cap Gris Nez in France to the Kent coast in 13 hours and 10 minutes.

The relay team was chosen from companies around the country and whipped into shape by a Miss B. Strutt, a physical education expert from Manchester University.

On the appointed day the first swimmer, Sally Rose, set out at 3.27am with the moon still up and a fog gathering on the water.

8 Language investigations and other coursework tasks

The following topics are covered in this chapter:

- What a language investigation involves
- Suggested topics
- Putting your investigation together
- Requirements for the task
- Other coursework tasks

8.1 What a language investigation involves

LEARNING SUMMARY	After studying this section, you should be able to:
	• understand what a language investigation involves for your specification
	• identify possible formats for your investigation
	• consider some of the issues raised by language investigations

Investigating language

AQA   **A P4**
AQA   **B P4**
Edexcel **P4**
OCR   **P4**
WJEC   **P3**

All specifications require that you carry out a language investigation as part of your A2 year. The main difference between the approaches taken by the examination boards is in how they ask you to present your investigation. For some it is a formal, academic exercise, and for others it needs to be aimed at a general audience. In some specifications your investigation will be all of your coursework, whilst in others it will be part of a portfolio.

Generally speaking, your investigation should:
- be an original piece of work based on your own ideas
- use data that you have collected
- have a specific focus – this may vary from board to board
- answer a question or test a hypothesis that you have generated
- be directed to a specific audience.

What you will investigate

Please read this information if you are studying the **AQA A** specification.

For the **AQA A** specification, your first task is an **investigation of spoken texts**, targeted at an academic audience. Excluding data, the investigation should be between 1750 and 2500 words.

Your second task is to write about a **language debate** in a particular form for a non-specialist audience. You can use up to 1250 words.

Please read this information if you are studying the **AQA B** specification.

For the **AQA B** specification, you can choose any relevant topic you like – either from elsewhere in the course or in any language area that interests you. The investigation should be aimed at an academic audience, and it should be between 1750 and 2500 words, excluding data and any appendices. It is submitted as part of a folder, which also includes a media text you have produced (750 to 1000 words).

Please read this information if you are studying the **Edexcel** specification.

Edexcel asks you to address two different audiences in the presentation of your investigation.

First, you are asked to write a short article, talk or presentation about your area of study, using between 600 and 750 words. This piece of work should be aimed at a non-specialist audience.

Secondly, you are expected to write an academic report that is between 2000 and 2250 words.

The first piece of work should deal mostly with what you are hoping to do, and the report should say what you did and what conclusions you were able to draw.

Please read this information if you are studying the **OCR** specification.

Your **OCR** coursework folder comprises two pieces of work, using a maximum of 3000 words.

Your investigation should consist of a sustained comparative analysis of three media texts from each of the three modes – spoken, written and multimodal. The original texts you study should be linked by a common theme or common topic. You must include all three of the texts you study in the coursework folder, but there is no prescribed length for them. You also have the chance to produce your own media text and commentary.

Please read this information if you are studying the **WJEC** specification.

For **WJEC**, you are asked to produce a study based on an area that interests you in spoken or written English (or a combination of the two) from the list below. You should aim to write around 1500 words.

The topic list comprises:
- language acquisition
- the study of accent and/or dialect
- attitudes to an area of language – such as accent
- aspects of language and gender – such as sexism or stereotyping
- language from the past, e.g. changing styles in a genre such as letter writing or advertising; also Anglo Saxon or Middle English
- black English or Ebonics
- language and political power
- the language of parliamentary debate – could also include speeches from the past
- political correctness in language
- spelling reform
- other 'Englishes'
- American and British English.

In addition to your study, you are also expected to produce a piece of writing for a specific purpose. This should be about 1000 words long and accompanied by a 500 to 750 word commentary.

KEY POINT

The research techniques you acquire in this chapter will stand you in good stead if you do a dissertation at university level.

The format of your investigation

AQA   **A P4**
AQA   **B P4**
Edexcel **P4**
OCR   **P4**
WJEC   **P3**

The following format can be used for **AQA A**, **AQA B**, **Edexcel** and **WJEC** investigations.

The **AQA A** specification gives very precise instructions on the format that your investigation should take. **This is necessary for AQA students, but it is a useful model for all academic investigative work.**

The format is as follows.

1. **Introduction** – this should briefly outline the topic to be investigated and explain why it is significant. It should then set out what question(s) your investigation hopes to explore or what hypothesis it will test. Finally, it should explain how your topic fits into language studies as a whole.

2. **Aims** – the aim of an investigation is what it is trying to find out. This will be the answer to the question you have asked, or confirmation or refutation of your hypothesis. Clear aims will ensure that your investigation remains focused and relevant.

3. **Methodology** – this section discusses the data you have used, how it was collected, and what precautions you took to make sure it was the right kind of data. The methodology section should also mention the linguistic framework(s) you used to analyse your data.

4. **Data** – if you are investigating spoken language this might consist of tapes and transcripts, or it may be copies of written texts. The data you have collected does not go towards your word count, and different boards have different rules on whether your data should be submitted as part of your final folder. There should be sufficient data to make your study valid, but not so much that it gets in the way of in-depth analysis.

5. **Analysis** – the analysis of your data will form the main part of your investigation and it will play a significant role in deciding your final grade. You are aiming for an understanding of your data in its context (a wide view) as well as subtle and insightful detailed analysis (an in-depth view). In this section you may need to refer to secondary sources of information and ideas about language.

6. **Conclusion** – the conclusion will make clear what the investigation has found out, or to what extent the hypothesis has been proved or rebutted.

7. **Evaluation** – in this section you should briefly analyse whether the investigation was a success or not (even disproving something represents progress in this sense) and whether the methodology was valid and reliable. It is also normal to suggest topics for further research at this point.

8. **Bibliography** – this will be a list of all the primary and secondary sources used in the investigation. This might include academic articles, books and websites. The bibliography is normally provided using a standard academic format.

9. **Appendices** – these contain data and other materials relevant to your investigation. You may wish to show, for instance, how you transcribed parts of your data, or allow readers to see your original collection of nutrition labels. The appendices are not included in the word count.

We will provide more detail about each of these sections of your study in Section 8.2.

The **OCR** investigation requires comparisons across three texts in three genres, connected by a theme or topic. For instance, the theme of 'persuasion' might involve you in comparing a political speech, a literary essay, and an illustrated brochure, using appropriate linguistic frameworks.

Investigation topics

AQA	**A P4**
AQA	**B P4**
Edexcel	**P4**
OCR	**P4**
WJEC	**P3**

Most investigations involve either a question you want to answer or a hypothesis that you want to test. If you can ask a good question or frame a testable hypothesis, a great deal will follow on logically.

Top-down approach

For example, you may have read Deborah Cameron's book, *Good to Talk?*,[1] and feel that it has some interesting things to say about the role of talk in modern society. However, you may wonder if Cameron's critical stance on the value of talk is just something that linguistics professors feel. Wouldn't it be interesting to explain some of her ideas to other A-Level students and then see what they thought of them? The idea of girls being positioned as 'better' at communication would certainly provoke some lively debate.

Your secondary reading would lead you to the first stage of formulating a question, such as 'Are girls better at communication than boys?', or, as Dr Cameron suggests, 'Has our idea of what constitutes "good" communication shifted recently?' This is a very big issue indeed, and could lead into areas like boys' underachievement in schools or the prevalence of women in call centres. Depending on your own interests, you would then narrow this basic idea down into something testable at A-Level. You might consider attitude surveys, or you could look at actual classroom behaviour. This might be described as a **top-down approach**, in which linguistic theories lead you to a specific topic.

Bottom-up approach

A **bottom-up approach** is one in which your own experiences of language lead you to a particular question or hypothesis. For instance, you might be a fan of cricket commentaries on the radio, but not of football commentaries. Is this because football is a game of continuous movement, whilst cricket is sporadic? Or is it because cricket commentators have developed a richer and more complex style of commentary than their football counterparts? Or, possibly, cricket fans are more inclined to listen. Once again, your interests will have led you to a question. You could simply compare styles of commentary, or you could analyse the development of commentary over time.

> **KEY POINT**
>
> The approach you choose will not affect your grade – examiners welcome them both.

1 Cameron, D. 2000. *Good to talk? Living and working in a communication culture.* London: Sage.

Suggested topics

Here are some other topic ideas that you may want to consider:
- Contrasting interview style of Jonathan Ross and Oprah Winfrey.
- An analysis of boys' and girls' language in a primary school classroom.
- Lexis and grammar in *Newsround* compared to *The Six O'Clock News*.
- What makes a good 'tweet'?
- Can English spelling ever be reformed?
- An analysis of accent and dialect use in one family, newly arrived in an area.
- A study of the grammar and orthography of lolcats.
- Fluency and hesitancy in answer phone messages.
- How has the Queen's use of language changed over time? A study of Christmas broadcasts.
- Developments in the language of film trailers across three decades.
- Is txt spelling becoming more common amongst year 7s?
- Attitudes and assumptions about local dialect speakers.
- How female characters have developed in *The Beano*.
- How the language of party political broadcasts has changed over time.

You may have several areas you would like to investigate, so at this stage think about practicalities. For example, you might find language acquisition fascinating, but can you study the language acquisition of a younger sibling/relative, or do you have a parent's permission to study the language development of their young child? Are all the Queen's Christmas messages available online or elsewhere? If you want to investigate 'live' language, do you have access to a tape or digital recorder? It is important to consider these kinds of issues before you choose a topic.

Overview of investigation stages

AQA	A P4
AQA	B P4
Edexcel	P4
OCR	P4
WJEC	P3

Once you have found a topic that you find interesting, and which is doable in practical terms, you will need to think carefully through the stages of your investigation.

Generally speaking, the stages comprise:
- conceptualisation
- data gathering
- data analysis
- preparing a first draft.

Conceptualisation is extremely important – it basically means knowing what you are doing in linguistic rather than practical terms.

For instance, a comparison of the language of menus from MacDonald's with Le Manoir Aux Quat'Saisons is a good idea, but it needs to be conceptualised – as a study in prestige forms of language, or even as an analysis of the importance of French terms in English cooking. In essence, you need to decide on a focus and stick with it.

Data gathering and data analysis comprise a major part of your investigation and we will look at this stage in detail now. The next section of the chapter focuses on the requirements for the task, to help you prepare yourself for writing a first draft of your investigation.

Data gathering and data analysis

AQA	**A P4**
AQA	**B P4**
Edexcel	**P4**
OCR	**P4**
WJEC	**P3**

Given that language is all around us, there is a temptation to gather too much data.

This is a bad idea for two reasons:

1. You will spend too long analysing data, which will reduce the amount of time you have to plan and write your draft.
2. You will simply not be able to address the data, given the word limits for all language investigations.

The converse is also true – you do need to have enough data in order to make interesting and informative comments.

Data types and approaches

In all investigations you will need to gather **primary** and **secondary** data.

Primary data is something that you personally have gathered and processed. From the point of view of your language investigation, simply obtaining a King James and a modern Bible could count as your data gathering stage. If you are investigating spoken language in the public arena, you may find everything you need on YouTube or BBC iPlayer.

If you are investigating the language of people you know, you will probably need a tape or digital recorder and you will need to make sure that the people you will be quoting have given their consent – or in the case of children, that you have obtained a parent's consent. Most schools will have a standard letter for this purpose, but you can also design your own.

In your report you should discuss your methodology – this is usually a question of whether the data you have gathered can be used to support the conclusions that you reach. You will need to think about this as you gather your data.

The fact that one three year-old that you have met can say 'Millennium Falcon' is not evidence that watching *Star Wars* films speeds up linguistic development. If you are studying one child, how typical is he or she?

If you have chosen a sample of a particular type of language, how representative is it? You could base your analysis on information from the 400-million word Bank of English and retrieve large amounts of quantitative data, or you could conduct a single in-depth interview and generate a large amount of qualitative data.

To illustrate some of the problems, imagine you have chosen to look at the grammar and orthography of lolcats. There would be no problem finding examples, as there are whole websites devoted to them – there is even a project to translate the Bible into lolcat.[2] Your problem will be to decide on how many lolcats to choose, and how to select them.

Using a **synchronistic approach** – taking a snapshot at a single moment of time – you could simply choose 100 lolcat images from the *I Can Haz Cheezeburger* website on a single day, and perform some simple statistical analysis on them.

You could, for instance, note statistics such as:

- deviant spelling (in this snapshot 86 percent)
- non-standard grammar (in this snapshot 27 percent)
- formulaic language (in this snapshot 36 percent).

2 See www.lolcatbible.com/

Using 100 examples is a good idea as it is a large enough sample to be statistically significant and you do not need to do any calculations to work out the percentages; 50 is also a good number in this context, but a sample of 25 would probably be too small.

Alternatively, you could take a **diachronistic approach**, and look at how lolcat language has developed over time. Finding evidence for this would be more complex, but not impossible, using websites like *Know your Meme* and *Wikipedia*.

You could also **cherry-pick** samples by applying appropriate language-based criteria. Here, you are more likely to be concerned with subtle points of grammar or representation, and with providing examples to illustrate your hypothesis.

It is up to you how you collect your data and process it. There is no right or wrong way of going about it. All you have to do is discuss the constraints you were working under in the methodology section, and how you used linguistic perspectives to inform your choices.

> **KEY POINT**
>
> Quantitative approaches are useful if you need a sharp focus for your work. Qualitative approaches do not impose limits, and so you have to be more disciplined in deciding on the depth and breadth of your work.

Figure 8.1 How typical is this child?

A second approach is to use qualitative rather than quantitative data. Here, you do not have to collect 'significant' amounts of data, but ensure that you provide a sufficiently linguistically informed account of your source material. This will often involve you in some background reading and **secondary data collection**. For example, if your primary source of language data is your four year-old sister, you will need to find out about four-year olds in general using standard text books. This will allow you to put the data you collect from her into context. Is her speech exceptional or normal compared to text book examples? This way of working can be used in an **ethnographic approach**, where you do your best to capture real language in real situations.

If you are going to make comparisons, it is very important that you compare like with like. This means that you should narrow down the number of variables that could plausibly account for the phenomenon you are studying. For instance, you might be investigating one of Lakoff's statements about women's language use. If your sample contains women and men from different age groups or language communities, your conclusions might be questioned, as there will be other possible explanations for the language behaviours you observed. In technical jargon, you will have failed to control for age, ethnicity and gender.

If you are investigating attitudes to language, you may wish to use a **survey**. This should feature a number of carefully targeted questions and a method of recording the data elicited.

Here are a few examples of good survey questions.

How do people respond to your Geordie accent?

Positively ☐
Negatively ☐
Impossible to tell ☐

People think that you are well educated if you talk in a 'posh' accent.

Strongly agree	Agree slightly	Neither agree nor disagree	Disagree slightly	Strongly disagree
☐	☐	☐	☐	☐

Giving people limited options in their answers makes your data analysis easier, but you need to be fair and also allow room for 'don't know' type answers.

In some surveys, you might wish to provide prompts.

What name do you give to the meal in the middle of the day?

A. Lunch ☐
B. Luncheon ☐
C. Brunch ☐
D. Snack ☐
E. Dinner ☐
F. Midday meal ☐
G. Scran (or other local word) ☐
H. Other ☐

A few well-focused questions are much more manageable than a large number of vague ones, particularly if you wish to administer a large number of surveys. It is also a very good idea to get a few people to 'test drive' your questionnaire before you send it out, to make sure that people respond to it as you expect.

Ethical considerations

If you are planning any sort of data gathering that involves people rather than texts, you need to make sure that you have the consent of the people involved (even if you are collecting examples of something that people would normally do, like leave messages on an answering machine). You should explain what you are doing beforehand, and ask them to sign a consent form after they have provided you with data.

A key ethical issue is the **anonymising of data**. This will not be necessary if you are quoting from material that is already in the public domain (for instance, television broadcasts or speeches in Parliament), but any conversation that is normally private should stay that way. You need permission to quote someone, and you also need to make sure that a third party cannot identify your respondent from the information given in your study. Names of people are usually replaced with letters, but place names should also be blocked out if they could lead to someone guessing who is speaking. Typically, this might be the name of a cafe or shopping centre where people meet.

Types of interview

The most people-intensive data approach is an interview. For this you will need a good quality tape or digital recorder – and patience.

The three main types of interview are:
- **structured** – this type of interview uses a pre-decided set of questions from which there is no deviation
- **unstructured** – the questions are on a single topic, but differ every time
- **semi-structured** – this type of interview uses a set of prompts so that each interview goes over the same ground, but the wording for each question may differ.

If you plan to utilise interviews in your report, you need to decide what to do with all the data. The main solution is to transcribe it. This can be a long process if you have several complex issues. Structured or semi-structured interviews are best if you wish to compare similarities across interviewees.

Writing a transcript

You will not need to transcribe long passages of your data, but make sure that you use the same format as your exam board if you do.

The usual transcript format is a modified and simplified version of the system developed by Jefferson[3] in the 1960s.

Common conventions include:
- **(.)** – micropause
- **(.h)** – pause with an audible intake of breath
- **(1.0)** – pause for time shown in seconds
- **She thou:::gt** – colons show elongated speech
- **//   //** – overlaps in speech of participants
- **CAPITALS** – to show speech that is louder than surrounding utterances
- **very** – underlined words show emphatic stress
- **=** – latch-on, i.e. no gap between two utterances
- **th.** – an incomplete word.

It is normal to label the participants at the beginning and then use contrasting letters thereafter. If text is omitted, this should be labelled in parentheses at the appropriate place, as should inaudible speech. Pragmatics such as gestures need only be labelled, again in parentheses, if they are necessary for the understanding of the passage. Do not attempt accurate phonetic transcriptions of the noises people make – an 'ah' or 'eh' will do.

3 Jefferson, G. 2004. 'Glossary of transcript symbols with an introduction', in Lerner, G.H. (ed). *Conversation analysis: studies from the first generation*, pp.13–31. Amsterdam/Philadelphia: John Benjamins.

Here is an example from an interview between Margaret Thatcher and the journalist Brian Walden shortly after Nigel Lawson resigned as Chancellor of the Exchequer.

> A = Margaret Thatcher
> B = Brian Walden
>
> B: I <u>want</u> to come on to future policy but I also want to clear this up which will not just go away (1.0) a last question (1.0) do you deny that Nigel would have <u>stayed</u> (.) if you had *sacked* Professor Alan Walters=
> A: =I don't know (1.0)
> B: you never // even thought // to ask him that=
> A: // I don't know //   =I (.) that is not (.) I don't know (1.0)
> Nigel had determined that he was going to put in his resignation (1.0h) I did everything possible (2.0) to stop him (1.0) // I // was not successful (1.0h) now
> B: // b //
> A: you're going on asking the same // question (2.0) I have nothing further//
> B: // of course but that's a terrible admission prime// minister (1.0h) er
> A: I don't know// (1.0) of course I // don't know=
> B: // you <u>don't know</u> //   =you could have kept your chancellor possibly if you had sacked your part-time adviser (2.0)

What does the fact that the two speakers interrupt each other and overlap frequently tell you about what is going on in this conversation?

Who to interview

If you decide to carry out interviews, it is very important that you choose the right person to talk to. A common error is to interview people who are willing, but not necessarily part of your target group. If you state that you are looking at the language of 'typical teenagers', then you will need to find a representative sample – just interviewing other English Language students is not acceptable, because your age range would be too restricted and, as English Language students, they would not be typical.

Finally, remember to record the time and date of each interview, and the names of those taking part, as part of your own record keeping.

PROGRESS CHECK

1. Identify whether each of these topics are worth pursuing as language investigation coursework, and, if so, what the primary focus should be for each one.
   a) The difference in speech patterns between Liverpool and Everton supporters.
   b) The language of horror films.
   c) A study of different ideas of politeness around the world.
   d) The role of play in children's language acquisition.
2. What are the three main types of interview?

1 a) Yes, but a very narrow topic. **b)** Yes, provided language is the focus and not, say, visual imagery. **c)** Probably not for an English investigation. **d)** Not if the focus is on play. **2** Structured; semi-structured; unstructured.

8.2 Requirements for the language investigation task

> **LEARNING SUMMARY**
>
> **After studying this section, you should be able to:**
>
> - understand what each part of your investigation requires
> - focus more clearly on your own investigation
> - start writing a first draft

Breaking down the task – introduction

AQA	**A P4**
AQA	**B P4**
Edexcel	**P4**
OCR	**P4**
WJEC	**P3**

Generally speaking, examiners are consistent in their praise of clearly formulated, cleanly executed investigations, placed within a coherent linguistic framework. One of the indicators for success is a good beginning and a good first impression.

A good place to begin is the linguistic area that you intend to investigate. If you are fascinated by language acquisition or enthralled by representation, explain this in your introduction. If you are going to conduct a convincing investigation, it should be in an area that you feel is important. For example, why is it vital that we increase our knowledge of how children learn to speak? What are the consequences of ignoring the way that language is used to position people in regards to each other?

If you begin by explaining what is important to you, your research question should arise naturally out of your concerns.

Do not be afraid to be slightly autobiographical in your account of how you arrived at your question.

> **KEY POINT**
>
> Remember that the introduction will form your reader's first impression of your work. Give some thought to its style and impact.

The question

Your question or hypothesis should be quite short, and expressed as clearly as you can. Do not be vague. Ask a specific question, which you have some hope of answering.

Below is an example of a question that is worthwhile, but would not work within the boundaries of this course – and a couple of questions that **are** achievable:

- 'Does thought come before language?' is an utterly fascinating question, but you simply do not have the resources or the time to answer it at A-Level.
- 'Are people more or less polite today than in the 1980s?' is a challenging topic, but it could be approached.
- 'How do theories of gendered communication strategies relate to boys and girls talking and texting?' is achievable, and already shows that you have done some theoretical thinking.

A hypothesis is not simply a theory plucked from the air, but a considered application of one of the areas of knowledge that you have considered during the course. It can often be expressed as a prediction that you wish to test.

Here is one example:
- 'If Brown and Levinson are correct, then teachers who focus on "win–win" solutions will have better behaved classrooms than those who use a more authoritarian approach.'

Having explained context and formulated a question, the final part of your introduction should briefly outline what linguistic frameworks you decided to use. You can opt for a narrow focus, and simply look at grammar and lexis for instance, or you can include everything from speech acts to graphology.

Breaking down the task – the aims section

AQA	**A P4**
AQA	**B P4**
Edexcel	**P4**
OCR	**P4**
WJEC	**P3**

The introduction sets up the question, and the aims section explains how you went about answering it. If you asked a reasonable question, then you should be able to achieve a reasonable answer.

If you are attempting to explore Brown and Levinson's ideas on politeness, your aims might have been:
- to identify the linguistic characteristics of 'win–win' strategists – this would have been done first of all by looking at secondary sources
- to obtain data from four different classrooms, taught by teachers who have good discipline but different reputations
- to analyse the language used in the different classes to see if it fits in with Brown and Levinson's theories, as identified earlier.

The main focus might have been a semantic one, with possibly some commentary on rhetoric and lexis.

Another way of looking at your aims is as follows:
1. I am interested in problem X.
2. To find out more, I have/will collect(ed) some data.
3. Then I analysed/plan to analyse the data using theoretical perspective Y.

You will need to decide at this stage of your writing if you are presenting a report of what you did (in which case you should use the past tense throughout), or if you are reporting on a work in progress (in which case you should use the future tense). In the aims section, you are only discussing the **ideas** behind your work. You will not need to cover what you found out until later.

Breaking down the task – methodology

AQA	**A P4**
AQA	**B P4**
Edexcel	**P4**
OCR	**P4**
WJEC	**P3**

This section follows on directly from step 2 of the above aims checklist. Essentially, you need to describe the data you collected or hope to collect.

The three key words in this section are **relevant**, **valid** and **representative**:
- **Relevant data** relates to your question directly.
- **Valid data** has been checked in some linguistically significant way.
- **Representative data** has been chosen sensibly from a larger set.

If you are looking at language over time, theoretically any texts from different periods would be relevant, but how do you know that the changes you spot are the result of the passage of time, and not, for instance, differences in register or geographical origin? To eliminate these possibilities, it would make sense to look at the same type of text in three different periods, for instance diaries, travelogues or even something like advertisements for breakfast cereal. Even better would be to look at a single text that has been updated. The various translations of the Bible are ideal for this purpose, but it might also be possible to find old editions of books in second-hand bookshops and compare them with the latest version. Handbooks like *Scouting for Boys* can often be found in this way.

Ethnographic approach

If you are using an ethnographic approach to collect primary data, the most valid data would be real language used in real situations. An investigation of politeness strategies will not produce good, valid data if all the people concerned are aware that they are being monitored for politeness – this is a well-known problem called the **observer paradox**. You could record conversations in secret, but this would be unethical and not allowed. Fortunately, people usually forget that they are being recorded after a while, and some fairly valid data can be collected with patience. In your discussion of methodologies, you do not have to solve all of your data-gathering issues, but you do need to show that you were aware of possible problems and that you took precautions to ensure validity.

Quantitative method

If you are using a quantitative method, greater validity is conferred by sample size. One example of a particular piece of linguistic behaviour can be the basis of an ethnographic study, whilst the gathering of thousands is a suitable task for corpus linguistics. If you are using questionnaires, you are probably aiming for the middle ground.

Representative data

Representative data is data that you can manage, but which you think tells a larger truth. Obviously, the most accurate way of telling if people still use the phrase 'golly gosh' in everyday conversation is to record every English speaker on the planet for about a year, and then listen to all the recordings. This would be accurate, but not practical.

Practical research depends on the idea of sampling and scaling up. Most modern opinion polls, for instance, use a sample size of 1000, which is carefully constructed in terms of age, sex, type of occupation and ethnicity.

In your own investigation you will not be able to work with such large numbers, but you should be able to say what you did to account for such variables.

Here are the types of questions you should be asking yourself:
- Did you make sure that there was a 50/50 split in terms of gender?
- Did you make sure that you had someone from every age from 13 to 19 in your study of teenagers?
- Did you account for the level of parental income if you were researching social class?

Texts in the public domain are perhaps more manageable than recordings you have made yourself, but they still have to be rigorously vetted before you use them.

If you are examining the way that different DJs introduce music or handle phone-ins, for instance, you need to make sure that there is nothing out of the ordinary taking place – such as a natural disaster or a political crisis – that might affect the way the DJs express themselves in the programmes you select.

If you are going to compare styles of different newspapers, perhaps a corpus-based approach using hundreds of articles would be best. However, three editorials or reports on the same subject would be better than articles chosen without consideration of how typical they were of a particular newspaper's style.

Unforeseen problems

The advantage of using the future tense in the methodology section is that you only have to discuss the problems that you thought of in advance. This gives you the opportunity to discuss **unforeseen problems** (if you had any) in the evaluation section. Equally, you can talk about whether your sample was representative enough in the end (as opposed to in your plans) to justify your conclusions.

Breaking down the task – data

AQA	**A P4**
AQA	**B P4**
Edexcel	**P4**
OCR	**P4**
WJEC	**P3**

You do not normally present your data in the body of your report, but it can be useful to summarise it in some way before you present your analysis. This could be a single sentence, such as the following.

> My primary data consisted of three newspaper advertisements for Persil detergent from 1926, 1968 and 2009 (see Appendix 1).

The key points in this sentence are what you will be discussing, and where it came from. The fact that there are three dates shows that you are carrying out a **longitudinal** or diachronistic **study**.

More complex data will require a little more explanation. Here is an example.

> My primary data consists of 30 questionnaires on the language of Valentine's Day cards, all of which were filled in between February 12th and 13th this year (see Appendix 1). In addition, I will be referring to three follow-up interviews, which were conducted on February 15th (see Appendix 2 for relevant transcripts). Each interview lasted approximately five minutes, and recordings of all three are included with this folder.

The key points here are to mention all the data that is going to be included in your report, the nature of the data, and when it was collected. In this example, the emphasis on the closeness of dates shows that a synchronistic or **cross-sectional** study is being attempted. Your teacher will advise you on whether your original recordings need to be submitted.

Analysing your data

The **analysis** of your data should be the longest and most detailed section of your report. It should begin by identifying the linguistic framework or frameworks that will be used, and then go on to apply it or them to the primary data that you have collected.

The framework you choose will depend on the **question** that you are attempting to answer.

If your aim was to find out if the 'poshness' of the language used by *Come Dine With Me* contestants matched the 'poshness' of their houses, you would be looking at social class markers in the language of contestants. You would need to apply some sociolinguistics, some semantic and lexical analysis, and some phonological analysis.

The question you asked in the first place required an understanding of how ideas of 'poshness' are constructed through language, as well as through factors like type of job and dwelling. The fascinating thing about *Come Dine With Me* is that it allows viewers to see into people's homes and listen to them speak. There are a number of theories around language use that you could invoke, ranging from the idea of 'U' and 'Non-U' speech, through to Lakoff's statement that women tend to use higher prestige forms of language than men. This could be investigated in depth using data collected from *Come Dine With Me*.

Your analysis would therefore begin with an outline of what makes language 'posh' in terms of its semantic field (e.g. foreign words on the menu), its phonology (e.g. hypercorrection of dropped 'h'), and sociolinguistics (e.g. 'serviette' or 'napkin'). Depending on the programme you choose, you might also have something to say on regional accent and even dialect. Finally, you would also have to use some non-linguistic definitions of 'poshness', but these should be easily found in a sociology text.

Your data would logically fall into three categories:
1. People whose language matched their apparent socio-economic status.
2. People who were trying to be 'posher' through their language.
3. People who were trying to play down their 'poshness' through language.

People in the second category can be described as aspirational, which means to aim higher. The semantic field of height and depth is one that you are likely to encounter. You might write about it in the following way.

> In transcript 1, Dawn criticises Anne for 'getting above herself' and then goes on to say that she herself is 'down to earth'. Semantically, social class is often linked with height – 'posh' people are said 'to look down on' their social inferiors. However, here Dawn is engaging in inverted snobbery. The connotations of 'down to earth' are steadiness and reliability, and are to be admired, whilst those of 'getting above herself' are flightiness and even arrogance. Dawn is, to use another spatial term, putting Anne in her place with her remarks.

Here we have a relevant piece of data, which has been selected and commented upon using appropriate linguistic terms.

This way of working can be summed up as follows:
1. I was interested in phenomenon A.
2. I devised some criteria for spotting A.
3. I applied these criteria to my data.

This is a robust formula, as long as the criteria you devise are linguistic ones. However, there are other approaches you can use.

A **data-based approach**, for example, begins by looking at one data set and noticing its common features. These are then used as the basis for analysis of another data set.

This is in effect setting up a hypothesis and testing it, and might consist of the following process:

1. I was reading text M when I noticed phenomenon B.
2. I wondered if all M-type texts contained phenomenon B.
3. I made a list of all the things that make up phenomenon B.
4. I collected some more M-type texts and tested them for B using my list.

You could easily apply this approach to the style of writing in science books or the characteristics of the final story in news bulletins.

A third approach is the **theoretical** one. This is when you decide to test out something that you have read with the aim of challenging it, confirming it or modifying it.

This is the method outlined earlier in this chapter (see page 245) in relation to Deborah Cameron's book, *Good to Talk?*, and consists of the following steps:

1. I read book P, which explained theory C.
2. I collected some more relevant data.
3. I applied theory C to see if it conformed to the account in P.

Your aim in this kind of work will not be to conclusively prove or disprove the theory, but to give it more depth.

Breaking down the task – conclusion

AQA	**A P4**
AQA	**B P4**
Edexcel	**P4**
OCR	**P4**
WJEC	**P3**

Your conclusion should not simply be a re-statement of points you made earlier, but a genuine attempt to sum up what you have discovered through your investigation. This may be limited, but you will receive credit for being realistic.

Here is a conclusion from a statistical analysis of newspaper styles.

> In general, many of my intuitions about the differences between broadsheet and red top newspapers were correct. My study shows that the average sentence length in red tops was as much as 50 percent shorter, whilst the levels of vocabulary needed to understand red tops were much lower than those for broadsheets. However, the study did not show that red tops were necessarily easier to read. They typically employ Bernstein's restricted codes, and need to be understood as part of a long-term conversation with their readers.

This highlights the main findings and applies some relevant and valid observations to make the conclusion seem balanced.

This is how a conclusion to an ethnographic study might read.

> This study of sixth-form common room talk has revealed a number of counter intuitive results. The boys in my sample seemed to indulge in support rather than status talk, and in the course of the study several girls seemed to indulge in conflict rather than compromise behaviours. Nevertheless, my findings are broadly in line with the categories described by Tannen.

In this example, a few exceptions are mentioned before the general conclusion is introduced.

Your conclusion should be quite short. It should serve as an introduction to your evaluation.

Breaking down the task – evaluation

AQA	A P4
AQA	B P4
Edexcel	P4
OCR	P4
WJEC	P3

Once you have arrived at a conclusion (for example, that politicians sometimes use metaphors to cloak their real intentions, or that the teenagers in your area use slang to be exclusive), you then need to say how reliable your conclusion is, based on research criteria.

These criteria include:
- size of sample
- typicality of sample
- effectiveness of your control factors
- appropriateness of selected frameworks
- subtlety of analysis technique.

Here is an example.

> I believe my conclusions are valid for all speakers in this age group, as I was able to record data in three different schools in three different socio-economic sets of background.

This is a carefully backed up claim about the validity of the writer's data. However, not everyone can be so confident or lucky.

> In the planning phase I hoped to get surveys from all three local secondary schools, but in the end I was only able to use data from two. This restricts – but does not totally invalidate – my argument about school sociolects.

This evaluation points out problems with data, but you might also discuss the difficulty of applying your chosen criteria.

> Although great care was taken with the recordings, sometimes it was impossible to hear differences between long and short vowel sounds.

There may also be other interpretations of the data.

> The changes observed are consistent with Trudgill's theory of overt and covert prestige, but it is also possible that gender was not the most important factor. The sample I had available was simply not large enough to rule out such things as regional differences.

The final part of your evaluation should suggest areas that can be improved, such as sample size or range of correspondents. Examiners do not want to see a grand statement that the whole project could have been improved if you had had more time, resources or energy.

With the time, resources and energy that you **did** have available, you should be able to come to sensible conclusions, and make some sensible suggestions for further investigations.

Breaking down the task – bibliography

AQA	A P4
AQA	B P4
Edexcel	P4
OCR	P4
WJEC	P3

Your bibliography is a list of all the primary and secondary sources used in your investigation. There is a standard format for this, which you should follow. Your school or local library will probably have a great deal of information on this topic, and your librarian will certainly be able to advise you on difficult or unusual texts.

This is the standard format for **books**.

> Author, date, title, place of publication, name of publisher.
> Crystal, D. (2003) *The Cambridge Encyclopaedia of the English Language*, Cambridge: Cambridge University Press.

Multiple authors are listed alphabetically.

> Goodman, S., Graddol, D. and Lillis, T. (2007) *Redesigning English*, 2nd ed., London: Routledge.

Journal articles should include the name of the journal, its volume number, and precise publication date, as well as the relevant page numbers.

> Nielsen, L. (2003) 'Subtle, Pervasive, Harmful: Racist and Sexist Remarks in Public as Hate Speech', *Journal of Social Issues*, 58 (2), pp.265–280, 7 June 2003.

Web page references should include the author, the title of the page, the web page address (omitting http:// unless the address doesn't include www), and the date when it was accessed.

> Stevenson, J. (2000) *The language of Internet Chat Rooms*, www.demo.inty.net/Units/Internet%20Relay%20Chat.htm (accessed June 15, 2010).

Breaking down the task – appendices

AQA	A P4
AQA	B P4
Edexcel	P4
OCR	P4
WJEC	P3

Appendices contain information that is relevant to your investigation, but which is not included in the main text. Usually this will be your primary data, drafts of letters, and a template of your questionnaire. The appendices will allow examiners to assess the processes you used to prepare your report.

> **PROGRESS CHECK**
>
> 1. What are the key criteria that need to be applied to your data?
> 2. What are three ways of structuring your analysis?
>
> 2 Question focused; data based; theory based.
> 1 Validity; relevance; representativeness.

Note: The next section relates to the OCR specification only, but it may be of interest to other students for its comments on text choices and comparisons.

8.3 The OCR language investigation task

LEARNING SUMMARY

After studying this section, you should be able to:

- understand what the language investigation task consists of
- develop some strategies for dealing with the task
- start gathering possibilities and ideas

What the task consists of

OCR   P4

Types of text

For your OCR language investigation coursework, you must choose three media texts – one each from the written, multimodal and spoken modes.

The following areas are suggested for study:
- For **written texts**, you might choose tabloid and broadsheet journalism, advertising, music or film reviews, magazines, leaflets, electronic texts (e-mail, web blogs, chat rooms and text messaging)
- For **multimodal texts** (a variety of media used simultaneously), you might look at TV presentations, films, music videos, cartoons, computer games and web-based texts.
- For **spoken texts**, you might choose news items, transcripts of political speeches, radio interviews, comedy sketches, music lyrics, CDs and podcasts.

The texts you choose should be linked together in some way, as the two examples below illustrate.

The theme of 'persuasion' might involve the following:
- Written – a literary essay on avoiding clichés in writing.
- Spoken – transcript of a political speech.
- Multimodal – a brochure advertising a service.

Texts addressing the theme of 'education' might be as follows:
- Written – an extract from *Tom Brown's School Days*.
- Spoken – a transcript of a radio interview in which a celebrity discusses his or her school days.
- Multimodal – screen captures of a school website.

You will need to include copies of your texts in your folder, so in practice the texts you choose should be in a written format. Spoken texts are texts meant to be spoken (or sung) and can therefore include both scripted and non-scripted materials. If you use a non-scripted spoken text, you will need to produce your own transcript of the relevant portions of the text (rather than a copy of, for instance, a television programme).

You will be expected to demonstrate a detailed understanding of factors such as audience and purpose, and you should be able to explain some of the complexities of the social and cultural contexts in which your texts were produced. This may be the result of your own research.

You will need to compare and contrast your texts using appropriate phonological, lexical, morphological, grammatical and discourse frameworks.

Example texts

Below are three texts on the theme of freedom for women. This idea could be interpreted very narrowly – it could look at bicycling literature from the 1890s or washing machine advertisements from the 1950s, for instance – but by focusing on political freedom it has ensured that there are large areas for comparison.

Ain't I a woman?

Sojourner Truth's speech, delivered 1851 at the Women's Convention in Akron, Ohio

Well, children, where there is so much racket there must be something out of kilter. I think that 'twixt the negroes of the South and the women at the North, all talking about rights, the white men will be in a fix pretty soon. But what's all this here talking about?

That man over there says that women need to be helped into carriages, and lifted over ditches, and to have the best place everywhere. Nobody ever helps me into carriages, or over mud-puddles, or gives me any best place! And ain't I a woman? Look at me! Look at my arm! I have ploughed and planted, and gathered into barns, and no man could head me! And ain't I a woman? I could work as much and eat as much as a man – when I could get it – and bear the lash as well! And ain't I a woman? I have borne thirteen children, and seen most all sold off to slavery, and when I cried out with my mother's grief, none but Jesus heard me! And ain't I a woman?

Then they talk about this thing in the head; what's this they call it? [member of audience whispers, "intellect"] That's it, honey. What's that got to do with women's rights or negroes' rights? If my cup won't hold but a pint, and yours holds a quart, wouldn't you be mean not to let me have my little half measure full?

Then that little man in black there, he says women can't have as much rights as men, 'cause Christ wasn't a woman! Where did your Christ come from? Where did your Christ come from? From God and a woman! Man had nothing to do with Him.

If the first woman God ever made was strong enough to turn the world upside down all alone, these women together ought to be able to turn it back, and get it right side up again! And now they is asking to do it, the men better let them.

Obliged to you for hearing me, and now old Sojourner ain't got nothing more to say.

'Ain't I A Woman?' by Sojourner Truth, feminist.com

Margin annotations:

Your historical research would reveal that there are several versions of this speech, and you could discuss dialect issues.

You could point out the deictic words here.

Repetition is used for rhetorical effect.

Non-standard language is used – 'head' rather than 'beat'.

She argues that black women work as hard as men – no one calls them the weaker sex.

There is restricted vocabulary, but not restricted understanding.

Arguments about capacity do not affect equal treatment.

She appeals to the Bible and to biology – women are vital.

Again, an appeal to the Bible and a call to action.

Research on rhetoric is necessary to determine how effective this speech is.

A room of one's own (1929)

ONE

But, you may say, we asked you to speak about women and fiction — what, has that got to do with a room of one's own? I will try to explain. When you asked me to speak about women and fiction I sat down on the banks of a river and began to wonder what the words meant. They might mean simply a few remarks about Fanny Burney; a few more about Jane Austen; a tribute to the Brontës and a sketch of Haworth Parsonage under snow; some witticisms if possible about Miss Mitford; a respectful allusion to George Eliot; a reference to Mrs Gaskell and one would have done. But at second sight the words seemed not so simple. The title women and fiction might mean, and you may have meant it to mean, women and what they are like, or it might mean women and the fiction that they write; or it might mean women and the fiction that is written about them, or it might mean that somehow all three are inextricably mixed together and you want me to consider them in that light. But when I began to consider the subject in this last way, which seemed the most interesting, I soon saw that it had one fatal drawback. I should never be able to come to a conclusion. I should never be able to fulfil what is, I understand, the first duty of a lecturer to hand you after an hour's discourse a nugget of pure truth to wrap up between the pages of your notebooks and keep on the mantelpiece for ever. All I could do was to offer you an opinion upon one minor point — a woman must have money and a room of her own if she is to write fiction; and that, as you will see, leaves the great problem of the true nature of woman and the true nature of fiction unsolved. I have shirked the duty of coming to a conclusion upon these two questions — women and fiction remain, so far as I am concerned, unsolved problems. But in order to make some amends I am going to do what I can to show you how I arrived at this opinion about the room and the money. I am going to develop in your presence as fully and freely as I can the train of thought which led me to think this. Perhaps if I lay bare the ideas, the prejudices, that lie behind this statement you will find that they have some bearing upon women and some upon fiction. At any rate, when a subject is highly controversial — and any question about sex is that — one cannot hope to tell the truth. One can only show how one came to hold whatever opinion one does hold. One can only give one's audience the chance of drawing their own conclusions as they observe the limitations, the prejudices, the idiosyncrasies of the speaker. Fiction here is likely to contain more truth than fact. Therefore I propose, making use of all the liberties and licences of a novelist, to tell you the story of the two days that preceded my coming here — how, bowed down by the weight of the subject which you have laid upon my shoulders, I pondered it, and made it work in and out of my daily life. I need not say that what I am about to describe has no existence; Oxbridge is an invention; so is Fernham; 'I' is only a convenient term for somebody who has no real being. Lies will flow from my lips, but there may perhaps be some truth mixed up with them; it is for you to seek out this truth and to decide whether any part of it is worth keeping. If not, you will of course throw the whole of it into the waste-paper basket and forget all about it.

Extract from A Room of One's Own *by Virginia Woolf*

The writer treats the readers as if they were the original audience.

She is playing with audience expectations. Brief research will reveal who is being alluded to, but how is Woolf positioning her audience here?

There is complex witty word play, using 'might' and 'may' and 'mean'.

Personal voice and opinions come through.

Persona as lecturer – 'nugget' on mantelpiece is an ironic choice of lexis.

A self-deprecating reference, but this is the main point of the piece.

Gentle ridicule of the original invitation to give this lecture.

She is signposting the discourse ahead and showing that her minor opinion might have a major import.

She establishes herself as an honest and open speaker, who is prepared to share both an idea and the process by which the idea arrived.

She proposes to pursue the truth via fiction.

The lexis – 'bowed down', 'weight' – shows that this is a difficult task.

She involves the audience in the search for truth.

This text requires further work on rhetoric and on the literary essay form.

Language investigations and other coursework tasks 8

Persepolis: the story of a childhood (2004)

This text will require background research into the Islamic revolution in Iran.

You will also need to do some research into graphic novel techniques. What is the effect of using black and white only, and no shading?

Would words like 'obligatory' be in a child's vocabulary – is this an adult's perspective?

Are these drawings consistent with how a child might remember events?

What do the ten-year olds' reactions to wearing a veil show about their attitudes at this time?

What does the school yard picture suggest? What does the inclusive class photograph remind you of?

What does the spokesman's lack of mouth suggest? Why is the audience shown agreeing?

Who, according to the author, is suffering because of adult concerns?

Extract from Persepolis: The Story of Childhood
by Marjane Satrapi

Preparation and planning

OCR   P4

Once you have chosen your texts and carried out the research needed to investigate them further, you should be able to formulate a plan for comparing and contrasting them. Your main point of contrast will be how each text uses the resources of its medium to convey its message.

In the spoken mode, this will largely consist of traditional rhetorical techniques such as repetition, rhetorical questioning and deixis. In the written mode, you might focus on how the writer creates him or herself as a speaker and how he/she positions their audience. In considering a multimodal text, you will need to look at how images and words interact to create rhetorical effects. Depending on your choice of texts, you might refer to a 'grammar' of graphic novels or a 'grammar' of advertisements.

An example of how you might organise your investigations and note taking at this stage is summarised in Figure 8.2 below. The more that you fit into the central section of the diagram, the easier your overall comparison task will be. Equally, you should have clear ideas about what is unique to each text.

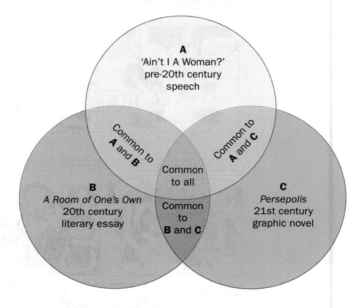

Figure 8.2 One method of organising your investigation at the planning stage

Comparing and contrasting

It is essential that you demonstrate a sophisticated understanding of all three texts in terms of their audience, purpose and the circumstances of their production. It is also necessary to compare the three texts. Comparing two texts is moderately demanding, but comparisons involving three texts need to be carefully thought out. In theory you could deal with each text on its own and then make some comparative points at the end, but this is not a good idea, as your reader is likely to have forgotten the precise details of what you said a thousand words ago. It is much better to organise your essay into major headings and discuss each work under each heading.

Suitable headings might include:
- Social and historical context
- Genre features

- Audience and purpose
- Rhetorical features
- Grammar, lexis and semantics
- Morphological and phonological features
- Discourse features
- Impact and effectiveness.

When you are comparing three texts, it is a good idea to organise your comparisons along a **continuum**. Using our examples, in terms of lexis, Sojourner Truth's speech is the simplest, Marjane Satrapi comes in the middle and Virginia Woolf comes at the end. In terms of linguistic rhetorical complexity, Woolf is the most complex and Satrapi is the least.

Do not fall into the trap of simply working through a checklist of features. The most important question to keep in mind is, 'What is this text trying to achieve?' Sojourner Truth expresses anger and frustration at the treatment of women in general – and of black women in particular – but she is thoughtful in her comments; Woolf is playful and ironic in her opening remarks, but she promises a serious investigation into the impact of wealth and privacy on artistic production; Satrapi is recalling a childhood where things she did not approve of happened to her and to her society in general. Each writer or speaker uses the means at her disposal to **protest**. If you do not keep this purpose in mind, your commentary may ramble unnecessarily.

PROGRESS CHECK

1. What sorts of text must you choose for the OCR coursework?
2. Why is a narrow focus sometimes a good idea?
3. How should you organise comparisons of three texts?

3 Along a continuum. 2 It can make comparisons easier. 1 One spoken, one multimodal and one written.

8.4 Other coursework tasks

LEARNING SUMMARY

After studying this section, you should be able to:
- understand what the other coursework task for your specification is
- develop some strategies for dealing with the task
- move towards a drafting stage

What does your specification require?

AQA   **A P4**
AQA   **B P4**
Edexcel **P4**
OCR   **P4**
WJEC   **P3**

All specifications require a language investigation, and we have already covered this part of your coursework in this chapter. The other piece of work that makes up your coursework folder differs, but in general you will need to produce a media text.

For the **AQA A** specification, you must write one or two **interventions** into **language debates**, addressing a non-specialist audience in a recognised form in up to 1250 words. To prepare for your writing you will need to look at examples of texts written to inform, argue, instruct and persuade. These will include articles, editorials, letters to the editor and scripts, and you should think about how to

Please read this information if you are studying the **AQA A** specification.

express your specialist knowledge in an accessible way. You can choose any topical language issues that have appealed to you during the course.

The table below shows examples of assignments that have been suggested by AQA.

Type of writing	Language issue	Location
Feature article	Are regional dialects dying out and does it matter?	Quality newspaper
Feature article	Do women speak differently from men?	Lifestyle magazine
Policy statement	Words used to describe different groups of people	County Council web page
Script	Has World English replaced British English?	Radio 4
Book review	*Between You And I: A Little Book of Bad English* by James Cochrane	Quality newspaper
Short story	Highlighting attitudes to accent and dialect	Magazine or anthology
Information text	Extract from a children's book on attitudes to language change	Children's book

> Please read this information if you are studying the **AQA B** specification.

For the **AQA B** specification, you must produce a 750 to 1000 word media text – such as a newspaper or magazine article – to further explore the language ideas and issues surrounding your investigation topic. You should write for a non-specialist audience, and your text does not have to reflect your investigation findings.

Along with your text, you will need to submit a bibliography of your preparatory reading material.

Here are a few suggestions for titles from the AQA B board:
- Men vs. women: who talks the most?
- How do children learn to read? A parents' guide.
- What do your text messages reveal about you?
- From 'perfect' to 'pukka': how the language of food writers has changed over time.

In preparation for this writing, you should have studied:
- the structures and conventions of media texts
- how to evaluate and synthesise complex ideas from different sources
- how to paraphrase and summarise, and to control register and style
- re-presenting specialist material for new audiences, genres and purposes
- referencing skills.

> Please read this information if you are studying the **Edexcel** specification.

Edexcel requires you to produce a short article, talk or presentation of 600 to 750 words about your language investigation, aimed at a non-specialist audience. This is very similar in scope to the AQA B task, but you are encouraged to consider a wider variety of presentational techniques.

Please read this information if you are studying the **OCR** specification.

For your **OCR** coursework, you will write your own media text and commentary. No specific word limit is given, but your folder should not exceed 3000 words in total.

In terms of range of text, you can select from those given on page 260. If you have been looking at a theme in your investigation, for instance persuasive texts, it is a good idea to follow on with the theme in your media text, in this example by producing a persuasive media text. The theme of performance, for instance, might result in a film review, and the theme of weather conditions might result in a broadsheet newspaper report on the effects of a hurricane. Some media texts – such as advertisements – can be very short, but you must make sure there is enough text to justify around 500 words of commentary.

Please read this information if you are studying the **WJEC** specification.

For **WJEC**, you will produce an 800 to 1000 word piece of writing for a specific purpose, accompanied by a commentary of 500 to 750 words.

Examples of possible genres or areas of language use include:
- travel writing
- reportage
- newspaper reports
- diaries/journals
- magazine articles
- articles for broadsheet/compact newspapers
- sports writing
- reviews (of books, films, theatre, music, etc.)
- biography/autobiography
- speeches (written to be spoken, with an emphasis on rhetorical features rather than delivery)
- obituaries
- a guide.

In addition to studying the genre conventions of your choice, you may have to carry out additional content research. For instance, you could research:
- a place (for travel writing)
- a person (for biography and obituary)
- performances (for book or film reviews).

You should not attempt personal writing, as this was assessed at AS level. If you attempt a diary, journal or autobiography, it should be in the persona of someone famous, such as a historical or literary figure.

Studying media texts

AQA	**A P4**
AQA	**B P4**
Edexcel	**P4**
OCR	**P4**
WJEC	**P3**

All boards allow you to produce a media text for the non-investigation task. In preparation for writing it, they expect you to look at the genre conventions that your chosen text employs and the types of media in which it occurs.

This is a very simple first step, but one that some candidates fail to observe. For instance, it is no use producing a tightly argued, erudite, literary essay on recent developments in the study of morphology, and then claiming that it would be suitable for publication in the *Sun* newspaper!

Your first step should therefore be to decide on what type of media text you are going to produce. Then do some research on that kind of media text in situ.

Knowing your audience

If you decide to write a film review, there are plenty of examples to look at.

You can read reviews:
- in daily or weekly newspapers
- in specialist magazines – for instance, *Sight and Sound* or *Total Film*
- online – either through listing sites, blogs, or a review aggregating site like *Rotten Tomatoes*, or in the user comment sections in the Internet Movie Database (IMDb).

In practice, newspaper and magazine reviews can also be accessed via the Internet.

All reviews work on the principle that a critic has watched a film, or read a book, or attended a concert to help readers decide whether the work in question is worthy of their attention. Many magazines and newspapers use a rating system – usually from one to five stars – to facilitate reader decision-making. Five stars is 'unmissable' and one is 'avoid at all costs'. You should pay attention to these external features when you write your *Empire* or *Times* or *Guardian* style review.

Below is a film review from *Empire* magazine. It is a review of a film that is based on the second in a trilogy of books written by Stieg Larsson. The books are best-sellers, and the first film adaptation – *The Girl with the Dragon Tattoo* – was generally well received. Notice how the reviewer mixes specialised language with his highly developed sense of what the audience knows and would be interested in.

> Notice the prominent placing of the star rating. Would you bother to read a one-star review?

> Headings and boxes help readers to find the information they need quickly – some readers might wish to avoid knowledge of the plot, for instance.

> Actors' names are placed in brackets after the character has been mentioned.

The Girl Who Played With Fire (15)

Plot
Lisbeth Salander (Rapace) returns to Sweden, becomes a suspect in three murders and goes on the run. Journalist Mikael Blomkvist (Nyqvist) is sure Lisbeth is innocent, but realises she is being pursued by dangerous criminals who have a connection to her troubled past.

The review begins with context and background information.

The reviewer identifies a reason for being unhappy with the film.

Critical lexis: set-up, trilogy, cinematic, plot.

Gossipy reference to another film that the reader is expected to know.

Technical discussion involving knowledge of film production processes.

The film involves writers, so words from the **semantic field** of literature are used.

Details of plot and character development.

Cinematic/comic book lexis – super power, reference to *Star Wars*.

More cinematic gossip, and an overall assessment of a character's performance.

Character compared with what the audience is familiar with.

Secondary characters are considered and some possible highlights revealed.

Overall comment justifying the star rating.

Review

This follow-up to the Girl With the Dragon Tattoo (the second of Stieg Larsson's novels about Lisbeth Salander and Mikael Blomkvist) suffers from middle-chunk-of-the-trilogy woes as it runs from the ending of the last story to the set-up for the next without quite telling this one properly. Niels Arden Oplev's ...Dragon Tattoo was confidently cinematic, taking its time over a complex plot; here, Daniel Alfredson — brother of Tomas, director of Let The Right One In – seems in a hurry. The Girl Who Played With Fire was made as a cinema release, but also as a longer TV serial: sub-plots, supporting characters and incidents are present but abbreviated. For the low-down on key chunks of story, you'll need to watch Swedish TV or hope for an expanded DVD.

The first film was a mystery with editorial content; this is an action film with footnotes. Lisbeth, the breakout character, is now at the heart of the story, with the present-day plot about sex trafficking and political corruption turning out to be a way into Lisbeth's hitherto-mysterious past. The abused, paranoid girl whose traumas turn her into a heroine (she even has a super-power: photographic memory) gets a Luke-and-Darth face-off with an all-purpose monster who is responsible for all that's happened to her (and everything bad in Sweden, if not Europe). The Social Network's Rooney Mara will replace her for David Fincher's in-progress remake, but it's likely Rapace will be the definitive Lisbeth: if this is a choppy vehicle, she's still uniquely fascinating, admirable and tough. Unlike most Hollywood actresses, she goes up against enemies twice her size and is as likely to take a brutal beating as prevail — and the film really grips in the climax, when she's in the sort of dire peril which would seem terminal if Part Three weren't on the way.

Blomkvist, the moral centre, is removed from the action: emails and mobile phone pings cover the fact that the leads are separated for most of the movie. Larsson strays slyly into Ian Fleming territory, which gives a pulpy verve to characters like the kickboxing lesbian (give her a spin-off) and the blond hulk born without a capacity to feel pain (cue a great uh-oh moment with a stun-gun).

Verdict

Entertaining and powerful, if hurried. It needs a killer Part Three to make it a trilogy, not a hit with sequels.

★★★☆☆

Reviewer: Kim Newman

Film review of The Girl Who Played with Fire
by Kim Newman, Empireonline.com

The key aspect of this film review is the way in which it deals with its audience's knowledge and expectations.

In the following review, the writer cannot be so sure about his readers' expertise.

Txtng: The gr8 db8 by David Crystal

The Sunday Times review by Marcus Berkmann
Published: 20 July 2008

It's almost comic to imagine how annoyed some people will be by the title of this book. But texting (the idea of it, the practice, the mere word sometimes) does get people's goats. David Crystal quotes two such commentators with relish. "[Texters are] vandals doing to our language what Genghis Khan did to his neighbours 800 years ago," said John Humphrys, possibly with foam-flecked lips. "Texting is bleak, bald, sad shorthand which masks dyslexia, poor spelling and mental laziness," wrote John Sutherland (how v irrtbl he mst hv bn th@ am).

Good grief, an entire generation of young people not only can't read or write proper sentences, but are developing repetitive strain injury in their thumbs. And does "LOL" mean lots of love or laugh out loud? It's all too appalling for words.

Of course, we've been here before with rock'n'roll, psychedelia, space hoppers, the charleston ...for every youth craze, there were oldsters who decried it. Similarly, there have always been people who wished to protect the poor, vulnerable English language from assault by barbarians. If texting is unique, it's because it has managed to unite these two discrete groups of grouches under a single banner. Thus far in this gr8 db8, we seem to have heard only one side of it.

So here's Crystal, honorary professor of linguistics at the University of Wales, Bangor, and prolific writer of books on the subject, to answer the charges. He says that all the popular beliefs about texting are wrong, or at least debatable. Its playful way with language isn't new. Most of the hated abbreviations have been around for years. "They are part of the European ludic linguistic tradition, and doubtless analogues can be found in all languages that have been written down."

As it is, most of the dafter emoticons and abbreviations aren't actually used by most people: they turn up only in the text-messaging dictionaries, which seem to have been designed specifically to exclude everyone not taking part. "Faced with a new kind of communication problem...people all over the world have set about solving it...not by inventing a new language but by adapting old language to suit the new medium." Texting doesn't erode literacy: it actually challenges literacy skills. "I do not see how texting could be a significant factor when discussing children who have real problems with literacy. If you have difficulty with reading and writing, you are hardly going to be predisposed to use a technology which demands sophisticated abilities in reading and writing." An obvious argument, but not one I remember seeing before.

Crystal's polemic is backed up by a formidable body of research. This is clearly the fashionable academic subject of the moment. (If only spacehoppers had received the same attention.) But he also quotes some

---

Annotations (left margin):

General comment about attitudes of some people to texting.

Quotations from the book to back up initial comment.

Reviewer uses textese to show that review is not anti-texting, and to draw reader in on this side of the debate.

A comic parody of a stuffy response to texting.

Placing texting into its social and historical context.

Lexis – 'grouches' shows anti-texters unfavourably.

Telling the reader who the author is and what expertise he holds.

Quotation and repetition of information gained from reading the book.

Further explanation in simple language of the linguistic principles identified in book.

Extensive quotation to prove a particularly strong point.

The reviewer adds his support to Crystal's point, albeit a little begrudgingly.

The lexis shows precise identification of the book genre – polemic.

delightful texting poetry, which, he points out, differs from poetry written on the page in that you can't see the last line when you read the first: you have to read it strictly in order, and this gives it an entirely different narrative thrust. There are also some terrific glossaries of texting abbreviations in other languages. In French, d100 is descend, gt is j'étais and, of course, edr is écroulé de rire – laughed out loud. Well, I smiled at least.

This is a brief book that sometimes feels like an overextended magazine article. At times, Crystal, who probably has another three books to write before the end of the year, just seems to be filling the pages: we hear that two-thirds of texts are only one sentence, that 82% use no capital letters, and so on. But it's a work that needed to be written, it's wholly persuasive in its arguments and it makes the blusterers look a bit silly. Besides, I rather like a book that tells you that, essentially, there's nothing to worry about.

…

Txtng: The gr8 db8 by David Crystal
£9.99 pp239

Extract from 'Txtng: The gr8 db8 by David Crystal – The Sunday Times Review'
by Marcus Berkmann, times.co.uk

> The reviewer points out some of the pleasures and highlights of the book.
>
> Some minor criticisms.

> Why it is an important and useful book.

Although the writer does not know if his readers are pro- or anti-text speak, he takes the pro-text side and uses a number of rhetorical devices that make disagreeing with him difficult. The first is to set up two straw men (people who have ideas that are easy to attack) and use their own extreme comments against them. John Humphreys is described as speaking 'possibly with foam-flecked lips', as if he were a mad man, and John Sutherland is described in text language as irritable. Later, these kinds of commentators are called 'grouches'. David Crystal, on the other hand, is described as a hard-working, highly qualified expert on language who has access to a 'formidable' body of research.

The reviewer, having aligned himself with the writer, then has to explain the writer's views in the space of a review, rather than in the 239 pages of the book. As English Language students, you will recognise some of the points being made about exclusive language or language play, but the reviewer has to explain these in general terms. This is done using a combination of broad paraphrase and close quotation. These skills are the ones that you will need to deploy in your language interventions and media pieces.

Kim Newman's film review is mostly informative, although it does try to persuade the readers on some points. In comparison, Marcus Berkmann's book review is mostly persuasive, with some informative aspects.

Presenting ideas

Information texts use a variety of techniques to convey information – ranging from fully animated 3D graphics and historical re-enactments on television programmes, through to carefully worded explanations.

The following example is from a grammar text aimed at upper primary level school children.

Playful use of language in title, suggesting a non-serious tone.

Author directly addresses reader as 'you'. Use of repetition for emphasis ('very, very'), colloquial language and mild rudeness about other grammars – suggesting the reader has made a good choice.

Suggestions of fun and mysteries unravelled, encouraging reader to continue.

Use of headings to aid navigation.

Facts are conveyed simply and directly, but mystery remains.

The first example includes leading questions followed by an unusual thought. Verbless sentences and graphic adds to informal tone.

Questions are asked, but not answered yet.

Same technique used in second example.

Semantic field of fishing – catching something.

Previous questions are answered and some knowledge of Bible stories assumed – not all answers are spoon fed. New vocabulary explained in a footnote – 'dancy' invented.

Conversational discourse markers, e.g. But...

There is further semi-serious criticism of other books – authorial use of 'I'.

Complicated play on words and spelling conventions.

Layout features are used for ease of comparison.

Author 'shares' personal details to seem friendly.

Short concluding sentence – use of 'we'.

Make Grammar Make Sense

What this book is about

This might be the first book about grammar you've ever opened – if it is, you are very, very lucky as nearly all the others are, to be frank, not very useful. If you *have* seen any of the other books you will know that they just start without any kind of explanation of what grammar is for or what makes it fun. By the time you reach page two you are knee-deep in proper nouns without any inkling of the deep mysteries that lie behind such words as 'word' or 'thing', let alone how a word could possibly name a thing – which is what the other grammars will tell you.

Words and things

People have been using words for over thirty thousand years, so you would think we would know what they are by now. But we don't. We don't know when words start and we certainly don't know where they stop.

Take the word ball for instance. Think about it – do you get an image in your head of a round thing? Possibly a red round thing? Does it look something like this?
What if I say 'have a ball'? Is that a red round thing? Is the new ball word the same as the old one, or are they just sound coincidences?

OK. What about grass? Green stuff right? But what if someone grassed you up? That person would be a grass wouldn't they? Would they be green?

Words are slippery and grammar is the net we use to stop them getting away. There is a grammatical relationship between the verb grass meaning 'to tell on someone' and the noun meaning 'a person who tells'. There is only a sound relationship between a bouncy ball and a dancy ball, but there is an interesting etymological[4] and possibly even mythological relationship between 'a grass' and green grass (think snakes).

But to get back to other grammar books. They will often say things like 'a noun is the name of a thing' or 'nouns are naming words', usually on page 1 in the 'parts of speech section'. But do these statements actually make sense in practice? I don't think so.

Take the word 'dog' for example. This is not the name of a thing (unless you happen to know a dog called 'dog' that is, in which case it would be spelled Dog). It is possibly the name of a type of thing. Equally, dog is not a naming word, it's a word that exists in a grammatical relationship with other words.

If it's **a dog**, it's just a general don't-really-care-what-you-think-about sort of dog.
If it's **the dog**, it's probably one we've mentioned before.
If it's **my dog**, it's a border collie, but if it's your dog I've no idea what breed it is.
If it's **that dog**, then it's definitely the one over there.

The best thing that we can say about nouns is that they have a naming function.

---

4 To do with a word's meaning over time.

This information text uses a number of techniques borrowed from fiction writing in its introduction. The subject matter is introduced, but there is an implied promise that some of the 'deep mysteries' of language will be unravelled. The author contrasts this exciting journey with the less pleasant prospect of being 'knee-deep in proper nouns' in other texts.

A friendly and colloquial tone is maintained throughout – the reader is addressed directly as 'you', the writer refers to himself as 'I', and by the end of the passage 'we' is being used. Readers are not patronised, however, and some questions are left for readers to work out for themselves, such as the connection between betrayal, snakes and the Garden of Eden.

Moving forward

AQA	A P4
AQA	B P4
Edexcel	P4
OCR	P4
WJEC	P3

Once you have chosen a particular media genre and studied enough examples of it, you should be able to draw up a rough checklist of genre features that you will need to employ.

Here is an example of a checklist of features that you might use for an obituary. The focus is on the genre features, so the main text is illegible deliberately.

Title

Funeral details - flowers / donations to charity, etc.

Fuller chronological account with achievements noted

Family and family history – 'is survived by...'

Positive ending – journey metaphor?

Notice of the death and basic details about the person. Phrases used - 'passed on...', 'after long struggle with...', 'peacefully... among friends...'

Overview of person's life and accomplishments

Detailed accounts of notable events - anecdotes, etc.

Character and personality
Useful euphemisms:
- colourful - 'drank'
- larger than life - 'fat'
- tireless storyteller - 'boring'
- did not suffer fools gladly - 'grumpy'

Subject matter for the specifications

If you are studying with WJEC or OCR, you have a wide range of possibilities in terms of subject matter. For Edexcel and the two AQA specifications, you will need to use a media framework to discuss a language topic. Probably the easiest media formats for the AQA approach are feature articles and reviews, but as long as you present language issues you can use any format you like – you may want to consider writing an obituary for the death of the apostrophe, for example. If you make an oral presentation for Edexcel, you should hand in a copy of your script, along with a print-out of any presentation software (such as PowerPoint) slides or visual aids you use.

PROGRESS CHECK

1. What is the main function of a review?
2. Why is the plot section of a film review separate?

2 Some people do not like to know anything about the plot before they see a film.
1 To help readers to decide whether to see, listen to, or read a work of art.

Note: As this chapter is about coursework tasks, we have not included a sample question and model answer, or an exam practice question.

Exam preparation

The following topics are covered in this chapter:

- **Types of exam questions**
- **Approaching exam questions**
- **Useful strategies**
- **Final preparations**

9.1 Types of exam questions

LEARNING SUMMARY	After studying this section, you should be able to:
	- understand what type of exam questions to expect for your specification
	- understand what the assessment objectives are for your written exam

AS papers

AQA	**A P1**
AQA	**B P1**
Edexcel	**P1**
OCR	**P1**
WJEC	**P1**

All specifications for AS English Language have one assessed piece of coursework and one written paper. See Chapter 5, *Language production* (pages 140–159), for further information on the coursework element.

There is a considerable variety of approaches and topics at AS level, but all papers involve some data response work, and most require extended essay type answers. Only the AQA B specification offers any options.

The examination details for each specification are as follows.

> Please read this information if you are studying the **AQA A** specification.

The **AQA A** examination lasts 2 hours:
- **Section A**: Language analysis task – comparing two texts.
- **Section B**: Language development – data analysis and essay.

You answer two questions in total – one from Section A and one from Section B. There is a choice of topic in section B – initial language acquisition or children's writing.

Each question is worth a maximum of 45 marks, giving a total of 90 marks for the paper.

The assessment objectives are AO1, AO2 and AO3 (see pages 277–278).

> Please read this information if you are studying the **AQA B** specification.

The **AQA B** examination lasts 2 hours:
- **Section A**: Text varieties task – grouping exercise.
- **Section B**: Language and social contexts – text-based commentary:
  - Language and gender
  - Language and power
  - Language and technology.

You answer two questions in total – one from Section A and one from Section B. There is a choice of three topics in section B (as listed above).

Each question is worth a maximum of 48 marks, giving a total of 96 marks for the paper.

The assessment objectives are AO1, AO2 and AO3 (see pages 277–278).

Please read this information if you are studying the **Edexcel** specification.

The **Edexcel** examination lasts 2 hours 15 minutes:
- **Section A**: Language and context – short answer data response.
- **Section B**: Presenting self – comparative essay.

You answer one question from Section A and one from Section B.

Each question is worth 50 marks, giving a total of 100 marks for the paper.

The assessment objectives are AO1, AO2 and AO3 (see pages 277–278).

Please read this information if you are studying the **OCR** specification.

The **OCR** examination lasts 2 hours:
- **Section A**: Speech and children – data-based response.
- **Section B**: Speech varieties and social groups – data-based response.

Each section has a choice of two questions. You answer one question from each section.

Each question is worth 30 marks, making a total of 60 for the paper.

The assessment objectives are AO1, AO2 and AO3 (see pages 277–278).

Please read this information if you are studying the **WJEC** specification.

The **WJEC** examination lasts 2 hours 30 minutes:
- **Section A**: The language of texts – analysis of texts on a theme.
- **Section B**: Language focus – analysis of a single text and how it works.

You answer one question from Section A and one from Section B.

Each question is worth 40 marks, giving a total of 80 for the paper.

The assessment objectives are AO1, AO2 and AO3 (see pages 277–278).

A2 papers

AQA	**A P3**
AQA	**B P3**
Edexcel	**P3**
OCR	**P3**
WJEC	**P4**

As with AS specifications, all specifications for A-Level English language have one assessed piece of coursework and one written paper. See Chapter 8, *Language investigations and other coursework tasks* (pages 242–274), for further coursework information.

At A-Level, four of the five specifications ask you to discuss some aspect of language variation, either over time or across cultures and in society. Two specifications ask you to discuss children's language acquisition, two ask you to discuss spoken language, and two look at various aspects of language discourse.

All specifications require you to answer two sections in the exam. Edexcel uses short and then longer answers, whilst OCR offers one compulsory section and three optional sections.

The examination details for each specification are as follows.

Please read this information if you are studying the **AQA A** specification.

The **AQA A** examination lasts 2 hours 30 minutes:
- **Section A**: Language variation and change.
- **Section B**: Language discourses.

You answer two questions in total – one from Section A and one from Section B. There is a choice of two questions in Section A, but only one in Section B.

Each question is worth a maximum of 45 marks, giving a total of 90 marks for the paper.

The assessment objectives are AO1, AO2 and AO3 (see pages 277–278).

Please read this information if you are studying the **AQA B** specification.

The **AQA B** examination lasts 2 hours 30 minutes:

- **Section A**: Language acquisition.
- **Section B**: Language change.

You answer two questions based on a selection of data relating to the topic areas – one on language acquisition and one on language change. There is a choice of two questions for each topic.

Each question is worth a maximum of 48 marks, giving a total of 96 marks for the paper.

The assessment objectives are AO1, AO2 and AO3 (see below and page 278).

Please read this information if you are studying the **Edexcel** specification.

The **Edexcel** examination lasts 2 hours 45 minutes:

- **Section A**: Language diversity over time and in global contexts.
- **Section B**: The development of children's spoken and written language.

You answer one question from Section A and one from Section B.

Each question is worth 50 marks, giving a total of 100 marks for the paper.

The assessment objectives are AO1, AO2 and AO3 (see below and page 278).

Please read this information if you are studying the **OCR** specification.

The **OCR** examination lasts 2 hours:

- **Topic A**: Language and speech (compulsory).
- **Topic B**: The language of popular written texts (optional).
- **Topic C**: Language and cultural production (optional).
- **Topic D**: Language, power and identity (optional).

You answer one question on Topic A, from a choice of two, and one further question from topics B, C or D.

Each question is worth 30 marks, making a total of 60 marks for the paper.

The assessment objectives are AO1, AO2 and AO3 (see below and page 278).

Please read this information if you are studying the **WJEC** specification.

The **WJEC** examination lasts 2 hours 30 minutes:

- **Section A**: Analysis of spoken language.
- **Section B**: Analysis of written language over time.

You answer one question from Section A and one from Section B.

Each question is worth 40 marks, giving a total of 80 marks for the paper.

The assessment objectives are AO1, AO2 and AO3 (see below and page 278).

Assessment objectives for AS and A2 papers

AQA   **A P1, P3**
AQA   **B P1, P3**
Edexcel **P1, P3**
OCR   **P1, P3**
WJEC   **P1, P4**

All specifications have the same assessment objectives for the written papers (AO1, AO2 and AO3). The objectives are detailed below.

AO1: Select and apply a range of linguistic methods to communicate relevant knowledge using appropriate terminology and coherent, accurate written expression.

Essentially, you must choose the right analytical framework – such as grammar or semantics – to use on each text. You must also use the right terminology appropriately.

AO2: Demonstrate critical understanding of a range of concepts and issues related to the construction and analysis of meanings in spoken and written language, using knowledge of linguistic approaches.

You must be able to show how meaning is created in a range of modes and be able to assess its effectiveness, and you need to be aware of debates about language

AO3: Analyse and evaluate the influence of contextual factors on the production and reception of spoken and written language, showing knowledge of the key constituents of language.

You need to be able to show your understanding of how texts are the products of specific places, times and technologies, and be able to express your analysis and evaluation in linguistic terms.

AO4, which relates to creative writing, is not assessed in these papers.

PROGRESS CHECK

1 What is AO1 mainly concerned with?
2 Which AO is tested via coursework?

1 Correct use and application of terminology.
2 AO4.

9.2 Approaching exam questions

LEARNING SUMMARY

After studying this section, you should be able to:

- analyse what particular exam questions require
- develop ideas and strategies for approaching your exam questions

Questions and how to read them

AQA	**A P1, P3**
AQA	**B P1, P3**
Edexcel	**P1, P3**
OCR	**P1, P3**
WJEC	**P1, P4**

Different exam boards assess different aspects of the specification in different years, so it is not possible to divide questions into AS and A2 sections. However, it is possible to make a number of general points about responding to English Language questions.

The two main types of question are data response and essay questions, with the majority of questions at both AS and A-Level being anchored in a text of some kind.

Decide what a text is 'doing'

When you are responding to a text you will need to identify its form, function and audience, and decide on key criteria for your discussion. For instance, if you are asked to analyse a spoken text, you should be looking out for some or all of the features shown in Figure 9.1.

Feature	Explanation	Examples
Discourse markers	• Words and phrases used to signal changes in topic. • The meaning of discourse markers usually depends on context. 'Well…', for example, can vary in meaning from 'I'm thinking about it' to 'that's all'.	• 'Well, anyway, right, so, now. But to go back to …'
Heads and tails	• Words and phrases at the beginning or end of utterances that help the listener keep up with the topic.	• 'That **girl**, Jill, her sister, **she** works in our office.' • '**It's** difficult to eat, isn't it, **spaghetti**?'
Deixis	• Language that points to things. It usually only fully makes sense when the speaker and listener are in the same place.	• 'that/this one', 'here', 'over there'.
Ellipsis	• Missing words out for brevity, usually to keep up the rhythm of talk.	• 'Are you going [to the cinema]?' • 'No [I have got] other plans.'
Spoken clause structure	• The joining of clauses together, usually using conjunctions, often whilst developing ideas.	• 'Yeah, I got all the way to the shops **but** I didn't have any money with me **and** I was really annoyed **but** it was ok.'
Vague language	• Grammar and vocabulary that makes statements less definite and more negotiable, often as a politeness strategy.	• 'It's, you know, sort of rude not to be here on time. We've got stuff to do.'
Modal expressions	• Words, phrases and modal verbs that signal that the speaker is not definite. • Ideas of possibility can help people to get along with each other.	• 'Possibly', 'probably', 'I don't know', 'I don't think', 'I think', 'I suppose', 'perhaps', 'may', 'might', 'maybe' 'should'.
Adverbs	• In speech, adverbs are often added on to the end of utterances, rather than being placed next to verbs.	• 'I was worried I was going to lose it and I did **almost**.' • 'You know which one I mean **probably**.'
Prosodics	• Non-verbal aspects of talk.	• Gesture, body language, intonation, volume, pace.

Figure 9.1 Spoken language checklist

However, your task is not simply to identify features. You also need to show how the features are used to create meaning within a given social, cultural or historical context.

For most texts, you will be thinking in terms of:
• purpose
• audience
• genre/format
• formality
• speech

- writing
- multimodality
- representation
- linguistic areas (e.g. lexis, grammar, phonetics / phonology, etc).

This list is taken from the AQA B text categorising exercise, but it will also guide you on most other texts. Knowing about audience, genre and purpose is vital to understanding how any text works, and beyond these factors you will recognise unique factors such as how a text is determined by its technological format, or by how it represents a particular social group.

Use your linguistic tool kit

Having decided on what a text is doing, you can then use your linguistic tool kit to explain how it works.

For example, Figure 9.2, at first sight, has the **format** of an advertisement about beauty. However, on closer examination we can see that its **purpose** is to attack 'normal' beauty advertising, and therefore its **audience** is probably the more thoughtful type of consumer.

These two questions could be the beginnings of a traditional advertisement – they use an informal register and address the reader directly.

The next two statements subvert normal expectations by challenging the reader's assumptions about the truth and reality of advertising.

The reader is now being treated with contempt – as the 'puppet' of advertisers. Capitals are used to 'shout out' the unpleasant truth.

The reader is told that they should not be impressed by advertising.

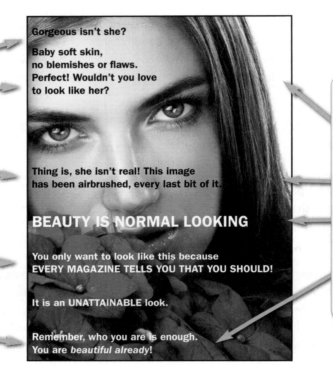

Gorgeous isn't she?

Baby soft skin,
no blemishes or flaws.
Perfect! Wouldn't you love
to look like her?

Thing is, she isn't real! This image
has been airbrushed, every last bit of it.

BEAUTY IS NORMAL LOOKING

You only want to look like this because
EVERY MAGAZINE TELLS YOU THAT YOU SHOULD!

It is an UNATTAINABLE look.

Remember, who you are is enough.
You are *beautiful already*!

The messages appear to be glued on to the image. The font is simple, which gives the impression of sincerity – not wasting money to impress.

This statement is surprising and puzzling.

The main message is in larger type.

The last statement is back to the friendly and informal tone of the top of the advert. Italics are used to emphasise the real message.

Figure 9.2 Anti-advertising advertisement

Having established these important factors, you can consider the advert's **multimodality**, the way it **represents** people by exploring their expectations, and its **graphology**, **lexis** and **grammar**. You will receive some marks for being able to identify the way this advert achieves its informal tone through simple choice of lexis and use of contracted forms, but you will gain far more marks if you can explain what the writer is trying to achieve, and assess how well he/she has succeeded.

Strategies for answering exam questions

AQA   **A P1, P3**
AQA   **B P1, P3**
Edexcel **P1, P3**
OCR   **P1, P3**
WJEC **P1, P4**

Focusing on a task

Below is a question focusing on a single text.

> The following text is from *The Guardian* newspaper. It was written at a time when there was a controversy about a mosque being built near to the site of the 9/11 attack on the World Trade Center in New York, Ground Zero. The author is a regular columnist with the newspaper.
>
> **Task**
>
> Analyse and discuss the use of language in this text to convey attitudes.
>
> You should consider in your answer:
> * how the language choices convey attitudes to the author's political opponents
> * what you can deduce and infer from the use of language about attitudes to politics in the early twenty-first century
> * your views on the power of language.

When you are faced with this type of question, the first thing to do is consider the question and establish its key words. In your exam it is a good idea to highlight or underline key terms.

In the example above, the key terms are:
* how language choices convey attitudes
* infer ... attitudes to politics
* power of language.

With these three points in mind, you might annotate the text as per this example.

Alliterative title.

Praise for opponents, but not for good reasons – 'misleading' is a key term.

General introduction – importance and the power of language.

Involves readers by asking them to visualise the author's idea.

Balanced periodic sentence to make first point.

Non-serious example introduced. Informal discourse markers and informal verbless sentence – chatty tone.

Buzzwords for blowhards

Rightwingers are brilliant at creating snappy-but-misleading nicknames – like fun-size chocolate bars and the Ground Zero mosque

At this point in human development, I think we can all look back on what we've achieved and agree that language is one of our better inventions – better even than Wi-Fi, the Dustbuster, and Super Mario Galaxy. Picture a world without language. Go on. No gossip. No chit-chat. No road signs. No newspapers. No theatre. No internet. The only forms of mass media entertainment available are slapstick …. Hang on, it's brilliant. I must be describing it wrongly.

But then, that's the beauty of language. It can change the way you see things without actually altering anything in the physical realm. It turns good into bad and bad into good and back again without anyone lifting a finger.

Take "fun-size" chocolate bars. They're tiny. Gone in a single bite. They don't last as long as a regular chocolate bar. Being individually wrapped, they're fiddly and environmentally unfriendly. And pound for pound, they're more expensive than their standard counterparts. But, back in the mists of

Illustrates that bad things can be made good through the power of advertising. The word 'genius' is used both ironically and semi-seriously.

Personal experience introduced to maintain friendly tone.

Once a concept has been absorbed, it affects all areas of a person's thinking.

Lexis – small = good; large = dull, hard work, boring.

High register – disapproving of 'calorific gluttony'.

Reversal of previous position – readers as victim of language. Lexis related to 'royalty', political power, technological prowess.

Informal discourse marker used to introduce second, serious example.

Oxymoron – 'horrible brilliance' – and balanced periodic sentence.

General point about conservatives' and liberals' use of language. The writer thinks that the right is better at this than the left because they are less concerned with the truth.

Audience involvement through another request to think independently.

Outright attack on right-wing attitudes – 'weevil'; use of alliteration; coining new word (crapgasms).

Liberal credentials shown by concern for truth.

General comment on the role of language in the media and the impact of technology on the pace of people's lives.

Lexis of advertising applied to politics and propaganda.

Return to the 'fun-size' idea.

---

time, some genius decided to label them "fun-size". And it worked. As a kid, the mere sight of a bag of fun-size Mars bars could work me into a flurry of excitement. These were dinky novelties you could eat! Hooray for fun-size!

But the magic of language didn't end there. As well as instantly transforming each and every shortcoming of these miniscule snacks into a thrilling bonus, the sly association of the word "fun" with the concept of "small helpings" had the side-effect of making regular-size chocolate bars seem less decadent, less naughty by comparison. If little ones were fun, regular ones were pedestrian slabs of edible workload.

Some time later, of course, king-size Mars bars hit the market, thus imbuing an act of calorific gluttony with an unwarranted air of imperial glamour. This was an imposing, statesmanlike snack to be reckoned with; a nougat mothership; the Mars bar of royalty. Language had worked its magic once again.

Anyway, I bring all this up because I've been thinking some more about the "Ground Zero mosque" debate. Specifically, I've been thinking about the horrible brilliance of the opponents' endlessly parroted, emotionally charged phrase "Ground Zero mosque", used to describe something which... isn't at Ground Zero and isn't a mosque.

Conservatives, generally, are far more adept at politically reframing concepts by giving them snappy-but-misleading nicknames than liberals. "Loony left". "Boom-and-bust". "Flip-flop". "Ground Zero mosque". All simplifications or outright lies – but they worked. Like advertisers, the right seems breezily unconcerned about the truth of the slogan, provided it rings up a sale. They slap the words "fun-size" on the packaging and wait for the public to buy it.

...

Have you tried doing it yourself? It's not easy. I was hoping to illustrate this article with some self-created buzzwords for leftwingers to use. The first one I came up with was "molehill mountaineer", a pejorative term to describe the sort of perpetually furious rightwing weevil who spends their life calculatedly conflating issues such as the "Ground Zero mosque" into gigantic media crapgasms. But then I realised that "molehill mountaineer" could equally be applied to many on the left too. So that's no good.

...

Which is a pity. Because in today's 2,000mph technological freefall, he who coins the catchiest buzzword generally wins the debate by default. Few people have the time to delve beyond the ticker-tape headline, to discover the reality behind a misleading brandname such as "Ground Zero mosque". There's a famous propaganda technique known as "the big lie": the bigger the lie you tell, the more the public will believe it. But today's audience is too distracted to digest big lies. Now the trick is to cram as much misleading information as possible into a succession of tiny verbal snacks, inaccurate but memorable.

In other words: Lies aren't big any more. They're fun-sized.

Extract from 'Buzzwords for blowhards' by Charlie Brooker, guardian.co.uk

Once you have annotated your text, it is a good idea to go back to the key words and apply them to what you have found. In a complex question it is a good idea to use abbreviations to label your points.

In the example on pages 281–282, the author has set up a simple opposition:
- Conservatism is clever but bad.
- Liberalism is less clever and concerned with the truth.

Advertising is viewed as a way of manipulating the world that is little short of 'magic'. It is also implied that readers are passive recipients of advertising or propaganda. This idea could be explored further with reference to nativist theories of language.

Making comparisons

If you have two or more texts to comment on, your comparisons should be used to highlight linguistic points in different contexts.

Here are some examples, based on the two texts we have looked at in this section:
- Both the beauty anti-advertisement and the Charlie Brooker piece **position themselves** as 'friends' of the reader, through **informal lexis** and the use of **personal pronouns**.
- Both texts assume a rather passive role for the reader/viewer, as if it is impossible to resist advertising's message. The poster claims that readers/viewers are made to want things ('EVERY MAGAZINE TELLS YOU THAT YOU SHOULD') and Brooker shows his attitude to Mars Bars flip-flopping according to the latest campaign. By **representing** the receivers of advertising as **victims**, they make the producers of advertising look more like **villains**.
- The linguistic **simplicity** of the poster is complemented by the linguistic **complexity** of the article. The article says that advertising creates false impressions by manipulating words like 'fun-sized'. The poster shows a 'false' face as a graphic example of the power of advertising. In this case a picture is worth several hundred words and shows one of the advantages that **multimodal** texts have over **written** ones.

Texts in time

Another frequent exercise is to place language in an appropriate historical context. This is obvious at the beginning of the Modern English period, when spellings were not standardised, but more difficult after Dr Johnson's dictionary was published.

Here are some pointers to help you place language in its historical context.

In **texts between 1600 and 1700**, punctuation is less complex, with fewer full stops, no semi-colons, and commas often used where Modern English would use a full stop.

Look out for:
- 'u' and 'v' being used interchangeably – e.g. 'priuate'
- doubling of consonants – e.g. 'dispossinge', 'sonne'
- single consonants – e.g. 'super' for 'supper', 'busenes'
- final '-e' – e.g. 'eate', 'spirite', 'goinge', 'toune'
- extra '-e' before plural '-s' – e.g. 'feeldes', 'sarvantes'
- lack of final '-e' – e.g. 'cam', 'som', 'wher'
- 'y' for 'i' – e.g. 'byshop', 'vyle'
- the use of archaic third person (an '-eth' inflection) – e.g. 'hath', 'giveth'

- more frequent use of words from the semantic field of religion
- the possibility of 'inkhorn' terms.

In **texts between 1700 and 1800**, the writing is generally formal. The language of the King James Bible was a strong influence on texts in this period – there is some use of 'thee' and 'thou', particularly in religious texts.

Look out for:
- 'so' as an adverb – e.g. 'and so to bed'
- frequent subordinate clauses – e.g. 'in which', 'after which', 'before which'
- prepositions often being different – e.g. 'read of the bible', 'walk in to the air'
- use/misuse of genitive – e.g. 'Michael his book' instead of 'Michael's book'
- capitalisation of all nouns, not just proper ones
- many very long sentences with subordinate structures
- past tense forms – e.g. 'did' hit, 'did' go
- fronted adverbials – e.g. 'waking this morning', 'my cold being better'.

In **texts post 1800**, most modern spelling conventions are in place. Long sentences are more frequent, but punctuation is more forensic. Formal Standard English is the norm, except with 'low' characters or dialect speakers.

Look out for:
- technological developments and associated lexis – e.g. times reported by the minute, steam train metaphors
- words that have changed in meaning – e.g. in the nineteenth century, 'nice' meant 'precise'.

In **texts post 1900**, there are distinct English and American spellings. There is also a gradual decrease in levels of formality (which has accelerated since the 1960s). There is less concern about language 'rules' – like splitting infinitives – and more concern over political correctness (use of 'he' and 'she', etc.).

Look out for:
- elision – e.g. 'he's', 'didn't', 'what's', 'I've'
- the impact of technology – e.g. from telegrams to texting
- shorter sentences and avoidance of the passive for clarity
- a wider range of punctuation marks and, eventually, emoticons
- the use of the modal 'will' in the future tense – e.g. I 'will' not be going.

Phonemic symbols and signs

In many responses, you will need to refer to actual sounds represented by spellings.

Some exam boards provide you with a list of Standard English phonemes. You do not have to learn this off by heart, but being able to discuss the fact that many words end with a voiceless /ə/ (known as 'schwa') is likely to impress the examiners, as is the ability to distinguish between /ð/ as in '**th**is' and /θ/ as in '**th**ank'.

The lists below comprise the symbols and signs that you may want to familiarise yourself with.

The phonemic symbols and signs for the **consonants of English** are:
- /f/ – 'fat', 'rough'
- /v/ – 'very', 'village', 'love'
- /b/ – 'bad', 'rub'
- /d/ – 'bad', 'dim'

- /θ/ – 'theatre', 'thank', 'athlete'
- /ð/ – 'this', 'them', 'with', 'either'
- /s/ – 'sing', 'thinks', 'losses'
- /z/ – 'zoo', 'beds', 'easy'
- /ʃ/ – 'sugar', 'bush'
- /ʒ/ – 'pleasure', 'beige'
- /h/ – 'high', 'hit', 'behind'
- /p/ – 'pit', 'top', 'spit'
- /t/ – 'tip', 'pot', 'steep'
- /k/ – 'keep', 'tick', 'scare'

- /g/ – 'gun', 'big'
- /tʃ/ – 'church', 'lunch'
- /dʒ / – 'judge', 'gin', 'jury'
- /m/ – 'mad', 'jam', 'small'
- /n/ – 'man', 'no', 'snow'
- /ŋ/ – 'singer', 'long'
- /l/ – 'loud', 'kill', 'play'
- /j/– 'you', 'pure'
- /w/ – 'one', 'when', 'sweet'
- /r/ – 'rim', 'bread'.

The phonemic symbols and signs for the **pure vowels of English** are:

- /iː/ – 'beat', 'keep'
- /ɪ/ – 'bit', 'tip', 'busy'
- /e/ – 'bet', 'many'
- /æ/ – 'bat'
- /ʌ/ – 'cup', 'son', 'blood'
- /ɑː/ – 'car', 'heart', 'calm', 'aunt'

- /ɒ/ – 'pot', 'want'
- /ɔː/ – 'port', 'saw', 'talk'
- /ə/ – 'about'
- /ɜː/ – 'word', 'bird'
- /ʊ/ – 'book', 'wood', 'put'
- /uː/ – 'food', 'soup', 'rude'.

The phonemic symbols and signs for the **diphthongs of English** are:

- /eɪ/ – 'late', 'day', 'great'
- /aɪ/ – 'time', 'high', 'die'
- /ɔɪ/ – 'boy', 'noise'
- /aʊ/ – 'cow', 'house', 'town'

- /əʊ/ – 'boat', 'home', 'know'
- /ɪə/ – 'ear', 'here'
- /eə/ – 'air', 'care', 'chair'
- /ʊə/ – 'jury', 'cure'.

Let the exam boards help you

All examination boards have websites where you can download copies of the specifications you are studying, and a variety of support materials. This varies from board to board, but at the very least you will be able to look at specimen papers and mark schemes. Some boards add past papers and mark schemes as time goes on. Some boards also provide exemplar material showing what high grade responses look like.

It is extremely useful to try and gain an insight into your examiner's thinking by reading through this material and applying it to your own studies. Your teacher may, however, be planning to use some of the past papers as practice papers for you, so check this before you look – practice papers will help you most if you come to them fresh.

Here, as an example, is some advice to markers from the WJEC specimen paper.

What distinguishes the best answers from the merely competent would usually be the ability to:

- compare the texts effectively
- engage with the evaluation of the language
- show understanding of the style and conventions of the specific genre
- **make a large number of points and to group them**, rather than plod through line by line
- choose the most appropriate illustrations
- show understanding of variations in the forms and meanings of language from different times in specific contexts
- discuss and explain language features accurately and interestingly.

The most useful advice is to make a large number of points and group them, rather than plodding through your answer. Note also that the examiners expect answers to be interesting. Being interesting is difficult to plan for, but one way of achieving it is to be interested in your own observations and discoveries about the text.

Here is some advice to Edexcel examiners about awarding marks on language change over time.

Indicative context

Candidates must choose 2 examples representing key constituents of language.

These could be:
- lexis
- syntax
- grammar
- spelling.

(Phonology – there is some evidence in the spelling of changing pronunciation patterns, but this is specialist knowledge that an A-Level student would be unlikely to have. If a student does select and analyse this accurately, then reward.)

The students must give an example and analyse it closely using appropriate linguistic terminology.

In each case the candidate should comment on current use and speculate briefly as to why the change has occurred:
- **Lexis:** words that have changed their meaning or use, or words that are no longer used.
- **Grammar:** verb endings for 3rd person, subjunctive 'be'.
- **Syntax:** word order, sentence construction.
- **Spelling:** don't reward for simply identifying differences in spelling.

The candidate must be able to identify a pattern, for example the substitution of 'y' for 'i', 'v' for 'u', the use of final 'e':
- **Lexis:** increase in the word stock, words falling out of use, change unscientific understanding.
- **Grammar:** language moves towards simplification, loss of inflections.
- **Syntax:** word order similar to modern, sentences longer, clarity when giving information.
- **Spelling:** process of standardisation of spelling, changes in printing conventions and technology.

AO2: shows awareness of concepts and issues relevant to the selected data of why and how language changes, using appropriate structural linguistic analysis.

AO3: shows knowledge of the context of language change relevant to the selected data and of the key constituents of language.

Remember that spotting a feature is not rewarded – fitting it into a commentary about language change is.

Final preparation – practise, practise, practise

Using the resources that your teacher and the exam board provide, you should be able to practise your exam several times before the real thing. The more often you practise under timed conditions the better. First, familiarise yourself with the format and shape of your exam, and then you will be able to get some idea of how you will perform.

In terms of timing, it is always tempting to finish off Question 1 before you move on to Question 2. This is often a mistake. Give yourself half of the available time for each question and stick with this. At the midway point stop, and start the second question. As Figure 9.3 shows, your marks per minute tend to tail off as you run out of fresh things to say. It is far better to start on the second question and generate some high scoring points than to linger on the first question. You can always return to the second question if there is time at the end.

Figure 9.3 Why it makes sense to be strict with timings in an exam

When you have completed a practice paper or practice question, always look carefully at the feedback you are given:

- What are you good at – how can this be improved?
- What are your weaknesses – how can they be improved?
- Is more revision needed or just more practice at expressing ideas?
- Are the answers well structured?
- Are examples appropriate?
- Can your timing be improved?
- Are you making any obvious spelling, punctuation and grammar errors?

The more you practise, the more you will build up a stock of successful strategies. You may feel that you are repeating the same strategies in your exam practice work, but remember that the examiner will only see your writing once, and it will seem fresh to him or her.

> **PROGRESS CHECK**
>
> 1 Where are you likely to find examples of ellipsis?
> 2 What is usually the effect of using a speech-like style in writing?
> 3 What is the name of the unstressed 'uh' sound that comes at the end of many words?
>
> **1** In spoken language **2** The writing seems more friendly **3** schwa' – spelt /ə/.

Note: As this chapter is about exam preparation, we have not included a sample question and model answer, or an exam practice question.

Exam practice answers

The answers provided below give an indication of some of the ideas that you might explore in a response to each question. They are not meant to be prescriptive or exhaustive.

Chapter 1

This message is written in text language, but it does not appear to be a text. In 'normal' spelling the message reads as follows:

> Our Christmas holidays were a complete waste of time. Last year we went to Los Angeles to see my sister, her boyfriend and their two screaming kids face to face. I like Los Angeles, it's a great place.

This reads more like the beginning of a story than an SMS text. Text messages are the result of a particular combination of circumstances, which have led to millions of messages being written as a short form of communication. The many shortcuts to be found in texts are the result of texters using the 12-key keypad found on mobile phones to reproduce the letters and numbers of a typical computer keyboard, which will often have over 100 keys on it.

Experienced texters can produce texts very quickly, but because of the way letters have to be accessed through multiple key presses, it can still be very laborious. For instance, on most keypads one of the most common letters in English, 's', requires four key presses. As a way of coping with the difficulties of entering texts, texters have adopted a number of strategies, and these can be seen in the message in the question.

The first strategy is the use of initialisms. These are set phrases that are represented by the first letter of each word. Common examples of these are LOL, meaning laugh out loud, and OMG, meaning Oh my God. The message uses CWOT for complete waste of time, FTF for face to face and ILLA for I like Los Angeles. The second of these examples is quite common in texts, because meeting FTF is something people do. However, both CWOT and ILLA take a bit of working out. This is always a problem with initialisms, particularly if you don't know the person texting you and you aren't used to the range of abbreviations that he or she uses. However, initialisms are not completely the product of texting technology. For instance, many letters between a boyfriend and girlfriend used to have SWALK – sealed with a loving kiss – written on them. Also, people used to say things like TTFN – ta ta for now – when they were saying goodbye.

A second response to the time-consuming nature of the mobile keypad is the use of abbreviations, for instance 'Xmas hols wr' in the first sentence. The writer has missed out vowels in words and has used a standard shortening of holidays. The writing of words without vowels goes all the way back to ancient Hebrew, which was never written with vowels, and the shortening of words also has a long tradition in English as in, for instance, the school subjects 'geog', 'biol' and 'maths'. Anyone doing a great deal of writing is likely to use such shortenings, as they are generally unambiguous and are easy to understand.

The use of letters or numbers for phonemes is known as a logogram, and the message contains several of these. 2 for 'to' is obvious and easy to understand, as are 2C for 'to see' and gr8 for 'great'. These logograms are characteristic of texting, but the idea of using letters for sounds occurs in many rebus-type games. The writer Kurt Vonnegut wrote a short story in the 1960s called '2B or 0 2B' in reference to the speech in Hamlet that begins 'To be or not to be'.

One relatively recent technological feature of the message is the emoticon ':-@' for screaming. Emoticons are definitely the product of keyboard use, as they use common keyboard symbols to make up sideways faces. However, they are not really the product of SMS texting habits, as they came originally from people who had keyboards. Texting an emoticon can be quite tricky, as often several extra key presses are required to get to the punctuation marks on keys.

The writer of the message seems to be using text messaging techniques quite deliberately, and is quite good at sentencing and punctuation. Many texters do not bother with commas and full stops if the meaning is clear, and many spellers might have missed out the apostrophe in 'it's' through confusion or ignorance, rather than cutting down texting time. The content of the message remains puzzling. Generally speaking, people do not tell stories like this via text. To talk about your holidays you might want to speak FTF or at least talk over the phone.

In conclusion, all the non-standard aspects of the message can be seen as a response to the difficulties of entering text using a mobile phone, but in none of the examples are the techniques unique to mobile phone technology. Some of the shortening techniques – such as shortening words and missing out vowels – are clear and unambiguous, whilst others – such as initialisms – can have their drawbacks when addressing strangers.

Chapter 2

The text consists of both words and pictures, and is therefore multimodal. The scene seems to be set in a hot air balloon and it features two seekers of truth. The one on the right is attempting to 'literalize all speech', whilst the one on the left is trying 'to find the meaning of life'. The literalist thinks that he can solve the problem of the meaning of life by looking up the meaning of the word 'life' in a dictionary. This is because he has responded to the literal rather than the figurative meaning of his companion's statement. The seeker of the meaning of life probably realises that the literalist will not understand the underlying meaning of his words and so he resorts to irony in his response. He appears to thank the literalist, but in fact he is expressing disappointment after his raised hopes about finding the meaning of life have been dashed. Of course, the literalist cannot see anything other than a thank you, and seems to think the seeker of meaning has succeeded in his quest.

The way in which the cartoon is drawn enhances the ideas in the text. The two characters are in a hot air balloon, and useless debate is often described as nothing but 'hot air'. The seeker of the meaning of life is drawn with a large thrusting nose and prominent eyes. These features suggest that he is looking around the world and sniffing out its secrets. He also appears to have a rucksack on his back, which suggests that he is a serious and slow traveller. The literalist is probably the owner of the hot air balloon and he is drawn with a cloak and a slightly odd looking flat hat. His nose is an aristocratic roman one and he is wearing thick glasses. The hat and aristocratic appearance might remind some readers of traditional illustrations of Don Quixote, the knight who went off on fabulous but ridiculous quests. The quest mentioned in the cartoon is a project 'to literalize all speech', which should strike the reader as ridiculous and linguistically impossible. The fact that the quest is being undertaken in a hot air balloon, which floats above difficulties, also undermines its seriousness.

The cartoon follows the normal conventions of its genre, such as reading from left to right and showing speech in consecutive bubbles. The conversation is set up with an establishing image to show where it is taking place, and the main exchanges enable the reader to see the expressions on the speaker's faces. The failure of the attempt to find the meaning of life is underlined by a wordless wide angle drawing, showing the two speakers facing each other but no communication taking place. The final exchange returns to a closer viewpoint. These drawing conventions are very similar to what might be found in a film of the scene and would be easy to follow for most audiences.

The exchanges between the two men are speech-like in that they proceed in turns and consist of a variety of conversation strategies, such as question and answer and exclamatory and declarative sentences. Given the available space, there is understandably no speech-like redundancy. The speech in the middle panel is laid out like a dictionary page to show that the speaker is reading from a dictionary. It is not clear how you would pronounce '(noun)', for instance, but for readers of the strip this device makes perfect sense. Unlike real speech, almost all sentences are grammatically complete, except for the seeker's first utterance which contains an ellipsis in response to a question.

The two men talk about their goals in life. The idea of moving towards something worthwhile is shown through the images of travel in the cartoon, such as the rucksack and the balloon, but the two men actually make no progress. The literalist has chosen an impossible quest, as almost all language is metaphorical to some extent – the word 'goal', for instance, is metaphorical in his first sentence. One possible interpretation of his quest is that he is trying to ensure that there is a concrete equivalent for all words, so that metaphors would disappear. More realistically, perhaps he is trying to stamp out people's tendency to misuse the word 'literally' when they mean metaphorically, in statements like 'I was literally over the moon'.

The literalist has obviously taken the seeker's search for the meaning of life literally. Word meanings can be found in dictionaries and the literalist responds to 'life' as a word whose meaning can be found. The seeker is concerned with the meaning of the phrase as a whole – to search for the meaning of life in this sense is to be on a quest to find life's ultimate purpose. The literalist has paid attention only to the denotations of the words, whilst the seeker is concerned with the connotations of the phrase. The seeker, on realising that his companion will not be able to understand him, resorts to irony. The word 'well' before 'thanks' in his final speech bubble indicates that he is not being entirely sincere in his gratitude. Of course, the literalist cannot understand irony either, as it is not contained in the literal meaning of the words spoken.

The pragmatics of the exchange show, in an amusing fashion, a common communication problem. Even when two people speak and understand the same language, communication is not possible if there is a wide difference in world views. The two men in the cartoon are both searching for a goal, but the literalist cannot see beyond his self-limited literal viewpoint. This is illustrated by his thick glasses and by his mode of transport, just as much as the words he says. The seeker has wider perspective and knows that

communication has failed, whereas the literalist must genuinely think that he has helped his companion.

The purpose of this cartoon is to amuse and to make the reader think. Anyone who is interested in communication will recognise and be amused by the situation of people talking at cross purposes, and the project to literalise language is certainly food for thought.

Chapter 3

The idea that children acquire their language skills by imitating adults seems to be based on common sense and general experience. Children do listen to adults saying words and later on produce them for themselves, but it does not fully account for how they acquire a rich vocabulary so quickly, and how they acquire grammatical knowledge.

In 1957, the behaviourist theorist B F Skinner suggested that language acquisition was a matter of operant conditioning – children are 'rewarded' by praise when they successfully imitate adult language production, and they are 'punished' by lack of response when they get things wrong. When 'rewarded' for saying something, they are motivated to repeat that behaviour. This view explains how children build up basic vocabulary and even such things as local accents, but there is a large discrepancy between what parents say to children and what children actually learn. This poverty of stimulus argument was one of the main points of Chomsky's attack on Skinner.

In 1960, Noam Chomsky attacked Skinner's ideas from a nativist standpoint, suggesting that children have an innate ability to learn language, and that language acquisition was a creative process in which children did not simply imitate, but worked out rules and produced their own words. Chomsky suggested that human beings are born with a universal grammar, or a level of linguistic competence that allows them to work out and apply the rules of any language that they are exposed to. This language acquisition device (LAD) needs to be 'activated' by exposure to language at the right time, and if this does not happen (as in the case of feral children) subsequent language acquisition is very difficult. The LAD explains why children apply regular grammatical rules to irregular words, and produce words like 'goed', which they cannot possibly have heard from adults.

A major difference between Skinner and Chomsky is that Skinner was actively involved with research into children's language, whereas Chomsky was much more concerned with theoretical issues. Chomsky's ideas overlooked the importance of social context, for instance. In 1977, Bards and Sachs reported on a child known as 'Jim', who had deaf parents. He was exposed to language through television and radio, but his linguistic progress was slow until he was able to interact face to face with a speech therapist.

Skinner's theory would seem to suggest that if a particular child received a great deal of parental input, he or she would make faster progress. This is not the case, and children go through the same stages of language development at approximately the same time wherever they are throughout the world. Skinner's view can also not account for children's regularisation of grammar, or their use of recursion in language. However, it is clear that vocabulary and phonological sounds are acquired through interaction with adults.

Exam practice answers

The role of interaction was explored by Vygotsky and Brunner, who argued that parents and carers provided a context for successful language acquisition. Work in this area seems to support Chomsky, as parents will often correct their children for truthfulness and for pronunciation, but rarely for grammar. An interesting example of this is quoted by McNeil:

> Child: Nobody don't like me.
> Mother: No, say, "Nobody likes me."
> Child: Nobody don't like me.
> (Eight repetitions of this dialogue)
> Mother: No, now listen carefully: say, "Nobody likes me."
> Child: Oh! Nobody don't likes me.

The child in this example simply does not understand the point that the parent is trying to make, in spite of being given nine chances to imitate the mother. The above quotation also illustrates observations by the cognitive theorist Piaget, who suggested that children need to be 'ready' for a particular aspect of language before they can learn it. No amount of explanation to a child will cause him or her to learn if the child has not developed sufficiently.

On the other hand, Brown and Berks in the 1950s found that children develop understanding of the sounds they deal with in advance of their ability to say them. This was shown by a discussion with a young boy who pronounced 'fish' 'fis'. When his carer said 'fis', the boy tried to correct him, but he was still unable to say 'fish' himself.

Accent, dialect and even idiolect all suggest that the adults and carers closest to a child have a strong influence on what a child says, and the way he or she says it. In later life, when we learn a foreign language, imitation and positive feedback are the main ways we make progress. However, the way in which all children go through the same developmental stages, and the fact that children invent their own grammar, are strong arguments in favour of the idea that there is more to language acquisition than imitation.

Chapter 4

The first extract is from a novel by a male writer and is his attempt to imagine how a particular type of Victorian woman might feel about herself and her surroundings. The second text is by a contemporary woman looking for a man on a dating website. Both texts are written from a first person point of view and are examples of women presenting themselves to a wider public.

Esther Summerson seems to be a very lonely person who has been emotionally – and probably intellectually – deprived all her life. She is an orphan, brought up by a godmother, whose principal companion has been a doll. In contrast, Phoenix26 is a well-travelled, well-educated and self-confident woman who enjoys vigorous intellectual and physical exercise. These two women could hardly be more different. Pheonix26 is confident and competitive, whereas Esther is keen to emphasise her inferiority and intellectual limitations. Even when Esther does mention one of her strengths – 'a noticing way', she immediately minimises it by stating that it was 'not a quick way'.

As a novelist, Dickens is artful in the way he sets out Esther's character, compared to Phoenix26's presentation of herself. There are notes of irony in the description of the extreme goodness of the godmother, and given the detail in which she is able to write, we are not convinced by Esther's modesty at the beginning. Her approach is generally chatty and discursive, with asides addressed to the doll, and even imagined conversations. The sentence structure is loose and informal. The second paragraph concludes with a short sentence that casts doubt on the rest, and reinforces Esther's modesty. Esther's hesitancy about herself is often expressed through repetition, as in her assertion that she is not clever, and the emphatic distance between her and her patron: 'I felt so poor, so trifling, and so far off that I never could be unrestrained with her.'

Pheonix26 uses long, balanced sentences, and in the opening paragraph uses groups of three to enumerate her likes, dislikes and preferences. The second paragraph opens with balanced compound sentences, using 'but' to emphasise the moderation of her tastes. In the sentence beginning 'I like...' she bundles several ideas together in an informal and loosely structured way. The paragraph ends with another compound sentence using 'but'. Particularly in the second paragraph, Pheonix26 is attempting to sound easy to get on with – she has enthusiasms, but does not pursue them to the point of fanaticism.

Esther's strengths are presented by implication rather than direct statement. Although she appears not to have been supervised, she seems always to have worked at school and at home 'busily' stitching, and she mentions a loving disposition on two separate occasions. In the Victorian period, Esther's modesty might have been thought charming, but in the modern era it seems cloying and even downtrodden. Some men might find Phoenix26 to be assertive and outgoing, but as this is a dating website there is no point in her pretending to be modest and unassuming if she is to attract the attention of a compatible man. Women like Esther probably did feel that they had to be modest and unassuming.

In terms of transaction theories on gendered writing, Esther's writing seems more typical. Lakoff stated that women tend to apologise more than men, and Esther is nothing if not apologetic. She is also excessively polite and even uses over emphasis when describing her godmother: 'She was a good, good woman!' Clearly, Dickens had a good ear for how Victorian women constructed their public personas. Phoenix26 seems to be almost the opposite of Esther, but there is some evidence of self-disclosure, as her interest in foreign travel is as much about relationships with people as it is about sight-seeing. Clearly, as she is on a dating website, she is comfortable about talking about her feelings.

Both women present themselves implicitly and explicitly. Esther is clearly brighter than the opening paragraph suggests, and Phoenix26 is more typically female than she might appear at first sight.

Chapter 6

This web page uses a number of techniques to make it appeal to adolescent girls. The choice of colour for the heading, the image of a heart and lips, and the photograph of a smiling, friendly, non-threatening boy all make the page seem warm and inviting. This is reinforced by the first words of the text (in purple), which specifically exclude boys ('Tips for GIRLS only!!!') to create an air of shared intimacy and secrets.

The exciting nature of these secrets is emphasised by the use of three exclamation marks after the heading. The use of pre-modifiers in the second part of the heading – 'his own special guy-way' – packs in a great deal of information into a short space. The meanings of 'special' and 'own' in this context are very similar, but the phrase comes across as emphatic rather than repetitious. Another 'exciting' word is 'Bingo!'. In the penultimate point about shy boys, the word DEAD is capitalised to make it emphatic, and the text as a whole uses a few general statements followed by bullet points. The idea communicated is that this is important, exciting and interesting information.

A friendly, informal tone is established by using slang words and colloquial expressions, and the reader is addressed directly as 'you'. Only one boy is implied in the advice – it is always 'he' rather than, say, shy guys in general.

The writing frames girls and boys in a number of ways. This text assumes that boys can easily be categorised into 'types' – presumably there are other pages on other types of boys. 'Shy' boys are assumed to be all actions and no words in a classic Deborah Tannen style opposition, but the advice given to the girls is all about passive observation of a boy's behaviour, rather than self-assertion and intervention. The girls seem to be being framed as shy too. Alternatively, as the girls reading the page are assumed to be inexperienced, they could be being given advice that will stop them from losing face.

The phrase 'They are hard to figure out!' implies that boys are a problem for girls to solve, and the conclusion 'you can put that puppy in your arms and take him home' implies that the solution will be getting a boyfriend. The choice of the word 'puppy' connotes a fairly innocent form of relationship, and is a further clue about the likely age of the readers of this advice. At one point, the author says 'remember when you were really young', implying comparative youth even now.

In many ways this is a very typical text aimed at girls. According to Deborah Tannen, such texts value support, intimacy, understanding and feelings, and all of these factors are well represented in this text. The advice is written by girls for girls, and it makes the assumption that girls will be primarily interested in boys. The use of modal verbs like 'may' suggest that this text is giving ideas, as opposed to hard and fast advice, which a text aimed at men would probably do.

Chapter 7

Both texts reflect attitudes towards women in the twentieth century. The Ladybird book was written before the advent of feminism, and portrays a boy and a girl in 'traditional' gender roles. The boy is helping his father with the car, whilst the girl is helping her mother with tea. Not only is the image accompanying the text gendered, it also conveys a message about social class – in 1964, few households would have had cars or, indeed, garages to put them in, so the family shown is quite prosperous. The tea set – and the fact that the girl is putting milk into a jug – shows that afternoon tea is a formal affair in this household.

The extract from *Something for the Girls* shows a high level of awareness of gender roles, and is consciously challenging gender stereotypes. Rather than pointing out that Girl Guides could get, say, a badge for making tea in 1966, the text shows Girl Guides working together to achieve a notable sporting goal. The text mentions six swimmers, but there are more than this in the photograph – presumably some were supporters. The photograph showing Guides grouped together in the face of a high tide sums up the nature of their achievement.

Both texts are educational to some extent. *Boys and Girls* exists to help children to learn to read, whereas *Something for the Girls* teaches lessons about female solidarity and achievement to a new generation of girls. *Boys and Girls* seems to be using the look and say method of teaching reading, in which a limited number of words are used in a variety of permutations. The focus of the page shown seems to be words beginning with 'g', as three of them are listed at the bottom of the page, either to help the adult see what is new, or to provide practice for the child reader. Simple and compound sentences are used with a high degree of repetition in terms of both structure and vocabulary, for instance 'Peter helps... Jane helps...' and 'good girl' used twice. This method of learning to read was popular in the 1960s and '70s, but was later displaced by 'real reading', and phonics-based approaches. There is even an element of B. F. Skinner's operant conditioning in the way that the girl is praised for fulfilling her traditionally feminine role.

The language of *Something for the Girls* is much more loosely structured, because it is aimed at competent, though probably still quite young, readers. The topic for the page is Girl Guides being presented with challenges, and this idea is explored through general examples first (earning a badge, raising funds and so on), and then through one specific example of six Girl Guides breaking a cross-Channel swimming record in 1966. Unfortunately for any feminist intentions in the text, the author has chosen to remind readers that 1966 was also the year in which the male England team won the World Cup. The very real – but not widely reported – achievement of the six Guides is thus placed in the shade by one of the most well-known events in English sporting history. The football reference is unnecessary and seems to imply that in the end things are judged by male rather than female standards. They may have 'scored a victory of their own', but it is diminished by the comparison.

The layout of *Boys and Girls* is non standard. Each paragraph is a single sentence, but the words seem to be right justified rather than left justified, as is normal. This is presumably to help readers who are following the words with their finger not to lose their places. Full stops and commas are used, but speech marks are omitted. The first paragraphs of *Something for the Girls* begins and ends with the idea of challenge, and emphasis is achieved by such things as en-dashes and starting a sentence with 'but'. The vocabulary is relatively simple and relates to things which would be familiar to Guides, such as the system of earning badges. The penultimate paragraph describes the swimmer being chosen from 'companies around the country' – this underlines the spread of the Girl Guide movement and its general meritocratic philosophy. The idea of the girls being 'whipped into shape' sounds faintly bizarre, but is typical of the enthusiastic language associated with Guides.

The two texts are very different in their content and intentions, but they both illustrate how writing illuminates prevailing attitudes. The Ladybird text now seems sexist and old-fashioned, and the Girl Guide text illustrates modern writers' desires to avoid sexism and gender bias.

Index

Index

Acknowledgements

Page 21 Reproduction of a London street scene, 1835 by John Parry; **Page 29** Archive Images / Alamy; **Page 30** Extract from speech by Winston Churchill © Winston Churchill care of Curtis Brown Associates; **Page 32** Extract from 'Mrs. Dalloway' by Virginia Woolf. Reproduced by permission of the Society of Authors, Literary Representative of the Estate of Virginia Woolf; **Page 36** Extract from *Pulp Fiction* published by Faber and Faber; **Page 37** Atheist bus © Jon Worth / British Humanist Association, atheistbus.org.uk; **Page 44** BLOG extract posted by: Sarah N on: 19 June 2008, from 'thebestof' website. Reproduced by permission of 'thebestof' (www.thebestof.co.uk); **Page 58** Extract from *The Siege* by Helen Dunmore, published by Penguin, 2002; **Page 59** Extract from *If on a Winter's Night a Traveller* by Italo Calvino, published by Vintage Books; **Page 69** Photo by: Sipa Press / Rex Features; **Page 72** David Crystal article from Cambridge Encyclopaedia of Language is used by permission of Cambridge University Press; **Page 73** Extract from Caroline Spurgeon's book: 'Shakespeare's imagery and what it tells us'. Reproduced by permission of Cambridge University Press; **Page 76** Article 'Prisoner escaped from ambulance after cutting off part of his ear' by Martin Wainwright, 03 May 2010. Copyright © Guardian News & Media Ltd. 2010. Reproduced by permission of Guardian News & Media Ltd; **Page 79** © Dan Long www.eqcomics.com; **Page 85** Table: 'Phonological Process' adapted from Bowen, C. 1998: Developmental phonological disorders. A practical guide for families and teachers. Used by permission of Acer Press – Melbourne; **Page 87** Extract from Stoel-Gammon, C. and J.A. Cooper. 1984. 'Patterns of early lexical and phonological development', *Journal of Child Language*, vol. 11, pp.247–71. Reproduced by permission of Cambridge University Press; **Page 92** 3 wugs images are used by permission of Jean Berko Gleason; **Page 99** – Many thanks to John Mannion for allowing us to reproduce this work; **Page 100** Many thanks to Isaac Cowell for allowing us to reproduce his work; **Page 101** (Figure 3.6) Many thanks to Ella Cowell for allowing us to reproduce her work; (Figure 3.7) Many thanks to Jack Ireland for allowing us to reproduce his work; **Page 105** Reprinted by permission of the publisher from MIND IN SOCIETY: DEVELOPMENT OF HIGHER PSYCHOLOGICAL PROCESSES by L. S. Vygotsky, edited by Michael Cole, Vera John-Steiner, Sylvia Scribner, and Ellen Souberman, p. 85, Cambridge, Mass.: Harvard University Press, Copyright (c) 1978 by the President and Fellows of Harvard College; **Page 106** McNeil quotation from: http://cobcenglang.homestead.com/cla/clahowpage.html; **Page 109** Many thanks to Ella Cowell; **Pages 113, 114** Extracts from Man Made Language by D. Spender are used by permission of Routledge/Kegan Paul, a division of the Taylor Francis Group; **Page 116** Extract from *Verbal hygiene* by Deborah Cameron (page 201) is used by permission of Routledge, a division of the Taylor Francis Group; **Page 124** Quotation from Schulman, E. 2006. 'Measuring fame qualitatively, Annals of Improbable Research, Vol.12, No. 1, January/February, 11. Used by permission of Improbable Research; **Page 125** Extract from the article 'Madeleine McCann saga reflects our society' by Boris Johnson, 13 September 2007. Copyright © Telegraph Media Group Limited 2007. Reproduced by permission of the Telegraph Media Group Limited; **Page 126** © Alain Keler/Sygma/Corbis; **Page 129** Logos reproduced with kind permission of The Manchester Grammar School; **Pages 133–134** Extract from article: 'The real first casualty of war' by John Pilger © All rights reserved, New Statesman Ltd. Reproduced by permission; **Page 135** Extract from *My Booky Wook* by Russell Brand, HarperCollins*Publishers*; **Page 144** Article: 'Cheer up, it might never happen' by Lotte Jeffs reproduced by permission of the author; **Page 145** Extract from 'An Education' by Lynn Barber, published by Penguin Books; **Pages 146–148** Extract from Screenplay: 'An Education' by Nick Hornby, published by Penguin Books; **Pages 149–150** Extract from A, B and C, *The Human element in mathematics*, by Stephen Leacock, published in the collection Literary lapses (1910); **Page 151** Transcript extract taken from DoD News briefing – Secretary Rumsfeld and Gen. Myers; **Pages 152–153** Article 'I say, chaps, the queerest thing has happened...' by Lucy Mangan, 31 July 2010. Copyright © Guardian News & Media Ltd. 2010. Reproduced by permission of Guardian News & Media Ltd; **Pages 156–157** Worst openings: by 1990 winner, Linda Vernon, from Bulwer-lytton.com; by 1991 winner, Judy Frazier, from Bulwer-lytton.com; by 1992 winner, Laurel Fortuner, Bulwer-lytton.com; by 1993 winner, William W. "Buddy" Ocheltree, from Bulwer-lytton.com; by 1996 winner, Janice Estey, from Bulwer-lytton.com; **Page 161** George Bernard Shaw quotation from preface of Pygmalion, is used by permission of the Society of Authors, executors of the Bernard Shaw estate; **Page 172** left-hand photo by Snap / Rex Features, right-hand photo by Everett Collection / Rex Features; **Page 176** Extract taken from a letter by Coggle, P (1994) to *The Times Educational Supplement 4* Nov. Used by permission; **Page 177** Extract from 'Do you speak Estuary? The new Standard English – How to spot it and speak it', Paul Coggle, (1993). Reproduced by permission of Bloomsbury; **Page 177** photo by c.Weinstein / Everett / Rex Features; **Page 178** Excerpt of total 48 words from page 558 from "Dictionary of

Modern English Usage" by Fowler H.W (2009); **Page 189** Schoolmaster image was found at: www.luminarium.org/renlit/scholemaster1570.gif; **Pages 194–195** Poem: 'Chaos' by G. Noist Trenite. To be found on the English Spelling Society's website, (www.englishspellingsociety.org); **Page 196** Poem: 'How to Get on in Society' from Collected Poems, by John Betjeman © The Estate of John Betjeman, 2001, reproduced by permission of John Murray (publishers); **Page 196** Extract from *Absolute Beginners* by Colin MacInnes; **Page 197** Extract from 'A Clockwork Orange' by Anthony Burgess, published by Penguin Books; **Page 204** Extract from 'Text messages destroying our language' by Eric Uthus, in The Daily of the University of Washington, 7 May 2007. Reproduced by permission of The *Daily of the University of Washington*; **Page 205** *Nineteen Eighty Four* by George Orwell (Copyright © George Orwell, 1949) by permission of Bill Hamilton as the Literary Executor of the Estate of the Late Sonia Brownell Orwell and Secker & Warburg Ltd; **Page 209** Extract from *Holidays on Ice* by David Sedaris, 1997, published by Little Brown and Co. New York; **Page 213** Extract taken from *Language and power* by N Fairclough, page 5. Used by permission of Longman, a division of Pearson Group; **Page 215** Extract from the 'Our "Big Society" plan' http://www.conservatives.com/News/Speeches/2010/03/David_Cameron_Our_Big_Society_plan.aspx; **Page 216** Margaret Thatcher, Extract from Speech to Conservative Party Conference ('the lady's not for turning'), 1980 used by permission of the Margaret Thatcher Archive Trust; **Page 217** © STAFF/Reuters/Corbis; **Page 220** www.scottbaker-inquests.gov.uk; **Page 221** Extract from screenplay 'A Night at the Opera' by George S. Kaufman. Published by Viking Press, a division of Penguin Books; **Page 222** Extract from: Party of the First Part website: http://www.partyofthefirstpart.com/hallOfShame.html; **Page 223** Permission to use the following book covers from HarperCollins*Publishers*: *I heart Hollywood* by Lindsey Kelk; Smart swarm by Peter Miller; Breathless by Dean Koontz; **Page 227** Extract from article: 'Family fun as Barack Obama splashes around on a beach weekend with his daughter Sasha' published by *Hello Magazine* is used by permission; **Page 229** Many thanks to Richard Toms for writing the football commentary; **Page 229** Extract from BBC's *Life of Mammals* by Sir David Attenborough (2002). Used by permission; **Page 234** Advert for 'innocent smoothies'. Reproduced by permission of Innocent Ltd; **Page 241** Extract from *Boys and Girls*, Ladybird Books, Penguin; **Page 241** Extract from 'Something for the Girls'. Published by Constable & Robinson, 2009. Reproduced with permission of The Girlguiding UK; **Page 241** © Hulton-Deutsch Collection/CORBIS; **Page 251** Extract from "The Walden Interview" Brian Walden and Margaret Thatcher - produced by LWT, 1989. Used by permission of Margaret Thatcher Archive Trust; **Page 261** 'Ain't I a woman?', Sojourner Truth's speech, delivered 1851 at the Women's Convention in Akron, Ohio; **Page 262** Extract from 'A Room of One's Own' by Virginia Woolf. Reproduced by permission of the Society of Authors, Literary Representative of the Estate of Virginia Woolf; **Page 263** Extract from Persepolis by Marjane Satrapi, published by Jonathan Cape. Reprinted by permission of The Random House Group Ltd; **Page 268** Film review of *The Girl Who Played with Fire* by Kim Newman, Empireonline.com used by permission; **Pages 270–271** Article: 6 Txtng' from The Sunday Times online Allison and Busby Ltd. Used by permission of The Times and NI Syndication; **Pages 281–282** Extract from 'Buzzwords for blowhards' by Charlie Brooker, 30 August 2010. Copyright © Guardian News & Media Ltd. 2010. Reproduced by permission of Guardian News & Media Ltd; **Page 286** Extract from sample assessment materials, Edexcel 2007

Page 23 ©2009 Jupiterimages Corporation, © iStockphoto.com/Raman Maisei; **Page 29** © Archive Images / Alamy; **Page 31** ©2010 iStockphoto / Thinkstock; **Page 33** ©2010 iStockphoto / Thinkstock; **Page 38** ©2010 Digital Vision / Thinkstock; **Page 40** ©2010 Hemera / Thinkstock; **Page 81** ©2010 iStockphoto / Thinkstock; **Page 82** ©2010 iStockphoto / Thinkstock; **Page 96** ©2010 Hemera / Thinkstock; **Page 114** ©2010 Hemera / Thinkstock, ©2010 Polka Dot / Thinkstock; **Page 120** iStockphoto / Thinkstock, Comstock / Thinkstock; **Page 126** © Photos.com/Getty Images / Thinkstock, © Photos.com / Getty Images/Thinkstock; **Page 130** ©2010 Hemera / Thinkstock; **Page 131** iStockphoto / Thinkstock, Comstock / Thinkstock; **Page 181** ©2010 iStockphoto / Thinkstock; **Page 184** ©2010 PhotoObjects.net / Thinkstock; **Page 213** ©2010 Hemera / Thinkstock; **Page 213** © Corbis; **Page 230** ©2010 Comstock / Thinkstock; **Page 231** ©2010 Stockbyte / Thinkstock; **Page 233** ©2010 Photodisc / Thinkstock; **Page 248** ©2010 Digital Vision / Thinkstock; **Page 280** iStockphoto / Thinkstock